THE
TOE-RAGS

DAPHNE ANDERSON

THE
TOE-RAGS

THE STORY OF A STRANGE UP-BRINGING
IN SOUTHERN RHODESIA

ANDRE DEUTSCH

First published 1989 by
André Deutsch Limited
105–106 Great Russell Street, London WC1B 3LJ

British Library Cataloguing in Publication Data

Anderson, Daphne
 The toe-rags: the story of a strange upbringing
in Southern Rhodesia.
 1. Zimbabwe, Social life, 1889–1953. Biographies
I. Title
 968.91′02′0924

ISBN 0 233 98362 7

Printed in Great Britain by
St Edmundsbury Press Ltd, Bury St Edmunds, Suffolk

For my family

Memory, that uncertain accomplice which lives within our minds, confuses and distorts things past and present. We do not ever tell the truth about ourselves. We conceal the fears, the hidden images, the deceits, the little cruelties and the betrayals we live with. Unbidden, memories rise to the surface to escape us, then hover as tantalising as a will-o-the-wisp, and when least expected stir into life. We make a sudden leap back into the past, and ask ourselves did it really happen like this, was it another time, another place, was it in that sequence? There are moments of self-reproach, self-pity, confusion, and some of congratulation and immense relief that we are indeed what we appear to be.

I make no apology for any slight inaccuracies. My apologies are for the use of the words 'Boy', 'Nigger', 'Kaffir' and 'Coloured'. Happily these offensive words went out of use many years ago and belonged to a different people and a different time.

GLOSSARY

Askari: formerly a native policeman but later an African soldier
Biltong: air-dried venison.
Dassies: rock rabbits.
Drift: shallow crossing place in a river.
Inkoos: chief, later 'master'.
Inkossikaas: feminine of above.
Ishwa: flying ants, alive, dried or roasted.
Kia: native thatched hut or room.
Kopje: a hill.
Knobkerrie: a thick stick for fighting or protection.
Kraal: an enclosure, in this instance a native village.
Mahobohobos: small sweet fruit.
Ma-johnny: Shona slang for a white policeman.
Mbira: a musical instrument.
Mealies: loose maize, cobs or growing maize.
Mealie meal: ground maize.
Meerkat: a weasel.
Naartje: a tangerine.
Outspan: an area where domestic animals are turned out to graze.
Rondavel: a thatched hut for European occupation.
Sjambok: a rhino hide whip
Situpa: a registration certificate.
Taal (Afrikaans):   'the language'.
Tagati: a witchdoctor.
Tsoro: a game like draughts played with pebbles on the ground.
Tickey: an old threepenny piece.
Umfazis: African women
Umfaan: an African youth.
Voorlooper: small native child who leads the oxwagon team.
Voetsak: 'go away' usually said to a dog.
Kyria (Greek):   lady
Menina (Portuguese):   'little one'.
Noivo or *Novio* (Portuguese):   fiancé.
Sueto (Portuguese):   holiday.
Psikhi (Greek):   character or personality.

PART ONE

It was the creaking of the wagon which woke me, and I lay blinking up into the black sky looking at the twinkling and flickering stars and wondering where we were. My older sister and I lay in the bed of the wagon on the bundle of sacking the boys had put down for us amidst the rolls of barbed wire, the drums of cattle dip and the sacks of meal and flour. The swish of the wagon wheels through the thick sand and the gentle plodding of the oxen were the only sounds I heard and then I saw my grandmother sitting across the wagon bed from me, her head resting on the back of the driver's seat. She was watching me and put out her hand to touch me and smiled in the darkness, and then I remembered the day in the small town.

From our games under the kaffirboom trees at the back of the house at the farm, we had been called in, our faces washed, our hair combed and our clean dresses thrust over our heads. We were going into Rusape, Grandma said, and would see our mother who was making the journey from far-off Salisbury, especially to see us. She was coming on the mail train on its once weekly journey to Beira on the Moçambique coast, and the train would have to stop for a few hours to take on water, goods, passengers and wood for the steam engine.

For two hot, dusty days we had plodded through the bush now drying and brown at the start of the winter season, the kopjes in the distance indigo coloured, only streaked by the grey and red lichen-covered rocky outcrops and the pools here and there in the river now disappearing into a trickle in the sandy bed, the water brackish and fouled by the native cattle brought here to drink.

At midday the oxen were outspanned to graze on the scrub bushes; the boys lay under the wagon and slept. We three ate our meal from the basket Grandma had brought; hard-boiled eggs, cold boiled mealies and a drink of water. Then we too slept in the shade until the sun was lower in the sky when the span was caught and yoked up, and the wagon ready to move on.

My sister and I ran alongside the team, imitating the driver as he cracked his long whip over the heads of the oxen, brown, grey, dark red, palest cream, spotted and patchy, their long curving horns threatening, but their gentle eyes soft and calm. Where the road was very sandy, we jumped off the wagon to look for lion-ant holes and spent fruitless minutes trying to coax them out by twiddling pieces of dried grass in the holes. A whistle and a shout from the boss boy called us back to the wagon and we were hoisted up and told to sit still among the sacks and boxes of eggs we were taking to the store for sale to the townspeople.

The day had not gone well and my grandmother's hopes that her daughter would take her children back with her were not realised. My mother had knelt on the station platform where we had waited for the train, and kissed us each in turn, offering her soft powdered cheek to us and wrinkling her pretty little nose at our shabbiness. Our clothes were made by my grandmother on her treadle sewing machine and she used the washed-out flour and sugar bags, some of them still bearing the legend 'Rhodesia Milling Company' or 'Whightman's Best'. The art-work took a long time to fade.

Today we wore our best dresses made by the Indian in Rusape, cut from his roll of khaki drill. They were quite straight with two holes for our arms, a round neckline, no belts and they hung to our scrawny knees, covered, as the rest of our legs were, in scratches from thorn bushes, scabs and old veldt-sores. Our only shoes were veldschoen made by my grandfather from the skins of the buck he shot for the pot, but they covered our horny, scabby feet.

'No Ma,' said my mother, 'I can't take them back this time but I'll come back soon when Bill has finished the house. He's out of work again so it shouldn't be long.' She went on to say it was only her wages from the Greek at the Station Hotel in Salisbury where she worked as a waitress, which kept them going and they went on talking, their voices rising and falling whilst we children sat on the edge of the verandah, watching and wondering about the people who came and went, speculating about the tins and boxes on the shop counter across the road, eyeing the rows of jars of pink, red and green sweets and the rolls of brightly coloured cloth for sale to the natives for their women, and in awe of the trains hissing and puffing as they shunted grandly back and forth.

There was a long silence and I turned to look at my mother and saw she was about to cry, but my grandmother quickly got to her feet,

4

speaking crossly to her and then she hustled us down the steps and out into the road and across to the outspan. I turned to look at my mother again; she was laughing and looking up at the white farmer about to go into the store but when I waved timidly to her, she did not see me.

Soon the oxen were inspanned, the boxes, sacks, drums of cattle dip and the basket full of shop bread stacked, we were lifted up onto the wagon bed, the driver cracked his whip, the voorlooper took the leading rein and the oxen slowly plodded ahead. My grandma was sitting against the back of the driver's seat and as I looked at her again, she leaned forward to kiss me but I felt her tongue on my lips and slowly she slipped the sweet she had been sucking, into my mouth. 'What is going to happen to you?' she asked no one in particular but she had tears in her eyes as she hugged me to herself and I fell asleep again.

My grandparents worked hard on their farm to make a living, but had not sought advice in this new Promised Land. They had planted tobacco, a crop destined to enrich the many newcomers, but the soil on Rockingstone Farm was not suited to this demanding crop and very soon it withered and died from the drought and was laid waste by pests or locusts, so they turned to maize.

There were granite outcrops scattered over the farm, so the crop was planted in patches wherever level ground was found, but the best mealies flourished across the river on the edge of the bush where, miles beyond, lay a vast native kraal of many thousands of Mashona people. Daily my grandfather rode on his mule over the drift into the lands to inspect his crop growing there on some two hundred acres. 'At last,' he thought, 'these look a damn sight better than anything else I've had.' He rode between the rows on his mule, inspecting the mealies, their stalks risking to some nine feet, the tassels glistening in the bright sunlight and the new cobs fat and firm.

But when he rode over the next afternoon, he found his maize trampled and devastated. Furiously summoning the headman from the Mashona kraal, he demanded the culprits be handed over and even threatened to call the police from Rusape to find and punish the thieves. The headman, a proud and grizzled old man, stated his case, saying his men had not stolen the mealies. They were not thieves, he said, and they grew their own. Then he suggested my grandfather look up to the granite kopjes which ringed the farm. Puzzled, Grandad followed the direction of the outstretched arm and saw the dark shapes scampering through the bush on the skyline — baboons, hundreds of them. He reached for his rifle in the saddle bag and fired twice into the air. Baboons of all sizes scattered from the maize lands, from the trees and from the rocky outcrops, screeching and barking as they fled. The crop was annihilated but the remaining cobs were gathered and thereafter used as bait in traps of many kinds.

We squatted on our haunches watching the boys hollowing out a small hole in each pumpkin and then filling it with the mealies; when the baboon put his hand in to get the mealies, they said, he would not let go and was trapped, the clenched fist being too big to come out of the pumpkin and the baboon lacking the sense to release his prize. The pumpkins were tied fast to stakes in the ground and the baboons clubbed to death. We saw them all, big and small, crucified on the wire netting of the chicken houses, some of them pecked away by the fowls and some lying on the ground, greying and shrivelling in the heat of the day. They were a deterrent to their fellows and for the time being we were free of their depredations, but no crops were safe and when the river rose in the heavy summer rains, we watched them running along the further river bank as though trying to find a shallow ford to cross over by.

One afternoon as my grandmother sat sewing on her verandah, a cry from one of the boys made her look up to see a large male baboon swinging from a low hanging branch of a tree across the river. Slowly she picked up Grandad's rifle from his chair, sighted and pulled the trigger. The baboon caught the bullet as he made his downward swing and dropped like a stone into the swirling water as his mates scattered, screaming and chattering with fright.

Many immigrant farmers had arrived from England after the War and moved into the district. My grandfather, ever anxious to earn a little extra money, saw his chance to make bricks to sell to the new homesteaders for their houses and tobacco barns and he rode off on his mule to see what orders he could get. The farm boys dug the clay from the river banks and packed it into simple wooden moulds, then laid the soft, yellow bricks in the sun to dry. Two weeks later, dry and solid, they were built into kilns and, when our young uncles arrived back from the Cape on their holidays at the beginning of winter, the bricks would be fired.

As soon as the young men had arrived, a hunt to shoot for the pot was planned and many hours were spent cleaning their rifles, filling their bandoliers with bullets and cartridges, trying on their heavy boots. Their

6

shotguns were taken down and oiled and targets set up on the kaffir-orange trees. We hid while they tested their guns, frightened by the noise and flashes and, when we woke the next morning, the house lay quiet and peaceful. The three brothers and their father had risen long before dawn, summoned some of the boys and made for the high plateau many miles from the farm where they knew herds of eland, kudu, reedbuck and sable grazed. There, too, were buffalo but they avoided the big, grey beasts knowing them to be dangerous if wounded and they were hard to see in the dense scrub and mopani trees.

That evening the men returned, but with only one eland cow hanging on a pole by her feet and carried by several boys. She had had a calf at foot, my uncle said, but it had escaped them and run off into the bush when the mother fell. She lay in the yard and by the lamplight I could see her soft grey under-belly, her udder and teats creamy white and smooth. My sister fetched a spoon and, amidst laughter, knelt down to milk the dead animal, but there was no milk, only the soft empty pouch. The next day she would be cut up, the meat put aside for the making of biltong and the head, legs and offal given to the boys who had accompanied the men on their hunt.

My youngest uncle was delegated to help his mother make the biltong. The meat was carefully removed from the bones by running one's hands along the muscle line and slicing the meat into thick fillets. Handfuls of rock salt were thrown between the layers of meat in the tin bath, together with pepper and ground coriander from Grandma's small stock of herbs and the meat was then left to marinate for some days. My sister and I were shown how to bend thin wire into hooks; the meat was threaded on and hung in the shade of the mopani trees to dry out.

The remaining pieces of meat were scraped meticulously from the bones which were thrown to the dogs or given to the labour force, and those small scraps were stewed with wild onion and thyme. We enjoyed the change from the mealies, vegetables and occasional stringy Mashona hen which was our every day diet.

When the men went off to see to the firing of the brick kilns, Grandma summoned her house servant to help her kill and dress a pig, so that there would be enough to eat. He was a large pink animal and his screams of terror and anger filled the air as he was cornered in his sty by the servant. A sharp blow from a wooden mallet stunned him instantly and, before he had fallen to the ground, his throat was cut. We rushed to watch the grisly event, wide-eyed and wondering, but reluctant to forego the excitement of watching the butchery. The carcase was laid in a

7

strawfilled trench, boiling water poured over it and soon there was just a pile of pink meat lying on the grass. The blood was collected in a basin, put on the back of the Dover stove to cook slowly and then fed to the ducks. Guts were cleaned out and washed for the sausages we would make from the fattier meat and the bladder was rinsed out, a reed inserted, and given to me for a balloon. I ran about waving it in the air, but very soon the delicate skin cracked and the air escaped.

As we sat in the dark, waiting for the men to join us, the liver and kidneys were cooked on the open fire, and we savoured the smell and then the meat which we ate with our fingers. The house servant and the farm boys sat a little distance away, cackling and laughing as the events of the hunt were re-told. The dogs crouched in the darkness hoping and waiting for the bones which would be thrown to them, but soon we became sleepy and were taken indoors to bed.

The kilns had been successfully fired and, when they were opened to cool off, my uncles returned by train, a journey of four days and nights to the Cape to their schools and university, and life went on as before. We invented new games, running through the air tunnels of the cooled kilns, or hiding from each other amongst the piles of loose bricks which threatened to collapse at the slightest movement. When it grew dark and we heard the sound of tom-toms from the Mashona kraal in the distance, we took hands and ran as fast as we could back to the homestead, where we found our grandmother about to set off to find us. Seizing us in turn, she dragged us into the lamplight, to find we were covered in fleas and little brown ticks which had embedded themselves into the creases of our bodies. We were stripped of our dresses and knickers and made to sit outside the house in the tin bath, so recently occupied by the dead pig, and doused with hot water liberally laced with Jeyes Fluid. Paraffin was rubbed into our hair, our eyes watered and stung, our skin itched and our fingers and toes crinkled and turned grey, and then we were beaten and sent to bed.

'Come and see what Grandpa's doing,' called my sister and I pressed my eye to the keyhole in the door of the store room. There he sat, a large, pink, naked man in a very small tin bath, a candle on the floor beside him throwing up a grotesque shadow on the wall, as he carefully turned the pages of a very old newspaper he was reading. Next to the candle was a soap dish and a small towel. As we watched, he carefully removed one leg from the greying water and rubbed his toes, flexing them before starting on the other foot, slid down a little in the bath, adjusted the candle light and went on reading. He was a large elderly man with a long white beard and full moustaches, but no hair at all on his head which he now proceeded to soap and rinse and then pat dry. Carefully wiping his hands on the towel, he turned another page, adjusted his spectacles, moved the candle again and slid back into the soapy water.

We giggled as we watched him but, as there appeared to be no further action, we left him among his bathing paraphernalia, the sacks of dried mealie cobs to be used as rations for the labourers, the sacks of mealies for the grinding mill and which we would eat or sell to other homesteaders, and the stacks of dried cattle hides. Farm tools hung from the rafters, with spiders spinning their webs over reims made from the spoiled hides and used as we use ropes and chains today.

Often I had watched the boys cut and make the reims. The hide, still wet and fresh, was laid out on the ground under a tree and, starting from the outside edge, was cut in as long a strip as possible before starting again on another length. Ideally they should have been about ten feet long, and when it was all cut into strips, these were thrown over a branch and the two bundles of ends were gathered up and tied to a big stone which had been rammed into a sack. A strong pole was pushed through the sack and, with two boys at each end of the pole, it was twisted and released, until the reims were fully stretched and dry. They were used for hauling cattle out of the river, for harness for the ox team, for tying up bundles of corrugated iron which roofed every house, shed and barn throughout the territory, and sometimes for tying up a thief or criminal caught stealing maize, cattle or even my grandmother's precious fowls.

When a thief was caught by the farm boys, he usually turned out to be a man from a minor tribe and was thus dealt with by my grandfather. Grandma took us down to the river to play amongst the pools and waterfalls, splashing in the clear water, finding pebbles of all sizes and colours which we collected in our aprons, but we knew what was happening at the homestead. The thief was being tied to a fence post and my grandfather was going to take his rhino hide sjambok to him. The roar of the river and the waterfall drowned the lash of the whip, the screams and cries and pleadings of the victim and the slow handclapping and grunts from the farm boys, at every stroke as it fell. When the beating was over, the man would be untied and a bucket of water and Jeyes Fluid poured over his back and he would be escorted to the boundary and threatened with worse if he was ever caught again.

Word soon got about that thieves were severely dealt with by the Inkoos at Rockingstone Farm, and not long afterwards the district policeman would come riding up on his horse, his askari loping beside him, holding on to the stirrup iron. The policeman was a young Englishman not long out from England where he had been recruited into the British South Africa Police. His stiffly starched khaki jacket and shorts, his highly polished leggings, his bandoliers strapped over his shoulders and his white pith helmet with its shining badge gave him status as the Law itself. He came astride his handsome horse and was accompanied by his askari, usually a tribesman recruited in far off Matabeleland and thus unlikely to be prejudiced in favour of Mashonas. He wore khaki jumper and shorts, his pillbox cap jauntily to one side of his head, his blanket neatly over his shoulder and his feet bare.

The constable dismounted, handing the reins to the askari and joined my grandmother on the verandah for coffee; the askari went off to the native compound for a gourd of soured milk and to learn what he could of the recent theft and the subsequent savage beating. The horse was unsaddled and led by a very frightened picannin to the duck pond for a long drink and a roll in the sand. The terrified child held the halter as far from him as he could and then slipped it over a fence post to join the farm boys squatting on their haunches, passing the gourd and speculating about the white policeman, the askari and the horse, but he soon forgot his fear and joined in laughing at their ribald comments and antics.

The arrival of the policeman on his three-monthly visit did much to hearten my grandparents, who felt they were forgotten by the authorities. The young man, handsome and fair, covered a vast territory, listened to complaints about stock theft, and to grievances between master and servant, set broken legs and arms, promised to ask a doctor from Rusape to make a special trip for anything more serious, diagnosed measles, ringworm and malaria in the children of the white settlers, hookworm and yaws in the labour force. Depending on his taste, he eyed the daughters of the household, flirted mildly with the farmer's wife or repelled the advances of the lonely wife whose husband was away shooting for the pot. Sometimes he stayed for a meal before saddling up, calling to his askari and riding off into the bush to camp beside the river. He was the only link between the homesteaders and their neighbours and his askari the only link between the authorities and the Mashona people in their kraals deep in the bush and the surrounding hills.

On this occasion I had slowly and carefully sidled up to the verandah to hear what was being discussed, but was puzzled by the remark 'So many go over the river,' and then realised they were talking about the number of cattle they suspected the Mashona stole but the policeman politely suggested that this could not be so. More likely it was the work of dissident bands of men who had left the safety of their kraals and the suzerainty of their chief, he said, and who stole from outlying farms or moved in with the farm boys unbeknown to the farmer.

The headman, he said, sweeping his arm to the east where the Mashona kraal lay, was very firm with his people, and they lived by their own primitive code and would not steal from someone so nearby. They were afraid of my grandfather's reputation and his terrible weapons. Those tribesmen who had left their kraals for employment on the farms were treated fairly and firmly, but there was an unspoken acceptance that something shameful had happened a long time ago, to reduce them to a life of service to the whites. Often the grown-ups talked about the war, but I knew that that had happened long after the country had been colonised. No, it was something further back, and then I remembered the word 'rebellion' had been mentioned when my grandfather had stood and chatted to the storekeeper in Rusape. It was to do with the natives and the white people, the newcomers to the country, and was constantly in their minds. But, I thought, it must have been a great triumph for us to have reduced these proud people to a lifetime of servitude. We, who appeared as poor as they were, lived in a proper brick-built house, wore clothes and owned the farm, were their masters, ordering them to do whatever we wished. Even small children gave orders, and, when denied, uttered that ultimate threat 'I'll tell the Inkoos'.

That year, we were ravaged by bush fires started very often by tribesmen in search of honey which they knew to be hidden in certain trees. They watched and waited until they saw the honey birds circling and wheeling in the distance. Despite the go-way bird calling from a nearby bush, they eventually located the tree with the hive in the fork of the high branches, and when darkness fell they lit flares and climbed up to smoke out the bees. A hasty exit by thousands of enraged bees sent them falling to the ground where they had also lit smoky fires, and there they waited before despoiling the hive. Honey was poured into goats-kins, dead bees, wings and bodies, twigs and debris as well, the thick yellow slabs of wax comb was carried away wrapped in skins, and in great triumph the raiding party returned to their kraal.

My grandfather has seen many of the despoiled trees, some of them on his own land, and had thus insisted on a share of the honey from the chief. It was brought and poured into jugs, pots and basins whilst my grandfather shook his fist at the chief, uttering terrible threats and rattling the bolt of his rifle, but he gave the old man two scrawny hens and a handsome bantam rooster he wished to be rid of, saying jokingly 'His feathers will make fine plumes for your head when you no longer need him.'

My grandparents spent all their days working their farm with their labourers, but were making little profit, and times became increasingly hard. I heard them talking about my sister and me, looking at us and debating what to do. Then I heard my grandad say 'Lotte must have them back, this is no place for two little girls, it's time they went to school.' My grandmother was not ready to part with us and replied tartly to her husband 'She won't look after them, she'll turn them over to her servant.' But my grandad was adamant, saying that until the rains came there would only be the crushed mealies to feed us on, and reminded my grandmother that all her chickens were moulting, no eggs were being laid and that meerkats and weasels had taken her last ducks and that her vegetable garden had been devastated by buck in the night. There was nothing to take to Rusape to sell except, of course, he added, the honey. Instead of putting it in her storeroom, my grandma poured it into old jam jars, bottles and glasses found around the farm, and it was carefully packed into a large paraffin box and loaded into the scotch cart.

We were called in from our games under the blue gum trees, taken down to the river to be scrubbed from head to toe in the cold brackish water lying in the small pools, while the houseboy washed our clothes, drying them by spreading them over bushes in the garden. Grandad put on his cotton drill suit, slapped on his pith helmet, brushed out his straggly white beard, mounted his mule and off we set for distant Rusape, Grandma in the driving seat of the scotch cart. The oxen plodded through the sandy veldt, the yellowing trees and dying scrub stretching for miles, the kopjes surrounding us on all sides, purple and greying into the distance, but this time there were no eager joyous thoughts of nearing the homestead, no loving look from Grandma, whose face was grim and distant, and no accompanying boys to lift us up and down on the journey.

'Why,' asked my sister, 'are we going to Rusape?' My grandparents looked at each other and then Grandma said very mildly, 'It's time you went back to your mother and started school, and you will want to see your daddy and your little brother, won't you?' This was the first time I knew I had a small brother and we both grew excited at the thought of living and playing with Tom, but then I started to cry and whined into Grandma's neck, saying I wanted to stay with her and Grandpa. I didn't want a brother, nor did I want to go to school, but she gently eased me away saying, 'Grandad and I won't be able to stay on the farm much longer unless things improve, and it's all for the best for you to go back to your mother.'

I did not like it at all and sulked for a long time, but whenever I looked at Grandma she smiled and pulled me to her, saying: 'We'll try to come and see you soon, so stop crying.' But I knew in my heart that it was an idle promise; I knew how long it took them to make the trip into Rusape and I knew too that Grandad groused and grumbled, saying, 'It's such a waste of time and look what happens while we're away, all the boys drunk or loafing, the stock not fed, fences pulled down, the whole place going to rack and ruin the moment we turn our backs.' Nor did he react kindly when Grandma suggested she go alone into Rusape, taking with her the boss boy to look after her. 'I can't spare him,' he answered, and then hugging her to himself he added, 'and you are too precious to me, what would I do if something happened to you?'

This day there were no stops for games in the bush while the oxen were rested, and we ate our lunch in the cart as we ambled on. My Grandad rode on to find somewhere for us to rest for a few hours during the night, the oxen were hobbled and fed dried mealies, and we lay under the cart, huddled together on sacks.

In the early morning when we reached Rusape, and Grandma, after begging the Greek storekeeper for the use of his water tap at the back of the store, washed our faces, tidied us up and summoned a picannin to carry the box of honey into the shop. She set it up on the counter and exchanged pleasantries before bargaining with him.

'Mrs Williams,' he asked, 'you must have left the farm in the middle of the night to get here so early?' And when she explained that we had started out yesterday morning and travelled all day and most of the night, he tut-tutted, removed the toothpick from his mouth and bent down to have a better look at us. He straightened up and leant over the counter into a tray behind it from which he removed several hot, squashed, sugary brown doughnuts. Carefully placing them on a sheet of newspaper, he led us to the rear of the shop, placed the doughnuts on a stack of meal bags and bade us eat.

'You too,' he said brushing closely past Grandma as he went to the front of the shop. 'I'll get the picannin to bring you some coffee,' and I noted he poured lots of condensed milk into our enamel mugs, but into Grandma's he poured something from a green bottle he fished out from behind the counter. We ate the doughnuts quickly and were sent out to play while he discussed the price of the honey with Grandma, but she looked at us sternly and said: 'Wait by the front for me.'

My Grandad had in the meantime strolled over to the Station Master's office to hear the latest news and to talk over old times when he too had been an employee of the Rhodesia Railways and had lived at a shunting siding ten miles down the line in the Salisbury direction. Presently we saw him hurrying back towards us, and he sent one of the boys lounging at the front of the steps into the store to fetch Grandma.

There was an excited exchange of words between them, much shaking of heads, more talk and then she showed him the money she had been paid for the honey. 'It will pay for a lot of stuff we need, and keep us in food for a bit and you can start again with some new fowls,' he urged her as she handed him the money.

Hastily we were bundled back into the scotch cart, thanked the Greek for his kindness, the oxen were prodded to their feet and once more we set off, but this time down the Salisbury road, in the direction of the old siding where Grandad had once reigned supreme as the sole representative of the mighty Rhodesia Railways.

All through that hot afternoon we drove on, the sun burning our arms and legs, the sweat trickling down our faces and our meagre supply of water and food nearly finished. 'I thought you said we were going on the train,' I said to Grandma, fishing out the last crumbs of sugar from my apron pocket, but at this my sister started to whine and cry, saying she was thirsty and hot and wanted to go back to the storekeeper's shop. But then we saw the water tank of the abandoned siding in the distance, at the base of the kopje which had sheltered the old homestead from the wind, and we were lifted down from the cart and ran ahead to see if there was any water left in the rusting tank by the little house.

It was now almost dark, and our bundles were offloaded, the oxen hobbled again and turned loose, and we sat on the step of the old house with only the small pool of yellow light from the paraffin lamp to comfort us. Far away in the distance we heard the throb of the tom-toms in the Mashona kraals, the yelping and barking of the wild dogs and then, very faintly, the eerie whistle of a railway engine. 'Where are we going, Grandma?' I asked, but she only hugged me to her side and smoothed my hair, saying, 'Listen for the train, you can hear it if you keep very quiet,' and so we sat in the ever darkening gloom until there came a faint rumbling and presently we saw the yellow eye and its beam and heard the rumble become a thundering roar.

Grandad stood up with the lantern in his hand, waving it backwards and forwards, and slowly the train altered its pace, slowing down with a screeching of wheels and came to a halt; steam and smoke surged around us and we saw it was a goods train snaking back along the line to the dim light in the guard's van. The European driver leant down from the cab, calling, 'What's happened? What's the matter?' Ponderously my grandfather climbed up to the plate and for long minutes they spoke. At last, they smiled at each other, shook hands, made a thumbs-up sign and he clambered down to join us.

'It's all right, Margritte,' he said. 'The driver is an old friend and will look after you, but we must go back to the van and the guard will help you on board. I have given the driver ten shillings for his trouble, and he says he is making the return trip tomorrow night from Salisbury and will ask for you at Charlotte's work before he leaves.' Grandma started to cry and clung to him, but he patted her gently saying, 'Now, now, don't cry, I'll wait for you at the Greek's, he'll let me sleep at the back of the store when I get back.' But she went on crying whilst I clung to her skirts crying too. My sister watched us but said nothing.

The interested engine driver leant down to urge us to hurry, so we picked up our bundles and ran and stumbled back to the van while the driver and his mate blew off steam and leaned out to watch us. Grandma had not imagined such a nightmare journey when she had left the farm, and the thought of travelling another hundred miles to the City, sitting on the hard floor of the goods van amongst sacks of mealies, crates of vegetables, drums of petrol and paraffin, ploughs and pieces of machinery loaded at Beira, appalled her, but she stopped crying, wiped her face and smiled up at Grandad as he held her close to him and kissed her several times. He patted me on the head, wiped my nose with his handkerchief and hugged me for a long time. When he bent down to pick up my sister to kiss, I saw his face was red and his eyes were watering, and I started to cry because I knew we would not see him again for a long time.

We were hauled and pushed up into the van, the guard and Grandad lifted Grandma and our bundles up and the guard waved his lantern with its green shutter turned towards the engine driver up ahead, and with a rumble and many jerks the train set off.

'Well, missus,' said the guard, 'that was lucky, seeing you just in time, but what's the matter, one of the kiddies sick?' My grandmother only caught the gist of his question and nodded her head and thanked him for his help. He looked at us with pity in his eyes and patted me on the head. 'They look pretty tired and so do you missus, so I'll put these sacks down behind that crate there away from the door, and you can sleep there. We don't get into Salisbury until about seven-ish in the morning, so you'll be all right. And your hubby asked me if we could stop at the Brickfields crossing before we get to the yards; I'll let you down there, it's not far from the Station Hotel where he said you'd be staying.' She only understood half of what he was saying and merely nodded her thanks. The guard looked at us again and certainly knew we would never grace the portals of such a grand establishment. In our thin khaki dresses and veldschoens, with our dirty legs covered in scabs and scratches and our hair bleached by the sun we must have been the nearest he had ever seen to that great defeated, ashamed army of poor whites.

'Grandma,' I asked as we huddled together on the sacks, 'why did we have to come to the old house and why did Grandad stop the train and where are we going?' My grandmother, always so honest and truthful, who smacked us if we lied to her, pulled me closer to her, put her hand under my chin to lift my eyes level with hers and replied: 'My darling, I had to agree to Grandad's plan to take you on this train, you see we needed the money we got for the honey and it would have cost us a lot to go on the mail train. When Grandad was speaking to his friend in Rusape he said if we pretended we still lived at the old siding, and if we flagged down the next train coming down, it would stop to pick us up. I've already told you we are going to see your mother', and when I lifted my face to kiss her, there was no sweet to be passed this time, only her salty tears on her cheeks.

When the guard saw there was to be little coversation with us, he drew his lamp nearer on his table and continued to write in his little book. We took off our shoes and snuggled up to Grandma and drifted off to sleep. The slow train stopped at every siding, every water tank and woodpile, loading and unloading, and in the very early morning puffed its way into the outskirts of the capital city, stopping only for a few minutes while we scrambled down from the van and joined the many native labourers on their way to their work. A short blast of the whistle, a wave from the engine driver and the guard, and slowly and grandly the train drew away leaving us with our pathetic bundles by the side of the track.

It was still very early when we arrived at the back door of the Station Hotel where my mother worked as a waitress, and there we waited, shivering, thirsty and still tired from our long uncomfortable journey. Servants were arriving for work, windows above us were thrown open, doors banged and soon people began to appear on the street outside. Hot smells of cooking breakfasts wafted past, there were sounds of clattering plates and shouted orders and then, suddenly dismounting from her bicycle, there stood my mother. Calmly she propped her bicycle against the wall, unclipped her long skirt from where it was hooked into her waistband, looked us up and down and then glancing quickly around to see who else had seen us, she asked 'What the devil are you doing here Ma, what's happened, is Pa all right and where is he?' She bent down to take my sister in her arms, her elegant skirt trailing in the dust and dirt of the yard. I hid behind my grandmother and looked at Charlotte with wonder. 'The children and I are exhausted,' said Grandma. 'We had to come on the goods train, is there anywhere we can go and talk and not stand here in the yard? Can you get us something to drink?' I could see my mother was embarrassed by us, but she led us into an alleyway which ran along the back of the hotel, and there we stood whilst she kissed her mother, saying, 'Wait here, I will speak to the manager and see what I can do.' She disappeared and came back several minutes later to say we could rest in the store-room at the back by the gate but that she had to be at work in the diningroom and would send us out some hot food and coffee. Grandma's face got very red when the kitchen boy brought out a tray with three plates of mealie meal porridge and some bread, which he put down on the floor saying he would bring coffee and that madam would come as soon as she could. We gobbled up our porridge, and after some time we heard footsteps crossing the yard and my mother joined us.

'I wish I'd known you were coming, Ma,' she said. 'Could you not have sent a message with one of the train drivers?' My grandmother explained they had only decided a few days ago to bring us back to her and had only managed to catch the goods train at the last moment. My mother smiled at her mother, taking her hand, and then arose, saying she would not finish work until the afternoon, she would have to help in the kitchen after the midday meal was served and she'd see us then. 'I don't know how we'll all get home,' she added. 'We live about nine miles out of town, but Billy's brother Bob who stays with us meets me here at five o'clock so we can ride home together, there are so many kaffirs and loafers wandering around and walking through the bush where we pass, and Bob says it's not safe for me to ride home alone.'

'But where is your husband?' asked Grandma. My mother looked away for a few minutes and then replied, 'He's away in Hartley looking for work again, Ma.' 'And you are living in your home with your husband's brother?' 'Yes Ma,' said Charlotte, 'he pays me for his board and the money is a great help.' 'And does this Englishman you married agree to this arrangement?' asked Grandma. Tartly my mother replied, 'He has no choice Ma, he is away, and besides his brother works and earns good money.' Grandma said nothing, but she looked at her daughter for a long time.

All through the rest of the day we dozed or slept, too tired to go out and too frightened to walk up to the shops, afraid to leave the security of my grandmother. Some pieces of buttered bread and cooked meat were brought to us in the store room at midday and when at last my mother called us out in the late afternoon to say hello to Uncle Bob, she announced that she would take Stella on her carrier, Uncle Bob would take me on his bicycle bar and thus, with Grandma, we would walk the nine miles to her home.

'No Charlotte,' said Grandma. 'I will stay here and later tonight I will go down and wait at the crossing for the train. Your father said the driver will look out for me, and besides he cannot wait too long at Rusape, we must get back to the farm.' She would not be persuaded otherwise, although Charlotte cried and begged her to come with us, but Grandma eyed Bob suspiciously and would not speak directly to him. I was speechless with fright to find myself seated on the bar of this strange man's bicycle, his nearness and the terrible thought that Grandma was leaving us with this lady whom I could only remember having seen once before when she had come to Rusape. All my mother's pleadings fell on deaf ears and so, at last, we kissed our grandmother goodbye and set off for my mother's home. I waved timidly to the ever-diminishing figure as she stood in the gateway of the hotel, and at last she turned and went in.

We walked on, the grown-ups quietly talking to each other, past the row of Indian and Jewish stores where the traders sold hoes, axe heads, paraffin lamps, beads, coils of copper wire and yards of garish cloth to the tribesmen who thronged the pavement. Their owners stood in the dark depths of their shops eyeing the passers-by, the tribesmen in old cast-off European clothes, others in skin kilts and old blankets, and here and there a grey-haired old man wearing only a breech-clout and led by a small grandson. African women were kept safely in their kraals and their men haggled and bartered for the tawdry goods. A Bengali Indian

18

eyed us as we passed, his kohl-rimmed eyes dark and glittering, and he smiled quietly hoping for a new customer.

When we reached the outskirts of the city, bicycles were mounted and we rode through the brickfields along a sandy road, then turned off to take a short cut through the bush. Here my mother and Uncle Bob dismounted to rest for a while. Stella and I were told to sit on a fallen tree trunk and Uncle Bob set to pumping up his bicycle wheels. His head was down when I heard him say to Charlotte 'This is a fine how-do-you-do isn't it, did you know they were coming?' 'No,' she replied, 'I got the fright of my life when I saw them standing there in the yard. Mr Costas asked me who they were.' 'What did you tell him?' asked Uncle Bob. 'I said the old lady was my mother and she had brought the kids to see a doctor, but I didn't say they were mine.' He laughed as he looked at her, and then remarked, 'Now all we need is for the rest of the family to turn up.' 'No chance of that,' she replied, hitching up her skirt and mounting her bicycle. But why couldn't Ma have kept them for a few more months? she asked herself. What difference would it have made? She rode on in silence and then turned to say to Bob, 'They'll have to go to school. I promised Ma. If I add a bit to their ages, they'll take them. I'll say they're nearly six and eight, no one will know any better.' 'It's worth a try,' replied Bob, 'thank Gawd they don't understand much English.' 'Be careful,' advised Charlotte, 'they may understand more than we think.'

It was dark when we neared the house lying in a hollow off the road. A lantern stood alight at a gatepost and as we were put down to the ground and stretched our legs and arms, we saw a young native sitting on a box at the back door of the house. He was peeling potatoes and gently pushing an old pram backwards and forwards with his foot. Inside lay my two-year-old brother asleep, but my mother lifted him out crooning and kissing and held him down to see us. But he was shy and turned away to smile at Uncle Bob who took him from her and my mother turned to speak to the servant.

It was early the next morning when I awoke to the sounds of the servant's voice and heard Stella and Tom talking to each other. The native boy was called Jim and was about twenty years old and he looked after us from that day onwards when my mother went to work in the city. He cooked and washed, got us up in the morning, fed us, played with us and lived in a mud and thatched hut at the bottom of the vegetable garden. We were not allowed to go into his kia, said my mother, and he never invited us.

19

Our own house consisted of two round rondavels joined together by a long living room and we slept here on camp beds which were put up at night and folded away during the day. My mother's big double bed almost filled her rondavel and at the other end of the house was Uncle Bob's room which was also a store room where garden tools, sacks of meal, coils of barbed wire and a tin bath were kept.

My mother spoke to Jim as he stood in the doorway and then, turning to us, she said, 'Keep out of the house today, the umfazis are coming to do the floors. Listen to Jim and do what he says,' and she mounted her cycle and joined Bob who was waiting in the road for her. She wheeled her cycle along the road to meet the women whom she'd seen coming out of the bush and then she rode off, her white calico dress billowing out behind her, her hat pinned firmly to her thick black hair, her white shoes and stockings such a stark contrast to the native women in their animal-skin aprons with their heavy pendulous breasts, their short-cropped woolly heads and their pink-soled feet and hands. They carried baskets of wet cow dung on their heads and on their backs slept their fat babies in their skin slings.

All day they worked, fetching clay and water from the stream a long way from the house, and mixing it with the cowdung. They trampled it with their feet, and when it was ready they spread it carefully over the floors, smoothing it until there wasn't a mark to be seen. In the afternoon they fetched wood from the bush, built a fire in the yard and sat down to roast the cobs of mealies they had brought with them. Slings were undone and the babies suckled and were then set down beside their mothers. They spoke quietly to Jim, looking at us shyly, and then invited us to join them.

By late afternoon the floors were dry and they set about polishing them with rags moistened with paraffin. When my mother and Uncle Bob came home that evening, the floors shone, the few pieces of furniture were back in their places and the smell of the paraffin was still heavy in the air. The house was thatched and spiders, scorpions, tarantulas and myriads of fleas lived there happily, only visible when the rains came and water poured through the weaker parts of the thatch, dislodging the bigger insects which landed with a plop and then scuttled away into the darker corners of the house. Crickets chirped throughout the house and fleas were everywhere, on us, on the dog and on the fowls which lived in a dismal little coop near the back door, and although we had been told not to scratch, we did until our legs and arms were once again covered in festering sores.

With the onset of the rainy season everything started to grow. The trees in the bush turned from dark russet to orange, then to yellow and at last to bright green; lianas and creepers unfolded themselves from the ground and clung to the walls, fence posts and the pile of bricks which were to build the house my father had promised my mother a long time ago. Wild flowers of all kinds, pink, purple, yellow and red, appeared overnight, grass sprang up and we watched the Egyptian storks arriving from northern countries as they wheeled and circled and dropped lower and lower to search for frogs in the pools of water which lay everywhere.

The stream where Jim fetched our water turned into a frothing yellow torrent which flooded his small patch of mealies and crept into the rows of sweet potatoes which my father had planted many months ago. Everything inside and outside was wet, rain poured through the thatch and leaked onto the polished floor, mildrew grew on our clothes, fleas and ticks fastened themselves to us and the dog and we all had coughs and colds. My mother could not go to work and spent many hours taking her old dresses to pieces to make into new ones for us, and my Uncle Bob was laid off work.

The precious sweet potatoes were attacked by caterpillars and worms and my mother asked Jim to dig them up. For many days these were our only food, and when they were finished Uncle Bob packed up his few belongings, oiled and cleaned his cycle and kissed us all goodbye, saying he was off to find work and would send back some money as soon as he could. My mother clung to him, then walked as far as the gate where she stood for a long time looking after him until he became only a small blur in the distance, crying quietly to herself. I did not like him and he sensed my animosity, but he had taken me on his bicycle one day into the city and treated me to my first ice cream at the Greek café. I long remembered the icy coldness of that first mouthful and laughed with him when he held a lighted match under the spoon saying it would soon warm up. But I was afraid of him and not sorry when he went away.

Not long after he had left, my mother said we were to go to school and that she would be going back to work at the Station Hotel. Very early in the morning we were wakened and while my mother ironed the new school dresses she had made from one of her old calico dresses, we sat in our petticoats eating our breakfast porridge, excited but a little afraid. At last we were dressed, our hair plaited, and with our feet bare, we ran along the sandy track through the bush with Jim beside us carrying Tom on his shoulders. As we drew near to the school we became nervous, but when we heard the laughter and shouts of the other children, we were eager to join them; when we turned to speak to Jim, he was already disappearing through the trees, going back home with Tom running beside him.

'What is your name?' asked the teacher as she knelt down to speak to me, and when I told her she took her pencil from behind her ear and wrote a large D on a sheet of paper and told me to see how many I could make like that. From the calico bag my mother had made for me, I removed the carefully sharpened piece of pencil my mother had cut from my father's carpenter's pencil and carefully copied what the teacher had written. Inside my bag were also two pieces of bread and jam and an old mineral-bottle full of cold water.

When we came out of school at midday, there was Jim sitting under the blue gum tree waiting for us. We ran off to join him and when we got out of sight of the school, which was really the home of two maiden ladies, he carefully removed our dresses and draped them over his arm. We ran on through the thick sand, stopping only to pick the sour wild berries which grew close to the ground, or to search for wild custard apples. But my mother was nervous at having the house left empty for most of the morning, and after the first few days we went to school without Jim, quite unafraid until one day when we were stopped by a tribesman, wrapped from head to foot in an old grey blanket. He held out his hand to stop us. 'What do you want?' we asked, but he pointed to his mouth uttering frightening sounds and rolling his eyes. We dropped our precious bags at his feet and ran as fast as we could, crying and clutching at each other in our fright.

We did not always follow the same path home and often stopped to climb trees or pick flowers or to play; one day we decided to walk along the river bank and when we came to the drift where cattle usually crossed, we paddled in the cool water, leaving our bags on the sandy beach. I looked back to see if they were safe and then I glanced down the river, shimmering in the midday heat, everything breathless and still, and saw floating on the surface of the water a black, grinning disembodied head, turning this way and that. It sank, came up again grinning and showing its white teeth but we took to our heels and fled. My mother listened gravely to our story when she came home, then laughed and told us that it must have been a native boy swimming. But we were not convinced, having seen no evidence of a body or even arms or legs, just that frightening, grinning head floating serenely down the river. When I asked Jim about it, he too laughed and putting his fingers in the corners

22

of his mouth he distorted his lips, crossed his eyes and waggled his fingers at me.

Uneventfully the days passed and we got used to being with Jim all day, or at school; my mother went early on her bicycle to work in the city and returned late in the afternoon. We had no near neighbours or friends. I longed to see my grandmother and asked if the old people might leave the farm and come to see us. But she replied that there was too much for them to do and now that the rains had started, crossing rivers and drifts would be too dangerous.

I knew that the empty sandy river beds could be transformed within hours to raging torrents of brown muddy swirling water, carrying uprooted trees, islands of weed and grass, dead animals and sometimes, wooden out-buildings which had collapsed, their foundations eaten away by the white ants which ravaged and destroyed everything. Once I had seen a dead cow tossing and bobbing about in the swollen river near my grandparents farmhouse. Native tribesmen stood by the river bank, naked in the rain, urging each other to wade in and to try and pull the cow into the shore, but they were afraid of the rushing water and ran shouting and yelling down the bank to the narrow defile where the river poured over the rocks and thundered down to the silent pools, now flooding the banks and creeping ever further into the mealie lands and vegetable gardens below the farmhouse.

My grandfather had made a rule that journeys into Rusape for stores and supplies were only to be made during the dry winter season when it would not rain and the rivers would be low or completely dried up. He never deviated from this rule and rather than harness up the oxen to make an urgent trip to the little town, we did without whatever it was we thought we needed. Even accidents were dealt with by him, cut feet and legs were bandaged up tightly after being washed thoroughly with diluted Jeyes Fluid which was the universal cure. Cattle, chickens, pigs and even the labour force were dealt with by Grandad and I remembered the night when a tribesman was brought in and laid on the kitchen floor; the back of his skull had been crushed in by a blow from a knobkerrie during a beer drink. Grandad realised he could do little for him so he was given a stiff drink from the brandy bottle, laid upon the rough stretcher on which his brothers had brought him and returned to die in his kraal.

I had listened to my grandparents talking about the Barclays who were our nearest neighbours and who lived nearly twenty miles away in the east. Mrs Barclay had been sick and needed to see a doctor urgently so they had harnessed their mules and set off early in the morning. When they came to the river, they found it in flood but they urged their mules into the water and carefully and slowly they started to swim; but half way across, Mrs Barclay's mule had panicked and unseated her and she fell into the swiftly running water. Her husband tried to save her. He could just see her clinging to a rock, but when he looked upstream, he saw to his horror a large tree-trunk bobbing and bouncing along the waves and he realised that it would collide with his wife before he could reach her. She was shouting and looking towards him and did not see the tree. It struck her with such force she was hurled away and sank immediately. Poor Jack Barclay called and shouted and swam around desperately looking for his wife, but she had gone. Finally he had to turn his mule back the way they had come, dismounting and swimming with it until they reached the river bank.

My grandfather had told us many such stories, all true he swore, and also of the many tribesmen who had been drowned in flash floods, women and picannins washed up dead many miles from their kraals. But these elicited little sympathy from the settlers who considered it inexcusable that the indigenous people should act in such a foolhardy fashion. That is, if they thought about it at all. Rivers, therefore, filled us with a terrible fear and we were very wary of paddling or even attempting to swim. We knew crocodiles lurked in deep pools, leguaans lived under river banks among the reeds and a lash from their tails could seriously wound. Snakes too could be encountered, twined around branches and tree trunks which had fallen into the river, and there were many frightening stories of drowning people clutching at trees in the water, only to be bitten and killed by the terrified snakes desperate in their attempts to survive.

Snakes occupied our thoughts, the more so as we never wore shoes when we played around the house or in the bush, but our only encounter with a snake had been when Stella sat up a tree playing with her rag doll. She saw and reached for what she thought was a pretty little green belt hanging from a branch but as she leaned forward her doll fell from her lap on to the ground below and the snake slithered quietly and swiftly up to a higher branch where it lay flickering its forked tongue and waiting for small birds.

One day, without any prior warning, my father appeared in the yard carrying over his shoulder a kitbag full of clothes and a few groceries. As he hugged my mother we watched, interested but afraid of this man we could not remember. He explained that he had given up looking for work and was home for good this time. He was suffering from malaria and was put to bed and we rummaged through his kitbag. Quickly we discarded his clothes, his boots and his packets of cigarettes and matches and fell upon the loaves of bread, the tins of golden syrup and the few potatoes he had brought with him. My mother slapped us and took them away and proceeded to empty the bag herself. Wrapped in an old shirt was about ten pounds of rice and in a separate packet, three long bars of Monkey Brand Blue soap. This was the greatest prize of all. It was used throughout the territory on wash days, but we used it on ourselves, although the strong caustic made our eyes burn and our skin itch. It was greatly coveted by the natives whom we often saw standing naked in the shallows of the river washing themselves and scrubbing their feet with stones from the river bed.

Life took on a new dimension with the return of my father and many schemes and plans were discussed. The first task, said my mother, was to start digging a well on the plot; all our water for washing and drinking and for watering the garden and the crops was fetched daily from the river by the native labourers. At dawn they assembled and collected every empty paraffin tin, old half oil drums and the tin bath, and either on their heads or in the old wheel-barrow they carried them down to the river and filled them. Care had to be taken not to disturb the water too much, but even so frogs, tadpoles and water beetles were scooped up and only discovered when poured out from the kettle, hard-boiled and grey. Small branches were broken off the low hanging bushes and rammed into the containers of water to stop it spilling and the boys lurched home laughing and joking. This water would have to last until tomorrow morning and was never fetched later in the day because we knew that cattle drank upstream and fouled the water and that the tribesmen and their families used the river as a latrine.

When my father had recovered, he took himself off across the river to discuss the matter of the well with Viljoen, an Afrikaans farmer to whom he declined to give any title and whom he secretly despised, although he could not afford to do without his help. He knew the Afrikaner possessed a dowsing twig, and had even seen the very satisfactory well he had found and dug, and which was the envy of every homesteader in the village. My mother was friendly with Mynheer Viljoen. I heard her telling my father she hadn't seen him for many

25

months, but I remembered the day not long ago when we had come home from school early and had found her walking through the rows of mealies with him. He rested his hand on her shoulder and when he had left, she said we were not to mention that he had come to the house because my father would not like it and that Mynheer Viljoen had only come to look at the mealies. When he eventually arrived with his dowsing twig, she excused herself and went into the house. I wondered if they had quarrelled about the mealies.

Mynheer Viljoen walked up and down the garden with my father, muttering and shaking his head, through the vegetable patch, along the length and breadth of the plot and then at last he indicated that near the blue gum trees, there seemed to be a response to the twitching twig which he held firmly in his hands and this was where he thought the river bed might run.

The boys, lounging under the trees with their spades, sprang into action and dug through the sandy soil, scooping and piling the earth to one side and trying to stop it sliding back into the pit. After a very long time a small damp patch appeared in the sand. This was the signal to down tools, climb out of the hole and to retire to the shade of the trees where they sat panting and sweating. Tins of water from the kitchen were passed around and then tobacco, which some took to chew and others to roll into soft mealie husks which they lit up and enjoyed.

My father and the Afrikaner inspected the work; very slowly the damp patch spread and when the boys had returned to their compound and Mynheer Viljoen had ridden off on his donkey, there appeared a small pool of greyish blue water seeping through the sandy bed. A good thing, my father observed, and went on to say to my mother standing by that by morning the well would be full; and he scooped out a mug of the opaque water to prove to her that it was clean and good. But he said it was not necessary to put in a liner and he merely shifted some loose sheets of corrugated iron into place, saying that would do quite well. My mother asked if the farmer was to be paid for his services but my father ignored the question and did not reply. Charlotte looked long at him and then remarked that the water might do for washing; but my father said it was exactly the same as Viljoen's well, and thus the matter was closed.

The next day my mother wrapped a new loaf of her homemade bread in a cloth and taking her bicycle, announced that she was riding over to thank the Afrikaner for his trouble, knowing that in his mind my father had already dismissed him. She was away for most of the afternoon and when she came back she said she had had a puncture in her back wheel

26

and had had to wait a long time for it to be mended. No, she added, she had not seen Vrouw Viljoen, she understood she was visiting her mother in the south, but the farmer had thanked her for the bread, saying it would be very welcome, and sent his regards and hoped the well was filling nicely. My father cleared his throat and spat, saying Bloody Dutchman.

There had been an outbreak of scarlet fever in the village and we no longer ran back and forth to school. Our Uncle Bob returned from Umtali where he had been working, with a large shiny suitcase full of new clothes. He brought us children packets of sweets and for my mother, a pair of dark red satin shoes with very high heels. 'Now you can take Charlotte dancing on Saturday night' he said to my father, but my father who never joined in any of the local functions and considered himself superior to the homesteaders and farmers who lounged around the village dance hall, shrugged his shoulders and said, 'I don't dance'. My mother looked hopefully from one to the other and then asked meekly, 'Couldn't I go with Bob then?' but my father got very cross and scornfully asked, 'Do you want people to talk about you?' Bob and Charlotte, although crestfallen, looked at each other for a few seconds and then I saw him reach forward and squeeze her hand and wink at her.

My father had many get-rich-quick schemes but the latest had been the most foolish and had brought to an end any other ideas he may have had. His first enterprise had been to plant flowers; lupins, carnations, sweet peas and statice. When they grew and flowered he rose in the early morning, kicked his labour force out of their huts and with him they gathered and bunched up the flowers. They were stacked in my mother's tin bath and then hawked around to the homesteaders. When the weary boy returned late in the afternoon, with soggy bunches of wilted flowers still in the bath and very little cash, my father was disappointed. He had not appreciated that every settler grew his own small patch of flowers for the house and would never dream of buying them. Neither had he realised that my mother had little faith in his schemes and he turned a deaf ear to her pleas to grow some ordinary vegetables for the house instead. At least she said, we would always have something to eat, but he ignored her, saying he knew what he was doing.

His next venture was equally disastrous. He planted velvet beans which he hoped to sell to the other Afrikaans farmer across the river who had a large herd of pink and black pigs which he kept in his new brick styes. Before the pigs were able to enjoy the beans – assuming the farmer would have bought them – the army worms demolished the crop.

Surveying his devastated fields my father swore he would not be beaten and walked over ostensibly to have a chat with the Dutchman whom he found sitting on his verandah taking early morning coffee with his wife and contentedly puffing at his pipe.

Mr Westerhuis was much in awe of my father whom he considered to be an educated man; after all he had seen him cutting a pencil in half for his two girls whom he sent to the little school. He knew too that Mynheer Sadler could read and write – had he not read the notice pinned up at the Police Station, informing all settlers that their horses must be innoculated against tsetse fly? He himself did not believe in education, although he longed to be part of the Englishman's schemes, but he felt inferior and memories of the Boers' defeat in the war against the English were still fresh in his mind. But Westerhuis also thought his neighbour a fool where practical matters stood, and wondered how the school fees were paid.

Mynheer Sadler did not seem to spend any time at home and the servant had told him that the Inkoos was always looking for other work in the town or in the surrounding country towns. But was there not enough work for him to do on his own plot here? If he, like the Afrikaners around, would attend to his lands, grow vegetables, keep a milk cow and a few hens, he would have no need to go tramping the roads to search for other work. And what of his young wife? He allowed her to give lodgings to another man, and worse still, forced her to bicycle into the town every day to work as a waitress, leaving her small girl children in the care of a kaffir, and a young man at that!

Every morning one of the sad-faced little girls came over to the farm and stood there on his back verandah, where his wife was separating the milk. The little girl brought an empty bottle with her and timidly asked if there was any milk to spare, could they have a little? His wife was sorry for the feckless family and gave the child back a full bottle and a custard tart, but she never spoke to the children. She had once tried but they were very shy and did not seem to understand the taal, and spoke only to the kaffir boy who looked after them.

After the disaster of the beans, my father begged some sweet potato runners from the Afrikaner and he planted these where the ill-fated beans had been grown. The runners grew abundantly, their leaves green and plentiful and the tubers underground swelled and cracked the soil above. But there was no rain, the rain clouds built up on the horizon in heavy threatening masses only to drift away at the end of the day. It grew hotter, the skies remained blue and unclouded and slowly the swelling tubers shrivelled and died and the precious runners turned brown and perished.

Undaunted, my father then turned to maize which he planted at the end of the late rainy season, but he realised it would be some months before it bore cobs of any size and he debated whether he should return to Salisbury to look for work once again. While he pondered the matter the maize rose to six feet in height, the tassels appeared, golden and silky, and my father's hopes rose. One early afternoon we stood and looked at a small dark cloud gathering on the horizon, but as it came nearer it swelled into a whirring, whistling, rustling cloud of locusts and suddenly the air was full of small prickly bodies. They caught in our hair and covered our clothes.

The natives were not idle. They had seized every pot and pan, every piece of rusty iron – many of them relics of my father's hare-brained ideas – sacks and branches from the trees and they beat at the swarm, shouting and yelling in the vain hope that it would once again take to the air; but the locusts lay everywhere, crawling and clicking their way across the bush. Within minutes they had settled and everything green was eaten, the mealies, the vegetable garden, leaves from the sparse trees, buds on the new fruit trees and my mother's few precious plants on the verandah. Nothing was left. The locusts marched and ate their way across the land, their weight on the trees so great the branches bent and broke and the rusty brown bodies piled into drifts against the buildings and clung to the wire around the chicken house.

The boys with their wives and pincannins gathered them up by the sackful and took them down to their compound. There they spread them over sheets of corrugated iron and roasted them over the fires and we three children ran along with the pincannins and squatted down with them to eat and enjoy this bonus. They were delicious, crackling and juicy, and more so when my mother arrived with a bag of salt which she passed around. She said we were not to tell my father of this, he was an Englishman and would not approve.

Then came my father's tour de force. He had observed the wandering bands of tribesmen who passed our home every day, and he decided that here lay an untapped market, so he set about to put one of his latest ideas into action. He would make and sell bread to the passing men.

29

First he would have to build an oven and he was very hazy as to how this was done but he picked up scraps of information from the Afrikaner and worked out other ideas for himself, and soon had his workforce mixing the clay from the river with sand to make bricks.

He did not have them fired, supposing this would be done when the bread was baked. He sat under the blue gum trees explaining to his boys what he had in mind but they found it difficult to understand; he did not speak their language and in any case their women cooked over woodfires, balancing their clay pots on three stones, and furthermore, what they made out of clay was drinking vessels and pots, not these blocks called bricks. White men had such strange notions, they agreed amongst themselves, and they smiled with their eyes downcast as he tried to show them what it was he wanted done. They even laughed openly as he grimaced and shouted and aimed kicks at their backsides, almost beside himself with rage, shouting 'You stupid bloody kaffirs'. They understood not a word and when his back was turned they imitated him, kicking each other and mouthing curses and rolling their eyes.

Eventually the oven was built and my father set about making the bread. He had not bothered to buy any yeast or to beg any from his neighbours, but as he intended to bake every night for the morning trade, he added copious amounts of baking powder to the mixture and thought that as long as the end result looked and tasted like bread, the tribesmen would buy it for their families in the kraals. He had never considered what they would use for money. Logs were chopped in the bush and dragged to the homestead, bags of flour obtained on credit arrived on the storekeeper's scotch cart, and water was drawn from the river. My mother looked on, wondering how she could appropriate some of the flour to make some bread for the family, but my father ignored her and went on with his instructions to the boys.

They rolled up their sleeves or took their shirts off and without pausing to wash their hands, they mixed and kneaded the mixture and shaped it into loaves. Carefully the bread was pushed into the oven which had been lit earlier in the day, the door was shut and the Africans squatted on their haunches while my father lit a cigarette and settled himself nearer to the oven on a kitchen chair. We stood a little distance away feeling the heat on our faces and heard the crackling of the wood and the roar of the fire in the chimney. But when it was time to take the bread out, the doors were opened and all we saw amongst the gleaming embers, were small shining black lumps of burned dough. The recipe was changed, the flues were adjusted and experiments were made to control the heat but my father never mastered the technique and the unsuspecting tribesmen and their families were spared the machinations and intentions of the Englishman.

All the able bodied men, my father amongst them, were summoned one day to the Police Station, and when they had been called together an officer just arrived from Salisbury Town called for volunteers; he explained that the dam east of the capital was in danger of overflowing or breaching the earth walls, and volunteers were needed to fill and pile sandbags. He went on to explain that heavy rains and the flooding rivers to the north and east were pouring into the dam and if it was breached parts of the city would be flooded and next year's water supply would be lost. Every able-bodied man was needed, and would be paid five shillings a day, and my father was one of the first to volunteer.

Rushing home he told Charlotte the news and they scurried about looking for his work clothes, his heavy boots and the old army helmet he had brought back from the war. Next morning he arose at dawn. Taking his tin of sandwiches and a bottle of cold tea, he set off for the main road where the police sergeant would pick him up in his mule cart and take him into Salisbury along with the other men recruited. Uncle Bob was working at the new city jail near the railway station and some time after my father left, he mounted his cycle and rode off to work.

The men in the Sandbag Brigade were paid weekly and for the first time in her seven years of married life, my mother found herself with a substantial sum of money each week. But it only lasted six weeks and at the end of that time, my mother took us into the city. The long avenues bordered by flowering jacarandas, flame-of-the-forest and bauhiña trees, the motor cars parked against the wide pavements and the elegant shops left us almost speechless, but what impressed us most was the number of people we saw standing about talking in groups, women and children in fashionable clothes, open shops full of wonderful things and carriages drawn by mules and the general hubbub of a prosperous, growing town. My mother bought us our first shoes and socks, which we would wear to school, and for herself she acquired a length of dark red material to match the shoes Bob had given her. She made it up on her sewing machine, and put it on to show us, dancing around the room in the evening lamplight, twirling and lifting the skirt up high whilst we clapped at the performance. But no more was said about going dancing

31

and she kept the shoes in their box, only sometimes taking them out to look at and touch.

I was sitting on the kitchen table watching my mother making the lunches the men would take with them to their work. Into Bob's she put three or four tomato and egg sandwiches, a piece of last night's cold pie, two small pieces of cake and an orange. She snapped the tin shut and turned to my father who had come in, opened his lunch tin and was inspecting the contents; cold meat sandwiches, a hard boiled mealie and a bottle of cold tea.

'What's this supposed to be?' he asked. 'Your lunch for tomorrow,' she replied tartly, 'what's the matter with it?' 'You know I don't eat the cold meat you buy from the store,' he replied, and then turned to inspect the other tin. 'Oh I see, Bob gets all this and all I get is something I can't eat and a cold mealie.' He was breathing heavily and his face was red. She ignored him, but when she got to the door, she turned and said evenly, 'Bob pays his way and has always done so.' 'And what else does he pay for?' asked my father.

My mother said nothing but beckoned to me and said I was to go out and play with Stella and Tom and she would call us in later. I ran down to the well where they were playing in the sand, but I heard raised voices and shouting coming from the house and said to my sister, 'They are quarreling about Uncle Bob's lunch.' She laughed and went on building a cattle kraal with sticks and clay and I joined her, making two oxen and a donkey to put out in the sun to dry under the gum trees.

When the work at Cleveland Dam was finished, my father decided to lay out a formal English garden at the front of the house. We were very excited because my grandmother was coming to see us at last, and my mother asked Mynheer Viljoen if he would lend my father his mule cart so that he could fetch Grandma from Salisbury station. The farmer declined to lend his cart, saying only he drove his mule team, but he added he would be very glad to take Charlotte in to collect her mother, and they set off.

When they arrived back, we were washed and in our clean dresses. Grandma cried when she kissed us and, for the first time, I realised how different she was from the other women I had seen in the village and the two ladies who taught us at school. She sat there sipping a glass of the home-made wine Mynheer Viljoen had given my mother for a present, holding between her teeth a cube of sugar through which she sipped the wine. Her long black dress rustled as she moved and when she sat down I could see the layers of petticoats she wore underneath, some of them threaded with pink ribbon, and around her neck was fastened a narrow velvet ribbon with a brooch at the front. On her glossy black hair she wore a small beaded cap and she spoke very quickly and expressively, waving her hands.

When Uncle Bob came in, Grandma rose and took my hand, saying 'Come and show me the garden your father is laying out and I want to see the farm you girls are making'. We led her out and proudly showed her our newly dried cattle, the donkey and the little pig my father had modelled for us and which he had coloured with black shoe polish. The future garden was hardly in evidence although there were a few bricks placed as markers, and Grandma sniffed as she viewed her surroundings. She seemed reluctant to join the grown-ups. 'Do you like living here now?' she asked, and when I replied that I did, she said, 'You must always try and help your mother in the house, she's not very well and needs a lot of rest.' This remark puzzled me because my mother no longer went into town to work and had been at home with us for a long time. But she often looked as though she had been crying, and would go for long walks by herself.

I often lay in bed at night listening to my Grandma talking to Charlotte, but seldom did I hear my father join in the conversation. Their voices surged back and forth and when my father spoke, their voices became sharp and they got up and stamped around the kitchen, banging things about. During the days my grandmother sat sewing and chatting to my mother but I often noticed that Charlotte was crying quietly and sometimes, she just sat and looked at nothing.

The visit was cut short. Grandma returned to Salisbury to take the train home and Uncle Bob announced that he would be moving into Salisbury to be nearer his work. We were moved into what had been his bedroom at the other end of the house and there we slept far from the quarrelling voices. My father spent all his time working in the vegetable garden with his boys, the formal garden forgotten, and there was an air of unhappiness in the house. My mother continued to sit at her sewing and looking at nothing.

It was a long time after that I woke one night feeling my father shaking me and saying we were all to go into his bedroom; the gentle candlelight threw flickering shadows on the wall and there, lying in the big double bed, was my mother, her black hair spread over the pillow, her face red and blotched. At the washstand stood the tall lady I had seen

33

when she had ridden up on her bicycle to see my mother some time ago. She was drying her hands and turned to smile at us as we sleepily came into the room. 'Come and see your baby brother,' she said and as quietly as we could we moved up to the bedside and looked at the small red baby wrapped in an old towel, lying next to my mother. 'Where did you get him?' asked Stella. 'Mrs Grey found him in the mealies,' said my father smiling kindly at us. Poor little baby, I thought, imagine having to be found in the garden in the middle of the night.

Mrs Grey leaned over my mother and said, 'You'll be all right now but I'll come and see you again some time tomorrow,' and smiling at us all, she left. My father hardly glanced at the baby or Mrs Grey and was busily folding towels and emptying the wash basin. No one seemed very pleased that Mrs Grey had arrived here in the middle of the night and that she had found this squirming, redfaced little baby in our back garden, but presently we were taken back to our beds and fell asleep.

When Jim came in the morning to dress us, I asked him if he knew the place in the mealies where the baby had been found and would he show me? He looked surprised but he flicked my legs with his dish towel and said he had work to do.

The baby slept all day in the old pram under the blue gum trees and soon we began to take him for granted, although we were not allowed to hold him or pick him up when he cried. No name had been given him yet. When the policeman and his askari called on their three-monthly visit, we proudly showed him our new brother. We had not seen this policeman before but he was very friendly and lifted me up and let me sit on the saddle with him.

My father spoke to him briefly and curtly, and said he would soon be leaving to start work in Hartley in the new Tobacco Research Station and that he hoped that the sergeant would try to call regularly at the house to see that all was well.

In the cold of the early morning we stood at the front door and waited to kiss my father goodbye. He had done his early morning tasks, given instructions to the boys, brought Jim's pay up to date and now came to the door carrying his old kit bag with his few possessions in it. 'Well I'll get along then,' he announced and turning to us children, he knelt down until he was level with our eyes, and said, 'Help your mother and I will try and send you a present, what would you like?' 'Sweets,' said Stella, and he laughed and jokingly said, 'I'll send you something that will last a long time, nigger balls perhaps?' and then he was gone, striding down the path without a backward glance. He said nothing to my mother until he turned and called out, 'I'll send your money to the Police Station, you can collect it there,' and then he was through the gate on his way to the main road in the hope of finding a lift.

My father was a slight, fair haired man, his best feature his twinkling eyes. When he first saw Charlotte she was standing near her father's wagon in the transport camp outside Francistown in Bechuanaland Protectorate, holding two large black roosters by their legs and gently swinging them backwards and forwards. She was a small, slender girl, olive skinned, with her black hair piled high, and dressed in a silky white dress tied with a pink sash, and he realised she could not be English. 'My mother is selling these for three shillings each, do you want to buy one or perhaps both?' she asked. So as not to show his dependence on his own family, he had recklessly spent his last six shillings on the fowls and then he asked, 'Where are you from and how long have you been here?' She answered that they had come from Europe and were on their way up to the new colony, then she excused herself and ran off jingling the money in her pocket.

His family had laughed at his extravagance when he returned to the shack he called home, and he had had to wring the tough birds' necks and ask his mother to cook them for their evening meal. They had been in the country for two years, slowly making their way to Rhodesia from the Cape in their own wagon and hoped to reach the new colony before the start of the next rainy season. They had waited here for the past six months because their money had run out. His mother and sister had cooked for the transport drivers, earning only their own food, and his younger brother and he had worked for the wagon master, outspanning the wagons as they arrived from the south, putting the oxen and mules out to graze in the veldt and then arising before dawn to round them up, sort them into the proper teams and harness them to the correct wagons.

They had come to the Cape from Tilbury Docks, travelling steerage, and the Government had paid part of their passage which lasted six dreadful weeks. When they arrived in Capetown, his father had fallen ill and was the only member of the family who could not work. He lay in the shack in bed, bemoaning the fact that they had ever undertaken this journey and blaming himself for their hardships. My father hated Africa with all his heart, the vastness of it, the ever changing pattern of the country, from the towering mountains of the Cape to the arid desert of the Kalahari, the endless, treeless plains of the Free State and now to this country of sand, trees and native tribesmen who stood naked but armed with spears in the shade of the endless trees, watching them as they passed by in their wagons, in carts and on horseback.

A few days after he had first seen Charlotte, she arrived at the shack with her mother and asked if they could speak to his parents. It transpired that they were about to set off for Rhodesia with her father's transport wagons and needed a man along to help, and they wondered if either he or his brother wanted the job. Her mother wrinkled her nose and pulled up the hem of her skirt and declined to sit on the only chair in the one roomed hovel. She stood outside in the hot sun, fanning herself gently while Charlotte explained what it was they wanted.

His mother and father discussed the matter at length and it was decided that whichever man took the job he would earn more than the wagon master paid, and as he was the eldest, it should be him. It would be an opportunity for him to establish something for his own family in the new colony, his father said, so he gathered together his belongings and joined the Williams's wagon. He learned that Charlotte's father had saved a lot of his money and had a flourishing transport business, but he intended to buy a farm in the hinterland and to settle there with his wife and daughter while his sons finished their education in the Cape. The thought of living in the bush, miles from any other habitation, appalled Charlotte. She said nothing, and meekly did as she was told, but she longed to escape from the restrictions imposed by her parents.

Before they left the transport camp, the Williamses sold all their blankets and household linen, saying they needed the space in the chests and kists for the merchandise they were carrying to the north, and they set off. They had not been gone long, when a detachment of Police arrived from Mafeking and arrested the Greek owner of the transport camp's run down, seedy little tea room where he sold coffee, tea and his wife's meat pies to the local white population – and, as it turned out, whisky, brandy and rum to the natives. The liquor had been carried up from the Cape by the transport drivers, said the police sergeant and most of it taken on to Rhodesia and smuggled into the colony.

They had found out only by chance. One patrolling policeman had paid a visit to Chief Khama's kraal; it lay many miles to the north and when he had stopped to make a courtesy call on the all powerful chief he had noticed the children of the favourite wife playing in the courtyard of Chief Khama's hut. They had woven harnesses for their horses just like his, they said, from grass they found by the salt pan, and had also made heads and tails for their animals. The policeman bent down to admire the cattle kraal they had built, with the thorn bush piled up at the entrance, but the bodies of the animals had startled him. They were made from bottles, white and green, some still bearing the gold and red labels of a universally known brand, but the plaited harness was correct in every detail. Turning to the Chief he asked about the bottles, knowing that they were foreign to a native kraal, and then it was he learned that the Chief and his men had exchanged their cattle, hides, ivory and lion skins with the Greek in Francistown.

Mr Costopolos was arrested but would not say who his accomplices were, and when Charlotte's father returned from his journey to the north, he was summoned to the police camp and asked to show the manifests for his last trip up from the Cape. He still had the copies, he said, taking them out of his old Army jacket, its three pips and regimental flashes indicating his recent allegiance to the 5th Saskatchewan Rifles. The sergeant who was serving out his last month of service, and who was anxious to return to his family in England, was a little in awe of the imposing old gentleman before him, and appeared satisfied that this officer could not have been implicated with the Greek. He apologised profusely for his assumption. 'Captain Williams,' he said, 'the man we have arrested in connection with this liquor smuggling to the new territory mentioned your name when we questioned him. Can you tell me anything more sir?'

My grandfather drew himself up, smoothed his moustaches, and adjusted his monocle and looking the sergeant straight in the eye, asked, 'Do I look the sort of man who would engage in liquor smuggling, sir? Do you really mean to tell me that you think an officer of the King's army, in Canada admittedly, would have dealings with someone like a mere storekeeper, and a Greek at that?' 'But he did mention your name, sir,' said the sergeant again. 'Oh, I realise why he tried to involve me, I was obliged to take my shotgun to him when I found he was paying court to my daughter. She is, Sergeant, only seventeen and he is more than twice her age, and married.' (He did not pause to think that he was thirty years older than his own wife.) He slammed his hat on his head, shouting, 'Look elsewhere for your man sir, and let us honest citizens get on with our work,' and with that he stalked off.

When he returned to the Cape for more consignments, he felt happy about leaving his wife and Charlotte in Bulawayo to wait for his return. Young Mr Sadler had been a great help to them on the journey north, had managed his ox and mule teams well, and had proved a good shot too, bringing in small buck and guinea fowl for the pot. He had also ingratiated himself with the two women, bringing them washing water from the river as soon as they had made camp, putting up and striking tents when necessary and cutting the firewood for their cooking fires.

Monies from staging posts to pay for merchandise delivered were also collected and banked by the young man, the invoices of sale neatly and correctly issued, and Grandad could hardly find fault with his new employee.

So it was that he was completely devastated and angry to the point of apoplexy when he returned from the south to learn from a tearful Margritte that their daughter had run off with Billy Sadler to the registry office one Saturday morning and there they had been married by special licence. She was eighteen and had explained to the registrar that her parents had no objection to the marriage and that her father had left her, with her mother, in the bridegroom's care when he returned to the Cape. In any case she added, her mother did not speak English, but she had given her consent.

George Williams shouted and raved at his wife for the first time in their married life, banging doors and slamming the windows of their hotel room in his anger. He threatened to take his shotgun to his son-in-law, to send for the police, to send his daughter back to her convent in La Rochelle and even to have the marriage annulled.

When he had calmed down and sat thinking about it, he realised that it was bound to have happened sooner or later. Charlotte flirted with every man she saw, and he remembered with a shiver the episode with the Greek – and many others. It was with little grace and less forgiveness that he accepted the inevitable, but he was thankful at least that the burden of responsibility had shifted from his shoulders to that of a younger man. For the sake of his own pretty little wife who had borne the brunt of his anger and ill temper, the anguish of the ill-matched marriage and the loss of her only daugher, he shook hands with his very frightened son-in-law but he could not bring himself to face Charlotte and left the room in tears.

As my father trudged along the sandy road looking for a wagon to hitch a lift with, he must have wondered how he was ever going to support his family. A wife and four young children in eight years had put a brake on his hopes and ambitions, but he was sufficiently immature to blame Charlotte for the quarrels and bitterness of the past year, not realising that it was asking for trouble to leave her alone for months at a stretch; especially in a country where there were so few white women, and so many unattached men and where a wedding ring had such little significance. He knew many men who had African women they had bought from the chiefs and by whom they had had many children, but they kept these families safely hidden away in the bush, visiting them occasionally, taking gifts to the chief and rolls of copper wire and cloth to their families. In the white society they passed as single men and they never publicly acknowledged their families living in the kraals, but were accepted and very often married into the well-established European families.

He felt Charlotte was disloyal to him, but his own family ties were very strong and he could not deny his younger brother a home; he felt bitterness and sadness for the children, but not being able to see his own short-comings and faults he could not remedy them. When he got home again, he decided, they would all sit down and have a long talk about it and there would have to be compromises on both sides. Naturally, he would not mention that he spent a lot of time with his married sister and her family who disapproved of Charlotte and would not visit her. There would be no need to bring that into the discussion.

A few days after his departure Stella and I had been sitting by the gate since early morning, when at last two dark images appeared on the distant horizon, shimmering and quivering in the noon-day heat, and growing more distorted as they slowly drew nearer. We put our hands up to shield our eyes against the glare and presently my sister exclaimed, 'Those must be them,' and we stood waiting. One man, the smaller of the two, was carrying a heavy sack on his shoulders, the other – the older – walked freely by his side, his assegai and throwing sticks held in his hand. His dog loped behind him in his shadow, tongue hanging out and thin ribs panting against his rough yellow coat.

We stood patiently by the roadside, fearfully wondering who they were but hoping that they were the men my father would send. As they drew nearer, they stopped speaking to each other and smiled at us, two little white girls standing barefoot in the hot sand, our hair bleached by the sun, our dirty faces and crumpled dresses proclaiming us to be the children of the settler. 'What have you got in your bag?' I asked nervously, standing closer to my sister. 'Have you brought the nigger balls?' Perplexed, they looked at each other, then at us and asked in the vernacular 'What is it you want?' 'Nigger balls, my daddy said he would send us some, do you have them in the sack?' we asked. These were the first people to pass our house since my father had left and we had waited for many days.

The smaller of the tribesmen swung his sack to the ground and the

39

older man asked again, 'Do you wish to look inside the bag? I do not know what it is you want.' 'Yes,' we replied, feeling braver and surer that they were my father's messengers. He indicated to his young companion to undo the bark lashing which he did, and we peered into the depths. The bag was almost full of dried cowpats they had gathered for firewood in the bush. My sister began to cry and whimper and the old man knelt down and tapped his sticks against her face saying kindly, 'Run home little girl, you must not stand out in the road'; his companion re-tied the bag and they squatted down together and I looked at them.

The old man smiled at me, and I could see his yellow broken teeth and the dried sweat on his dusty body and smelt his strong feral odour. The skin on his body was wrinkled and grey. He wore a breech clout and his thin legs were covered in dust. 'Can we have some water to drink?' he asked and as fast as I could, I scuttled away to ask the boss boy to bring a bucket of water for the two men. The old man cupped his hands indicating that the water be poured into them and when he had rinsed them, he scooped the water from the pail and drank until he was satisfied. He stood up and tipped the remainder over his head, scrubbed at his teeth with his fingers and then raising his sticks in the air, he bade us farewell.

His companion had not said a word, although he eyed the bucket of water hopefully, but he lifted the sack back on to his shoulders and they trotted off into the heat and dust and soon disappeared into the shadows of the msasa trees bordering the bush. I walked to the house with the garden boys and asked, 'Why didn't he give his son a drink too, he was very thirsty, I saw him looking at the water?' The boss boy looked at me with scorn in his eyes. 'He is the father,' he said. 'It is not for the umfaan to take what his father needs.' But I thought about it for a long time, and remembered the water splashing in his father's hands, on his head and the sucking up and enjoyment of it, the drops glistening and twinkling on his dusty hair and body, and his son standing there silently, obediently and respectfully.

Stella was crying when I went into the kitchen, leaning against the table and snivelling at my mother who was busy at the stove. 'Daddy promised to send us the nigger balls and now he's forgotten,' she whined, 'we've been waiting a long time for them, it's not fair.' My mother was smiling as she knelt down and put her arms around my sister, who by now was hiccuping and wiping her nose on the hem of her dress. 'Do you know how big a nigger ball is?' my mother asked, and she went on to tell us that they were only little, as big as a pigeon egg, but much harder and as you sucked them they changed colour until you were left with a red one, no bigger than a pea. 'And ten would fill a very small bag so I don't know why you thought those men with that big sack would have them.' Then she laughed and said, 'That's not really what they're called, it's something else, but not nigger balls,' and she laughed again and added, 'You mustn't stand in the road so long, someone will come along one day and steal you from me,' and she hugged Stella. But I went back to the gatepost. There was no one in sight, only the big red sun sinking into the mass of dark clouds, the long shadows falling across the road and the sound of herdsmen calling their cattle in the distance.

Some days later we came home from school to find our mother sitting on the top step by the kitchen door, surrounded by several native women, some of them the women who had come to plaster the floors. They were laughing and giggling shyly behind their hands, passing their fat naked babies to her, their velvety skins glistening in the heat, their big round eyes serious and in awe of the white woman who held them on her lap. She handed the last baby back to his mother and went to the stove from which she lifted her biggest cooking pot, and spreading all the plates on the kitchen table, she shared out the hot, steaming potatoes. She passed them to Jim, who dealt them out to the women, and put his own share safely by the back door. We three children were handed our portions and told to sit up at the table and eat our lunch. My sister, her hands folded on her lap, sat glowering and scowling, and then suddenly got to her feet and holding her plate in her hand turned and said, 'Daddy said we were not to eat with kaffirs,' and left the room.

In a flash my mother was after her and we heard the sound of a stinging slap and a cry, and my mother came back into the kitchen. Calmly she shared out Stella's lunch and we went on eating, wondering if there was any more to come. The native women washed their hands when they had finished, had a long drink from the water bucket, fastened their babies into their slings, bobbed little curtsies in thanks and filed down the garden path, across the river and melted into the bush where their homes lay many miles away.

Charlotte ignored Stella when she came out of the bedroom, but when she had put everything away, she called her into the kitchen and sat her on her lap. 'Why were you so naughty?' she asked. There was no reply so she went on: 'I asked those women in when I saw them passing. When it got late I cooked all our potatoes to share with them, what's the matter with that?' My sister looked at her for a few moments and then said, 'Daddy was cross with us when we went to the compound and ate the locusts the boys had cooked and when we eat the ishwa, he says we're not to, we're not kaffirs, we're white and we're English.' My mother did her best to explain her motives to her little daughter, but secretly in her heart, she must have wondered if it was right that the child should look down on the blacks. After all, she said to herself, they're people too and sometimes the only ones I see to talk to all day long.

A few days later we were sitting at the back door, intently watching Jim who was trying to show us the intricacies of Cat's Cradle with a piece of string he had found. I left them to wander through the garden, and noticed two native women standing at the bottom of the plot outside the fence. I recognised them as two of those who had sat in our kitchen, and they raised their arms in greeting and called out for the Inkossikaas; they carried a small bag and when my mother came down the path carrying the baby, they squatted down and undid the bag to show her the contents. There were some pounds of ground rapoko meal, grown in their own kraal they said, and they had stamped and winnowed it to this degree of fineness themselves. It was a gift, they said and my mother thanked them, shaking their hands as she did so, and they walked back to the fence. I watched them go, their skin kilts swinging over their fat bottoms, their big breasts bouncing as they walked, their black skins oiled and shining and their babies fast asleep in their slings on their backs. My mother's hand was on the shoulder of the smaller of the two and then they were through the gate and disappearing through the shadows of the bush.

The rapoko was cooked for our main meal and we ate it with the last of our store of tinned milk; I sat with Jim on the door step as he ran his finger around the empty tin, licking up the last dregs of the sweet milk. 'I am going to find mahobohobos tomorrow,' he said, 'when the sun gets there' – and he pointed to the horizon – 'we can all go together and bring back plenty.' My mother had been working in her flower patch near her bedroom window and joined us to say that she wished Jim to take a note to the Police Station for her and that he was to await an answer, but he returned very soon to say that the white ma-johnny was out for the day and he had found only the native constable on duty. My mother frowned and looked anxious, but she said nothing.

We went back to our game and soon my mother came out of the house with her hat pinned on and wearing her white dress. She said she had to go out and would not be back until very late and if she was not back when it got dark, we were to go to bed. No mention was made of any food for us but she said the baby's boiled milk was in the kitchen and Jim knew how much to give him. We were to listen to Jim and help him as much as we could, she added. She wheeled her bicycle down to the gate, mounted it and we returned to our game, intent on learning all the stages of Cat's Cradle.

When the sun had gone over the horizon, the wind started to blow, sighing through the rows of mealies and stirring up the dust in the yard. In the distance we could see the glow of veldt fires a long way away and we smelt the smoke which drifted away and hung in the still night air. Jim sat the baby on his lap and gave him his bottle while we three undressed and got into our beds. But it was cold and we lay there shivering in the flickering candlelight, wondering when our mother would return. Stella lay the baby in his bed, Jim stood the candle on the table and came in to see if we were all right but my sister was crying, saying she was cold and could not get warm. He went into my mother's bedroom and returned with my father's old army coat which he threw over her bed, urging us to all get in together, and he smiled as he rubbed Tom's hair saying, 'You look like three little birds in their nest.' He said goodnight and locked the back door and shuffled off through the sandy yard to his kia, whistling as he went.

The candle had burned itself down to the stub, the melted wax falling like a small cascade into the saucer and it was still dark when I went into Charlotte's room early in the morning. The baby lay asleep in his orange box bed, my mother's apron lay across the bottom of her bed but the room was empty, her bed had not been slept in; frightened and crying I ran into the kitchen to look for her but bumped into Jim who caught me by the sleeve of my nightgown and put his other hand over my mouth. 'What's the matter? Why are you running about crying, it's still early morning' he said as he picked me up. But as I sobbed into his neck, he told me not to be a baby, our mother would be back soon, he was sure she had been afraid to ride through the bush at night and that I would wake the others if I made such a noise. I sat on his lap, hiccuping and trying not to cry and he patted me gently on my head, making soothing noises such as he made when he carried the baby about.

We were still sitting there when I heard the familiar sound of bicycle wheels on the sandy yard and freeing myself from Jim, I ran out to see my mother leaning her bicycle against the wall. She stood fanning herself with her hat and smiled at me. 'I'm here,' she called softly. 'Don't wake any one else up, let's all have some tea.' She spoke quietly to Jim as he blew on last night's ashes and fed in sticks and kindling and then went out to bring in the packages from her carrier basket. We drank the bitter tea, sugarless and without milk, but it was hot, and then she drew from her dress pocket a small packet of shop biscuits. We ate only one each, keeping the rest to be shared with Tom and Stella. I sat on the chair swinging my legs and happy that she had returned, my fears dispelled, and then I asked, 'Where did you go?'

She pulled my chair closer so that our voices would not wake the others, broke her biscuit in half, passed one half to me and dipped hers in her tea before replying. She frowned again and then said, 'Your father promised to send me money for food but when Jim went to ask yesterday, there was nothing at the Police Station where he said he would send it. The boys haven't been paid for months and now we have nothing in the house to eat. I was so worried I went to see if I could find Uncle Bob to ask him to help us, but when I got there all the men had knocked off and I couldn't find anyone who knew where he lives. I was so worried I didn't know what else I could do and when I rode past the station I saw Mr Costas standing in front of his hotel. He called out to me and I stopped and went back to speak to him.' She started to tremble and I saw tears in her eyes and she leaned down to make me look up at her. 'I am telling you this, because you are always asking questions. Mr Costas is a very kind man, and he said he would send one of his boys with a note to Uncle Bob's work in the morning so I went in to write it in the hotel lounge. Mr Costas has loaned me some money and gave me some food from the hotel kitchen to bring home for you and when I realised how late it was, Mr Costas said I had better sleep in one of the spare hotel rooms. But I worried about you all night and couldn't sleep. This morning when it was still dark I took my bike out of the shed and rode home. It got light when I reached the railway crossing, so I wasn't too frightened but I came like the wind.' She wiped her eyes and smiled at me, putting out her hand to caress my cheek. 'But you had Jim to look after you, I would never have left you alone and he is a good boy.'

In single file we walked behind our servant through the bush. He carried a small can of drinking water, two hessian sacks and a digging tool he had made from a piece of old iron pipe, and we were searching for mahobohobo trees. When we found them, he stopped to examine the fruit which hung in clusters, but many of them were quite green and we went into the denser bush where he said he knew there were many more trees.

Stella hung back until she was quite a long way behind us and I ran back to hurry her up, saying she would be left if she didn't move but she stood there and then said, 'I'm not coming with you; long ago when Mrs Grey came here, I heard her telling Mummy about the three children who went into the bush with their boy to find berries. He killed them and left them lying there and he ran away to his kraal and the police never caught him. How do we know Jim isn't going to do the same to us? He's a kaffir just like the other man was.' She started to cry and I looked at her in horror. 'But Jim wouldn't do that,' I said. 'Why wouldn't he?' she asked. 'He's brought two sacks and that sharp piece of iron,' and she turned and ran back through the yellowing grass, leaving me alone amongst the trees and rocks. I remembered my little brother, so trustingly following the boy who looked after us, who dressed us and fed us, and who had so recently taken care of us when my mother had not returned from the city. Perhaps that wasn't the right time, a little voice in my head said, perhaps he hadn't got the piece of iron sharp enough then, perhaps he's just been waiting all this time to get us into the bush. Horrified, I realised the trend of my thoughts and I watched my sister disappearing towards the house, then I turned and ran back towards the dense bush hearing Tom's piping little voice calling to Jim to wait for him. When I reached them Jim was almost at the top branches of the tree reaching out to break off the clusters of fruit, and Tom stood in the shade, surrounded by fallen leaves, broken twigs, the can of drinking water, and two sacks, one half full. He was holding the sharpened piece of piping.

'That's all there are,' I heard Jim calling as he slid and climbed down the tree, and when he reached us, he looked about and asked, 'Where's Stella? Call her to come and help us pick up the fruit to take home.' And then, said the voice in my head, we'll all be together and it will be easy for you to kill us at once, and you can run to your kraal through the bush and we won't be found until it gets dark, and I went to stand next to Tom to protect him. 'Stella's gone home, she's got thorns in her feet,' I said. Now I saw Jim as a savage, intent only on murder, an uncivilised creature filled with hate and evil and practised in the art of deceit. His cheerful face and happy-go-lucky ways were only a mask for his true intentions. Suddenly I was terrified and wanted to go home.

'Come on,' he urged, as he gathered up the fruit and stuffed it into the bag, discarding the big palmate leaves, the twigs and smallest fruit. We stood there, my fear now imparted to my brother who had started to cry and whimper. 'What's the matter with you two?' he asked, 'don't you want to help me? Some of these are for you as well.' Suddenly I was ashamed to think I had entertained such dreadful thoughts about Jim, so confused that I had listened to my sister and believed the words she had spoken. My insides turned to water with the shame which overcame me, but all I could say was 'I'm sorry Jim.' He would never know why I was

45

sorry – he thought I was apologising for my tardiness – but in my heart I knew I had done him a terrible injustice.

We paused at the edge of the bush to drink the water, and taking the sharpened piece of pipe, Jim dug three deep holes and tipped the mahobohobos into them. He stamped down the earth, covered it with twigs and grass and taking Tom's hand and carrying all our impedimenta he led us back to the homestead, saying that in ten days' time all the fruit would be ripe and we would come back and dig them up. He shuffled sideways, backwards and forwards, singing quietly to himself and doing his little dance. I looked up at him and he smiled at me, rubbing the tear stains from my face with his dirty fingers and asked 'Why do you cry so easily? Were you frightened in the bush? You must never be frightened when I am with you, I will always look after you.' I took his hand in mine, our pink palms together and wished for that moment to last forever.

The money the Greek hotel keeper had loaned my mother was shared out between the three garden boys and Jim, but she kept a few shillings for herself and explained to the men that if they wished to return to their kraals or seek other work, they were free to do so. She had thought long about keeping them on and realised she could not afford to. If my father neglected to send her money, he surely could not expect her to starve, while the boys ate the mealies and sweet potatoes. She signed their situpas, releasing them from their work knowing that they would return to their kraals where they had families who grew their own crops.

She called Jim in to the kitchen and explained her actions to him, asking if he too, wished to leave, but he stood for many moments, his eyes downcast and then said, 'I will stay and look after you and the children and when the Inkoos comes, he can pay me what he owes me, even if it is a long time to wait.' 'But we have very little food,' my mother told him 'and there may not be enough for you.' 'If the Inkossikaas wants me to go she has only to say so,' he replied, and then he looked at her and smiled. 'You have no one to fetch the water or to bring in wood, so it is better that I stay with you; I will also look after the garden and the children can help me but I will not ask them to, if they are sick.' Tears came into my mother's eyes as she smiled at him. 'You are a good boy Jim,' she said, And the subject was closed. For us, life went on as before.

As the weeks went by the weather turned colder. The wind whistled and whined around the house, there was no moisture in the air, our skins became dry and chapped, our hair lank and the backs of our heels and our hands bled where the skin had cracked. Every week Jim took a note to the Police Station but returned empty handed and then one day a police officer, whom we had not seen before, rode up to our house with his askari leading the pack mule. He was on an inspection tour he said and was stationed in the main office in the city, but he had brought a message from her brother-in-law he told my mother. He had not yet called at the local police station he added, deeming it a matter of urgency to see her first. He hoped it was not bad news, declined the offer of tea, saluted and mounting his horse, he rode off towards the settlement.

My mother read the note, first removing the pound notes which had been folded in the envelope. At last she smiled and said it was from Uncle Bob to say he was coming to see us the next Sunday so we must all look our best and not to forget to thank him for the money. She sang as she helped Jim in the garden, we recklessly ate up our store of mealies and with Jim we ran across the veldt to the village shop to buy sugar, flour and two of Mrs Parsloe's Mashona roosters. Their legs were tied together and we took it in turns to carry them home, already anticipating our Sunday lunch. Our faces lost their pallor and our sores healed and we waited for Uncle Bob.

He rode into the yard whistling, and seeing us sitting in our usual place on the back door step, braked and slewed his cycle around to call out 'Where are you Lotte?' My mother came to the door and put her arms around him and kissed him on the cheek, but he held her close and kissed her for a long time, ignoring our big eyes as we sat watching them. I had never seen my mother greet my father with such enthusiasm, and felt embarrassed at the display of affection. Dutifully, we lined up to greet him. 'Gawd,' he said to my mother, 'they're not looking too good.' I didn't know what he meant and hoped my confusion was not noticeable.

He unstrapped the large meal bag from his carrier and we carried his gifts into the kitchen and then from the depths, he drew out an old pair of trousers and a jacket which he handed to Jim, saying he had no further use for them and hoped they would fit. Jim clapped his hands together softly to acknowledge the gift and went off to his kia.

'Sorry I couldn't get in touch with you earlier,' Uncle Bob said to my mother. 'Costas sent me your note but I couldn't get away sooner, we've been working seven days a week for the last month; the foreman wants us to get the job done quickly before the rains start next month and there's still a lot of work to do.' He leaned forward to put his arm around my mother and he drew her close, saying softly to her, 'Pleased

47

to see me then Lotte?' She was on the point of tears, but she smiled up at him and they walked to stand by the window. 'Well, what's the trouble?' he asked her.

'Bob,' she said, 'I was desperate that day I went into town to see you. Billy has never sent me a penny since he left and I've been sending the boy to the Police Station to ask if anything has come for me every week, but nothing has. We were starving and the kids have all been sick. Stella's had malaria again and the other two have started ringworm on their arms. I just didn't know what to do. When I couldn't find you, that day, I decided to go and see your sister and ask her for help.' 'Fat lot of good that would have done you,' said Uncle Bob. 'You know what she thinks, don't you?' 'Well,' continued my mother, 'as I was riding up past the hotel, I saw Costas outside talking to that friend of his, and he called me over. Well, the long and short of it was that when his friend had gone, Costas offered me a cup of tea and I told him why I was in town. He lent me two pounds and gave me some food for the kids and I rode home through the bush that night, terrified and without a light. But at least I had got something for the kids.' 'How long were you there?' asked Bob. 'Only as long as it took to tell Costas that I was looking for you and to write you that note,' my mother said. Bob looked at her and then said, 'He might have offered you a bed instead of letting you ride back through the dark.' 'Silly,' said my mother, smiling at him. 'I didn't want to leave the kids alone all night.'

The clatter of plates brought my mind back to the meal Jim now set before us and I wondered why Charlotte had told Uncle Bob that story. But perhaps like me, she didn't like him, although in that case I could not understand why she let him kiss her for such a long time.

I heard my mother pull out a chair and sit down but Bob still stood by the window, looking out into the night. We were sitting around the kitchen table eating rice and gravy and then I heard Bob ask, 'So, what are you going to do then Lotte?' 'I just don't know Bob,' she replied, 'but one thing's certain, I can't go on like this much longer.' In a moment he was at her side and he leaned down to say to her, 'Come away with me Lotte, let's run away down south, we can live in Jo'burg where there's plenty of work for a bloke like me and you won't ever have to worry again. I'm good to you, aren't I? What would you have done all these years if good old Bob hadn't always come to the rescue?' He laughed and walked up and down the room, jingling the loose money in his trouser pocket. 'I can't leave the kids,' wailed my mother. 'What's to become of them?'

Bob stopped in mid-step and drew up the other chair. He sat down

48

beside her and put his hand over hers lying on the table. 'Lotte,' he said, 'from the first day I saw you, I've been in love with you. For eight years I've waited for you, watching you have one baby after another, having to work for that lousy dago, living in this collection of shacks, never seeing another soul from one month to the other, doing without, never got any money, only talking to the niggers. Why, you don't have even a husband to keep you company, just that loser who can't keep a job, who thinks he's too good for the likes of me. I just don't know why you stick it.' But he had the sense to stop there and not to tell her that he knew his brother frequently called in and spent days with their sister in Salisbury, saying nothing to his family but merely excusing his absence, saying he had been after a particular job in the city.

Jim had called us out to help him wash the plates and put them away, and presently we went to our beds and my mother and Uncle Bob rose to go into the kitchen. She came in to kiss us, saying gently, 'Wasn't today a lucky day for us? Uncle Bob will be gone in the morning so just go along and say thank you to him now.' We did as we were told and then huddled together in bed as they went to have their meal. I heard the back door bang and Jim called out that he had finished his work and I wondered if he was going to try on his jacket and trousers.

I heard the rise and fall of their voices from the kitchen and then I heard Uncle Bob say, 'I'll have to leave first thing tomorrow but I tell you what. Think about what I've said and I'll come out next weekend and we can make some plans.' At that point I went to sleep but the conversation continued. 'You'll have a week to think about things Charlotte,' he said. 'You're too overwrought now, I can see, but I tell you this. I'm finishing off my job at the end of the month, and I'm off down south whether you come with me or not.' 'But I can't just leave the kids here alone with the boy,' said my mother. 'What can I do?' Bob rose to adjust the wick of the lamp and he looked down at her. 'They're not only your responsibility you know Lotte, Bill's their father, so let him worry about them for a change. Send them to the Children's Home if you like, but don't saddle me with them. I don't mind the baby, suppose the poor little chap will have to come along with you, but the other three, no, definitely not.' My mother put her head down on the table and wept and Bob patted her gently on her shoulder saying 'I'm off to bed now Lotte,' and made to leave the room. She looked up at him and he smiled saying 'Remember the old proverb about not fouling your own nest?' My mother rose, put the lamp on the kitchen table and quietly closing her door, went to bed.

Her mind was in a turmoil as she lay there in the dark. She realised life would become more intolerable as the years went by. Speaking of proverbs, she thought, what about the one which says something about making one's bed and lying on it. What a mess everything was! But she felt she could no longer subject the children to the sort of life they were living, with all its deprivations and insecurity. The children lacked proper food and clothes, they had no friends, they spent all their time with a native servant and the two younger ones spoke better Shona than she did. If I stay, she thought, things will never change, but if I leave them, Bob is right, someone will take care of them and nothing they ever have to endure can be as bad as it is now. Even Ma would take them, she would love them and do her best but she'd never forgive me, whatever I do. She slept.

Jim was spreading green fig jam on slices of bread for us when Uncle Bob came into the kitchen the next morning. He looked very smart in his best clothes, his black hair gleaming and his face freshly shaven. 'Well, you kids,' he said, 'I'll just say cheerio to your ma, then I'm off to town. Got to work, you know,' and with a smile and a wave he disappeared to my mother's room where she was bathing the baby who lay naked on the towel spread on the bed while my mother was testing the water in her washbowl. 'Looks just like his pa, doesn't he,' said Bob as he bent down to tickle the fat stomach. The baby squirmed with delight, but Charlotte looked quizzically at Bob and said, 'I had a terrible night, but you're right about what you said. Come and see me at the weekend and I'll give you my answer.' 'That's more like it,' said Bob. 'Sorry I can't stay for lunch, but I've promised this chum to do a small job for him and I'd better get going.' He kissed her long and lovingly and hand in hand they stood there for a few minutes looking down at the baby on the bed. 'Poor little blighter,' said my mother.

She walked with Bob to the gate, leaving Stella to see to the baby, and we hung behind them; I felt sorry for Uncle Bob having to go back to work, remembering the rooster who sat trussed and stuffed on a roasting dish on the kitchen stove, while his erstwhile companion, now tethered by one leg to the pole of the wash line, crowed his head off and only paused to cluck contentedly to himself.

Charlotte sat by the gate watching my uncle as he cycled up the road and he turned once again and waved to her. She called us together, saying, 'After we've had our lunch, let's walk down to the river and see if we can find some lucky beans and I'll make you girls a necklace each.' All afternoon we searched along the banks of the river for the beans which Charlotte threaded onto cotton for us and we wore our new necklaces, each defying the other to say hers was the best. Stella took hers off and put it in her pocket to show Uncle Bob she said, but mine broke and the red and black beads spilled and were lost in the sand.

The short winter season was nearing its end and although the sun shone brightly all day and the skies were blue and cloudless, the nights were cold, the bush dry and withered, what grass had not been burned away was brown and sparse, the river levels fell and in some there was no water at all. Jim went further and further from the homestead for water, and at last my mother took her bicycle and rode over to Mynheer Westerhuis to ask if he would allow her to draw a few buckets of water from his pump.

'Nie missus, I cannot allow that, we are only pumping for a few hours a day, and soon our own water will be finished,' he said, holding back his big black boerhound who strained at his chain, growling and barking. My mother looked at the Afrikaner, unbelieving at first. 'But we have no water in our river and the servant has to walk miles every day to find a small pool,' she said as she turned to go. 'Well then, why don't you ask your kaffir friends to bring you some in their goatskins?' shouted the farmer at her, 'or better still, move in with them, it will save them many miles of trekking to come and see you,' and with that he slammed the screen door. My mother's face was white with fury as she got back on her bicycle, but Westerhuis was determined to have yet another last word. He opened the window and leaned out to shout at her 'Kaffir lover!' My mother ignored him and cycled on, near to tears but determined not to give him the satisfaction of seeing her cry.

More days passed, but my mother was quiet. No longer did she sing or chatter to us as she used to, and many times I saw her watching us and sighing. She seemed busy clearing out her chest of drawers and bundling up old clothes which she gave to Jim.

Then, true to his word, Bob arrived with his suitcase and a blanket roll. Very little was said but their conversations went on long into the night. Before we went to bed, my mother called us in and Stella reached into her dress pocket and took out the little lucky bean necklace to show Bob. 'Have you got one too?' he asked me, but I shook my head and said I'd broken it and at that moment, my mother reached out for the lamp and said 'It's not very dark yet, let's go and see if we can find it, it's still somewhere in the yard,' and firmly but unobtrusively, she guided me to the door.

We searched in the sand for a few moments, then my mother drew me into the shadows of the house and reaching for my hand she said, 'I want to ask you to do something very special for me. Do you think you can?' 'What is it?' I asked as I looked up at her. 'Do you remember that day quite a few weeks ago, when you woke up early and came looking for me and I wasn't in my bed?' 'Yes,' I replied, 'and Jim said I had got up too early.' 'Well,' she went on still holding my hand, 'please don't tell Uncle Bob about it; you see, if he or even your father knew that I had gone all that way into town and then ridden back in the dark, they would be very angry with me. Do you think we can keep it a secret just between you and me? And not tell anyone else?' Eagerly I nodded, remembering that I had not even mentioned my mother's absence to Stella or Tom, feeling ashamed that I had been such a baby and had cried on Jim's lap. 'We'll just have a little secret between us,' said my mother smiling at me, 'so we'll go in and say we can't find the beans.'

Early the next morning we walked to the gate with Jim. He wore the cast-offs Uncle Bob had given him and around his neck, tied by their laces, he carried my uncle's old pointed black patent leather shoes. He would put them on, he said, when he came to the entrance to his kraal, they hurt his feet if he walked far in them and he liked them very much. He had given us the reed whistles he had made for us and he was now going home for a few days holiday. He also carried a mealie sack full of old clothes my mother had given him and these were for his sister's children, he said. We waved to him and stood watching until he disappeared from our sight.

As we walked back to the house, I glanced up the road to see in the distance a small figure trudging along the road. Instantly I recognised my father carrying his kitbag over his shoulder and we ran to greet him shouting with delight. His face creased into a smile under his old dented felt hat and he picked my brother up and we carried his belongings into the yard.

'I hope you kids have been good while I've been away,' he said and we asked why he had been so long in returning. 'I've been looking for something to bring you, that's why,' he replied smiling at us. When he undid his kitbag, he drew out a small box of sweets for us to share and as I held out my hand for some, my sleeve exposed the under part of my arm. 'What's this?' asked my father, rubbing his thumb across the sores which itched and which I tried not to scratch. 'Tom's got some too,' I said in defence, 'and we're not to scratch or touch it,' I told him. 'Where's your mother?' he asked and then I looked up and saw her coming across the yard. 'Hello Bill,' she said as she leaned forward to kiss him lightly on the cheek. 'You took your time didn't you? I thought you'd left the country and I certainly wasn't expecting you today.'

'What's the matter with these kids?' he asked. 'These two here've got ringworm and they all look pretty done in, what's been happening?' My mother's face was getting red and I knew she was cross, but she controlled herself sufficiently to say, 'Let's get this lot unpacked,' and she took the bag from him. He stood looking down at us and then Stella said, 'Uncle Bob came the other day and look what he gave me.' She pulled down the neckline of her dress to show him the tawdry little necklace of green glass beads and then she asked, 'Did you bring us the niggerballs? We waited at the gate for a long time and the only people who went past didn't have them, did you forget Daddy?' My father looked perplexed and then smiled. 'I didn't forget, I have some for you in the bottom of my bag.' My sister's face lit up and she clung to his hand and rubbed her face against the rough skin.

As we went into the kitchen, Bob rose from the table where he had been drinking a cup of tea. 'Wotcher mate,' he greeted his brother, but my father only looked at him and asked. 'You here again? Didn't expect to see you,' and he turned to address Charlotte. 'Now perhaps you'll tell me why the kids are in such a state. Have they been sick?' My mother looked at him aghast. 'You said you would send me some money each week, you've been gone for nearly three months and we were almost starving. What did you expect me to feed them on? Ishwa, locusts or fresh air? If it hadn't been for Bob, here, I don't know what would have happened to us,' and she sat down quickly, on the verge of tears.

My mother turned to us as we stood open-mouthed in the doorway and said, 'Go and play by the gum trees, you can speak to your dad later when he's had a cup of tea. He's tired now and wants a rest, I'll call you in a moment.'

Then I heard my father ask, 'Is there any hot water? Where are the boys? Get one of them to heat some water for me, I'll need a good wash, I've walked all the way from town.' 'The boys were all signed off last week.' said Charlotte. 'Your kids could starve but the boys were not prepared to and they've all gone home, I let them go.' My father looked stunned, Bob sat at the table moving his matchbox about but not looking at either and then he rose and said he'd see them later.

'Well,' asked my father, 'call Jim and tell him I want some hot water I need a few tins full.' My mother rose to her feet. 'You'll have to see to that yourself,' she said, 'I've let Jim go home for two days, he's had no time off lately,' and she picked up the baby, adjusting his shawl and came out of the room to where we played under the blue gum trees. We

53

could see Uncle Bob wiping down his bicycle with a rag and after a few moments Charlotte joined him, carrying the baby, and they walked down to the gate. They stood there for a long time talking and looking towards the house and then they strolled back. Her face was red and I could see she was still angry.

There was no sound from the house until I heard the chink of a teaspoon against a cup and my father came out of the kitchen, carrying a cup of warm tea. He sat down on an empty box where we were playing, poured the tea into the saucer, blew on it for a few seconds and then noisily and quickly, he sucked it up.

'Looks like a few things've got to get straightened out here,' he said, hitching up his trousers. 'Stay here you kids, I'll just have a wash and unpack my bag and see if I can find those niggerballs for you. Won't be long.' And he sloped off back towards the house. I looked towards the gate but my mother and Uncle Bob had left and were standing quietly talking, the other side of the house, and I saw Bob put his arm around my mother and hug her gently. She made no response and then I saw my father rush out of the kitchen and walk very quickly towards them.

PART TWO

It was still very early in the morning when Sergeant Finch arrived on duty at the station. He had taken up his post only a month ago and was still finding his way. He drew up the mule cart in the shade of the syringa trees and as he jumped down was surprised to see, walking along the road towards the station, a sorry little group.

A young native was carrying a small boy on his back – a white child – and holding on to his shirt tail was a little girl, her face red and her eyes swollen from crying. Bringing up the rear was another small girl carrying some faded flowers she had picked at the roadside. When they drew nearer, the sergeant addressed himself to the bigger of the two girls, but she drew away from him to stand closer to the young native.

'What's the matter?' he asked the children, ignoring the young man, but they merely looked at him, their faces blank but frightened. He opened the back door into the office and shouted 'Call Constable Petrus here,' and presently the askari stood before him, stamping his feet to attention.

'Ask this boy what he's doing here so early in the morning with these white children, who are they and where's he come from?' There followed a quick exchange of questions and answers, the young man looking sullen and afraid, shaking his head and drawing in his breath.

There was silence for a few moments and then he asked 'Is the Big Ma-johnny here? I wish to speak to him.' The askari told him that there had been an exchange of policemen recently, the old sergeant had retired and this new man was now in charge. 'Can I speak to him?' asked Jim diffidently, looking sideways at the Sergeant, and when the askari nodded, he turned to Sergeant Finch.

'I am the Inkoos Sadler's boy but they have all gone and I did not know what I should do.'

'Gone where, and who has gone?' interrupted the askari. 'If you cannot speak English, speak to me, this officer is new here and does not speak Shona.'

Again there was that troubled look, but setting down the little boy and disengaging himself from the two girls, he asked, 'Will you ask your master if these children can have some tea or some bread, there is nothing in the house for them and there is no one there.'

At this point the Sergeant intervened to ask what had been said, and then he called through the office to the young cadet, newly arrived from the training school in England and now at his first post. He looked at the children and asked, 'Make some tea please Mr Speke, and bring it out here with some cups and one of the askari's mugs for the boy. And see if we have any biscuits or cake in the tin.' He was intrigued by the three children who huddled as close to the boy as they possibly could, the small boy in his arms and the two girls leaning against him.

Again he addressed the older girl. 'What does your mummy call you?' Stella looked away for a second, her big eyes still frightened, her pinched little face streaked with tears and dust, then she replied in a whisper 'Stella.'

'And this is your little sister and brother?'

'Yes,' she replied shrinking back against the boy's leg.

'And where are your mummy and daddy?' he asked.

At this she began to cry quietly again, her face pressed into the boy's body, and seeing he would get no answer from her, he turned to me to repeat the question. He was disturbed to find this sad little group at his tidy station; so far he had been faced with stock theft cases, matters between masters and recalcitrant servants, and one murder of a lonely homesteader living on the edge of the settlement, but never had he had to intervene in anything concerning small children. He wondered if they were running away from home.

Mindful of my promise to my mother, and confused about the events of the last few days, I became frightened and began to pick my flowers to pieces, scattering the petals over the clean floor of the charge office, but I did not answer.

Tea and biscuits were brought, noses were wiped and we were taken into an inner room and shown a bench to sit on. It was obvious that the Sergeant could not part us from Jim but there was nothing else on the charge sheet which needed attention and he had plenty of time to question us.

With his askari acting as interpreter, he learned that the boy was indeed the house servant of Mr Sadler. He recalled the family living in a

58

small house in the low-lying part of the settlement and he remembered that the husband was away a great deal of the time, and that the young wife lived in the house with her children and her brother-in-law. He knew too, that the children were left with the servant all day and remembered that the woman had recently renewed her gun licence. She rode into Salisbury every day, she had said, where she had worked as a waitress, and she carried the loaded revolver in her dress pocket. There were many tribesmen and loafers wandering through the bush and she used to cycle back and forth to the city unaccompanied. Then he recognised the boy, he was the same man who had called frequently at the station with a note asking if a letter had arrived for Mrs Sadler.

'Yes, I know your Inkoos,' he told the boy. 'He was here some months ago and spoke to us, and you too, are the boy who has been coming in to ask if there was a letter for the Inkossikaas.' Jim nodded.

He looked at the policeman for some time before replying and then the words came out in a rush.

'Two days ago, I went home to my kraal in the morning, and when I returned to my kia late in the evening, I found the children sitting on the kitchen doorstep in the dark. There was no lamp lit, no food cooked for them and their mother was not there. Nobody was there. When I asked where their mother was, they cried and would say nothing. We waited for a long time but no one came, so I cooked some of my own meal I had brought from my father's kraal and we ate it together in the kitchen of the house. Then I washed them and put them to bed. That is what I always do, every night. I put the lamp by the back door, and I went to my own kia and I went to sleep. The next morning when I went in to the house, there was still nobody in the Inkossikaas' bedroom, only the children sleeping where I had put them the night before.'

'Did your Inkossikaas give you the day off then?' asked the Sergeant.

'She told me that I could go home for a few days, but I did not wish to stay long and my parents were making ready to visit Chief M'Kathlhe's kraal where my older sister lives. We left my own kraal at the same time, my parents taking the east road and I came back here,' said Jim. The Sergeant looked at him and then indicated that he was to continue.

'All day we waited for the Inkossikaas but she did not return. There was no food for the children and I did not wish to leave them. They stayed in their beds and slept most of the day, and that night I cooked the last of my meal and we ate it as before. I went to wait by the gate but when it got dark, I put them to bed and I took my blanket to the kitchen and there I slept on the floor. This morning when we awoke, I did not know what more to do, so I brought them here.' He looked down at us as we sat there with out eyes downcast, the tears drying on our cheeks.

'Are you telling me the truth?' asked Sergeant Finch.

'I have no reason to lie to you Inkoos, it is as I have said.'

'What happened that these three children should be left alone in an empty house? Where is their mother, do you know?'

'Inkoos, I do not know. As I have said, I only returned in the late afternoon, when the sun was already down. But inside the house many things were thrown to the floor and the flower beds around the house have been trampled on as if a herd of cattle were driven through them.'

Once more the Sergeant asked Jim, 'And where were you the day before yesterday?'

'I have told you Inkoos, I stayed with the children during the morning and then their uncle told me I could visit my family for that day and the next. So I went.'

'Did they tell you when you were to come back?'

'The uncle and the Inkossikaas said I could stay two days with my family but there was a feeling of trouble. That is why I came back.'

'Why did you return? Was it only because your parents went to visit their daughter?'

'Inkoos, if I was not there, who will take care of the children? I am the servant and I always look after them.'

The Sergeant looked at Jim for a long time. A dreadful thought had entered his mind and he hoped and prayed that the native boy was telling the truth. It occurred to him that if the facts were not as they had been related, surely that boy would not have come to the station bringing the children with him.

He turned and asked, 'Does your Inkossikaas have some friends near whom she may have gone to visit and perhaps fallen sick?'

'Inkoos, she does not go to see friends. She has none and no one comes to see her. Except the Ma-johnny, who comes on his horse, and some times Mynheer Viljoen, but he has gone away now.' Jim paused and when I looked up at him, I wondered if he would say that my mother had also ridden into the town, leaving us alone for a night and that she had only returned at daybreak, but I remembered my promise. He felt my eyes on him and turned to look at me, a puzzled expression in his eyes. I shook my head very slightly so that only he noticed. He faced the Sergeant once again.

'One night many weeks ago, the Inkossikaas and the uncle took the children across the river to the house of Inkoos Boswell. They said I was to go with them to help to carry the children back when they had gone to sleep. But they did not go in. The house was shut up and the Inkoos called out something and pointed up to their roof. The yellow flag was flying and I heard the uncle say that there was a bad sickness there and we must return home at once.'

The Sergeant recalled that he had seen a note in the day book about the Boswell family. They lived in a number of decrepit shacks across the valley and arrangements had had to be made to take them into the lazarette in Salisbury; he shivered when he remembered that leprosy had been diagnosed. The huts and shacks had been boarded up and the yellow flag left to fly and warn any intending visitors to stay away.

'Have the children told you what happened that first day when you went to your kraal? Did they say if their mother had said anything to them about going out or when she would come back?'

Jim looked down to the floor, shaking his head and drawing in his breath; he clasped and unclasped his hands before replying.

'Many times have I asked them but they say nothing. They cry when I speak of the matter. But Stella told me that their father came home shortly after I left but I did not see him. These two say nothing when I speak to them, but they are very frightened.'

At this point we looked up at the Sergeant at the mention of my father, and rising to pass the biscuits around, he turned and spoke to the constable.

'Take this boy through and look at his situpa and find out everything you can about him. Ask him the name of his headman, his kraal and his father and this afternoon I want you to take Mr Speke with you and visit the chief and see what you can find out. Ask anyone in his kraal if they saw him that day, and verify the fact that his parents went to visit their married daughter. Come back and report to me to my house if I am not here.'

He spoke to Jim again and our servant knelt down level with our eyes and said we were to go with the Sergeant and to show him our house; he would take us in his mule cart, but he Jim, would wait at the station for us. We were to listen carefully to the policeman who wanted to help us, we were not to be naughty or cheeky and he would be waiting for us.

Before we realised what had happened, we found ourselves alone with the policeman. Feeling less afraid, I took his hand, my sister picked Tom up and we were lifted into the wagon now standing at the front step of the verandah, the two mules quietly mouthing their bits, their mouse-coloured coats gleaming from good grooming, the white cover of the

61

wagon seat stiffly starched and ironed by the station servant.

Slowly we trundled through the bush along the sandy road to the lower part of the settlement and the Sergeant, heartened by what little he had learned, turned to Stella and said 'I think your mother must have gone to visit friends somewhere, with your father and uncle, and for some reason, they can't get back. Does she often go visiting?'

'No,' said Stella timidly, 'hardly ever, but once my aunty came to see us. My grandma came a long time ago, but she didn't stay long, she had to go back to the farm.'

'But your aunty came, did she? Does she live near by?'

'No, not near.' said Stella. 'She lives at the brickfields, but it is too far to walk and she's got a motor car.'

Instantly the picture cleared. Sergeant Finch realised that there was only one woman who lived near the brickfields and who drove a car. Cars were very rare and he remembered seeing the lady in her dove grey Model T Ford scooting along the road into the town, raising a cloud of dust and stampeding his mules into the bush. He remembered too, that the family was reputed to be well-off and that she herself was an astute business woman, but he could not see where this sorry little family fitted in with the affluent Stotter family.

'Is your aunty called Mrs Stotter?' he asked.

'No,' I replied, eager to join the conversation, 'she's called Aunty Betty.' He looked at me and smiled and asked, 'Does she come and see you often?' I replied, speaking slowly, not sure of the right words, 'No, she came once. My daddy was sick with the fever. She gave me this,' and I opened the front of Tom's shirt to show the necklace of bright blue beads which I had put around my brother's neck. 'He liked them so I gave them to him,' I added, beginning to enjoy myself now that I had been spoken to directly, some of the fear I had felt now dissipating.

We had arrived at the front fence of our house and were lifted from the cart. Holding the Sergeant's hands, we led him up to the house. It was as Jim had said, the few pieces of furniture were still lying on the floor, our camp beds were unmade, the garden was trampled and disturbed, the kitchen was quite empty save for the mealie meal pot standing on the small Dover stove, shreds of the cooked meal clinging still to the wooden stick Jim had used as a stirring spoon. Nothing else. Even the water bucket was empty and the fire in the stove only a pile of grey ash.

The Policeman whistled quietly to himself as he looked about, then went into the back garden, He scanned the rows of the remaining sweet potatoes, looking intently at the disturbed earth where we had dug them out, poking the soil with his cane. Then he turned to inspect my father's supreme folly, the bread oven he had built many months ago. He bent down to open the door of the abandoned oven. I wondered what he hoped to find and thought back to the breadmaking exploits of my father. Tears came into my eyes but I wiped them away on my sleeve and turned to watch the policeman.

'Nothing here,' he said almost to himself, but he smiled at us kindly and with him, we climbed back into his wagon. 'I think I should go and see your aunty,' he said, but my sister and I started to cry again, and begged to go back to the station where we had been told our boy was waiting for us.

He took us to his house. 'Give these kids something to eat,' he told his wife. 'I don't think they've had a meal for days,' and he went down the steps and got into his wagon. 'Ask Amos to look after their boy, I'm going into Salisbury and may be back fairly late,' and with that, he turned his wagon to the city. After we had eaten the meal set before us, we sat with our boy on the verandah, and when it grew dark we huddled closer to him, and did not answer Mrs Finch's pleas to go inside.

The Sergeant drove as quickly as he could and arrived at the Brickfields an hour later. He drove straight to the wooden building which bore a sign 'Office'. Mrs Stotter was speaking to a client in the shade of the trees, and glanced up at him as he brought his mule cart to a standstill, but she ignored him until some minutes later, the deal completed, her customer raised his hat and turned to his own car standing nearby. A pincannin was summoned to use the crank handle, the car spluttered into life and he drove away, waving to Mrs Stotter as he went.

She looked at the policeman and asked 'What do you want? Is it about the boys? All their poll tax has been paid.'

He ignored her question and asked, 'Mrs Stotter? It's about your brother's children, but I really want to see your brother Mr Sadler, do you know where I can find him?'

'Is he wanted for something?' she asked.

'Yes, I have to see him urgently, it's about his children.'

'I don't know anything about his kids, but he's at my house. He's got a bad dose of malaria and has been in a fight, but he's in bed now and won't be able to talk to you. But what's it about anyway?'

'Perhaps you can tell me were Mrs Sadler is, then,' he asked.

'Yes,' replied my aunt, and the Sergeant's spirits rose, 'I suppose she's at home with her kids in Hatfield.'

'She's not there and hasn't been for the past two days,' replied the policeman.

My aunt sat down quickly on the step of the verandah. 'Good God,' she said. 'Where the devil's she got to then? Has she taken the kids with her?'

'No,' said the Sergeant. 'Their servant brought them to the station early this morning. They have been alone in the house with him these past two days.'

'Have you asked the kids where their mother went to?' asked my aunt.

'We cannot get anything out of them, Mrs Stotter; they have been badly frightened and cry when spoken to. Even their boy can't find out what has happened.'

My aunt was clearly upset and then she spoke. 'When my brother arrived at my house two evenings ago he was in a terrible state, shaking from the fever and I could see he had been in a fight. He told me that he and his brother had had a fight the very day he arrived back and that his wife had told him to go. Naturally he came straight to me as he has always done when there's been any trouble there. He told me his brother and his wife were still at the house when he left, but if they aren't, then we had better go and see him right away and find out more.' She reached for her hat and walked towards the car, parked in the shade of the building.

Sergeant Finch stopped her and said, 'Just a moment Mrs Stotter, I have to get back, it's late now and I think the children had better stay with us for the night. But tomorrow early I want your brother Bill Sadler at the station, sick or not, to find out what has happened. I am disgusted at the way these children have been treated and I think their servant is far too young to have the total responsibility of looking after them. I don't know what would have happened to them if he had not decided to come back to the house when he did. No one seems to have given a damn for three very frightened children and if we can't find their parents, I shall have no hesitation in applying for a Court Order to have them taken to the Childrens Home.'

At the mention of this authority, my aunt paled. 'What will people say,' she said to herself, 'if it gets out that they were alone in the house with only that kaffir boy to look after them, and that I didn't do anything about them? I can't afford to have people talking about me.

64

Everyone here knows Bill and I are related. It's not as though I don't do anything for them. It's all that bitch Charlotte's fault, I know she still holds it against me that I won't give Bill a job at the Brickworks, but I'm damned if I should; I do enough for him anyway. He should never have married her.' With these thoughts in her mind, she remembered the surge of pity she had felt for him when he arrived at her home and his explanation as to what had taken place.

She smiled up at the Sergeant and turned to beckon to the picannin waiting under the syringa trees. 'If you can keep the children for the night, I'll fetch my brother out to see you early tomorrow morning and perhaps he can find out from them where their mother has gone,' and as she adjusted the spark, the picannin turned the crank handle, the car started, and off she went.

Sergeant Finch turned his mules, cracked his whip and drove the five miles home. The sky was darkening and he saw rain clouds banking up in the south and heard the distant thunder rumbling through the hills and kopjes. 'Poor little blighters,' he told his mules who flicked their ears at the sound of his voice, and quickened their pace.

I awoke early the next morning in the Finch's spare bedroom, with my sister beside me and Tom curled up at our feet; faintly I heard voices in the next room and slipping my dress over my head, I carefully and quietly crept to the door. My father was sitting in a chair speaking to Mrs Finch and then I saw my aunt standing by the window talking to the policeman. There was no sign of Jim so I climbed out of the bedroom window and went around to the kitchen, thinking he would be there with the servant, but there was no one and then I saw through the kitchen that the Finch's cook was setting a table on the verandah for breakfast.

My father came into the kitchen, saw me and asked me where Tom and Stella were. When I had told him, he merely nodded and helped himself to a cup of tea from the kitchen table. He still wore his old khaki pants and shirt, one sleeve half torn out, a red bruise swelling on the side of his face, his eyes puffy and red and in the morning heat, he shivered. He cleared his throat, sniffed and wiped his nose on his shirt sleeve before addressing me again.

'Have you seen your mother since the other day?' he asked.

'No,' I said. 'She and Uncle Bob went away together the other night. I didn't tell Mr Finch because he didn't ask me. He spoke to Stella but she said she didn't know either, and she told me I mustn't say; we spoke like

65

we always do to Jim so the Policeman didn't know what we were saying.'

He cleared his throat again and took a sip of tea. His hand shook from the shivering which engulfed his body, and I could see the film of sweat on his face, but he continued to look down at the floor.

'Wake your brother and sister. Mrs Finch has some food for you and then Aunty Betty is taking us all to her house. She's speaking to the policeman now and then they're going to look at the house. And don't forget to say thankyou to Mrs Finch,' he added.

I turned to go but he called me back. 'And speak bloody English, none of us know what you're saying half the time.' Hesitantly I replied, 'But I don't know the words,' and at the thought of Jim, I began to cry. 'I can't find Jim, where is he?' I asked, but he shook his head and said he had signed the boy off and he'd gone back to his father's kraal.

'But isn't he coming with us to Aunty Betty's?' I asked, hoping Jim's return to the kraal was only temporary, and he repeated that the boy had been given his money and sent home.

'But I want to say goodbye to him,' I cried, suddenly feeling the chill of yet another parting and the fear of what would happen to us now that he was gone.

'Gawd Almighty, he's only a bleedin' kaffir,' said my father.

It was midday and we stood under the eaves of the police house waiting for Aunty Betty. Looking up the sandy road, I saw the shimmering waves of heat dancing and flickering in the distance, and presently the distorted picture of her car breasted the hill and came into view; slowly she drew up, turned off the ignition and got out. She wore a long white dustcoat, her silk stockings and buckled kid shoes matching the tulle swathed around her hat and she bent down to look at us. She smelt of violets and I saw where her face powder ended at her hair line, and noted her carefully rouged cheeks. She drew back and looked us over, wrinkling her nose delicately and laughing. 'What a proper lot of bleedin' toe-rags they are' she said to Mrs Finch, and went on to confirm that the house was exactly as the boy had said, and that she thought it was time they left. Mrs Finch smiled back but I saw how she looked at her husband who had just come in.

'Well that's settled then,' said the Sergeant. 'I hope you hear from your wife soon Mr Sadler,' and he turned to go, but not before my father had thanked him and apologised for all the trouble he had had. 'It's your boy you should thank,' the Sergeant said. 'It couldn't have been a nice situation to find himself in and I must say I was very suspicious at first.'

He knelt down to look at us and as my father and his sister stood by the car waiting for us, I asked quietly, 'Where's Jim?' He looked at me for a moment and then said 'Don't you worry about him, he's gone home and your father gave him some money; you're a lucky little girl, your aunt is taking you home with her, so don't worry about your boy, he's all right,' and he stood up and smiled, but I cried for my friend and protector, knowing that I would not see him again.

'Get in,' said my aunt, 'but don't sit on the seats, stand at the back, this is a new car and your clothes are too dirty.' My father swung the crank handle, the car spluttered into life, he leapt in and carefully my aunt turned the car and took the town road. My sister was smiling at last, all her fears dissipated; we were excited to find ourselves actually riding in a motor car, but soon, as we drove through the bush away from everything that had been our home, I began to cry again for Jim as I clutched all I possessed in the world, a paper pattern of a sailor suit still in its envelope, which my mother had bought many months ago. Tom snivelled and huddled close to me, fingering his beads and then for the first time in many days he finally spoke. 'Where are we going?' he asked.

No one answered, and the humming of the engine momentarily soothed my misery and fears, but suddenly from beyond the door in my mind shut firmly on what had happened those days ago, there arose the dreadful scene again, and I screamed. The car came to a jarring stop and my father turned around to give me a stinging blow on the side of my head. 'Shut up,' he cried, 'what do you think you're doing, do you want to kill us all?' But I could not stop the crying and a feeling of terror overcame me. 'Where's Jim?' I wailed, over and over again. My father pulled me from the car and beat me again, shouting 'Shut up, or I'll bleedin' kill you.' I struggled to get away but he held me firmly and at last pushed me back into the car where my sister and brother both stood, dumbfounded and quietly terrified at this outburst. My aunt slammed the car into gear and not another word was said while I hiccuped and snivelled on the floor, reducing my precious paper pattern to a sodden mass.

We drove on through the bush, then turned into a long avenue of jacaranda trees, their purple blossoms lying in drifts along the verges of the road, and came to a stop in front of a large house set back from the road. Its red brickwork was mellow in the afternoon sun, the corrugated iron roof was freshly painted, the garden was full of flowers, the brick edged paths swept and tidy, everything orderly and nothing out of place.

'Get out, you lot,' said my aunt, and to my father she added that we were to wait there for her while she put the car in the garage. We stood looking around us. I was still full of misery and unhappiness and my head ached from the beating I had had. Where was my mother and why had she gone away, leaving us with my angry father and his sister? Aunty Betty returned and seeing my father shivering once again from the malaria which racked him, she put her arm around him and kissed him gently saying, 'Never mind luv, you're better off without her.' To us she said nothing and he picked Tom up, and took Stella's hand, and led us into the house.

A wide verandah ran around it and there were many pots of flowering shrubs and ferns among the tables and cane chairs; cushions were piled on sofas and low stools and from the ceiling hung baskets of more ferns and flowering plants and in the distant corner stood a large ornate cage full of little yellow and green birds, all singing, their throats throbbing as they trilled. Tea cups and plates of sandwiches and cakes were laid out on the long low table and sitting among the cushions on a low divan near the window, was a young man petting and fondling a big brindle greyhound. It lay on the bed with him and looked up to lick him gently on his face and then I saw he was pulling off ticks and fleas and dropping them into a small jar of paraffin on the floor.

'Say hullo to your cousin Georgie,' urged my father, and as we did so, our cousin rose from the divan, carefully putting aside the dog. 'Wotcher kids,' he said twitching his fingers at the dog which got up and followed him. At the doorway, he turned to say, 'none of you kids sit on my divan or I'll wallop you, only me and my dog sit there.' I looked at him open-mouthed, I had not seen such a big white man in short trousers before, and seeing me looking at him, he came back and said, 'Empty this,' and handed me the jar of ticks and fleas swimming and drowning in the paraffin. 'They don't understand much English,' explained my father taking the jar from me. 'Poor little tripehounds,' said Cousin Georgie.

Soon we were joined by my aunt who had removed her coat and hat and now stood before us in a dove grey linen dress, and with her, a younger edition of herself. 'This is your Aunt Annie who will look after you,' she explained. 'Listen to her and do what you're told, and no more nonsense from you,' and she pulled me forward. I looked at Annie and noted that she was not at all as pretty as her elder sister, nor as my mother, nor even as my grandmother; her face appeared to have slipped

68

sideways and when she smiled, she showed only one side of her mouth. Her short straight black hair was held back by a large steel slide and her freckled face shone with enthusiasm. 'Where's yer things then?' she asked but we were too shy to speak and my father replied, 'That's all they've got, what's on 'em. Gawd knows what Charlotte did with the money I gave her, she certainly didn't spend it on the poor little bleeders.'

'Poor little devils,' chuckled Annie, leading us away from the luxury of that verandah, the abundance of the tea table and the awesome presence of our aunt, and presently we found ourselves being shepherded down a long passage and into her bedroom.

The room was completely bare except for a single iron bedstead in one corner, but two mattresses had been brought in and laid on the floor. Bending over them and putting the finishing touches to this task was a tall thin native servant, dressed in a very smart set of clothes, white shirt and trousers and shining buttons. 'This here's Vinyu,' said Annie bursting into giggles. 'He's Portuguese, he don't understand Shona,' this last to me who had addressed the servant in the vernacular; at the mention of his name, he smiled at us and said in perfect English 'You will sleep here,' and then in Shona he added, 'It is they who do not speak Shona.' He left the room.

We had never heard a native speak English before and as I looked at his departing back, I realised how different he was to all the tribesmen we had known and who had worked for our grandparents and my mother and father. He was taller than average and lightskinned, but his most distinguishing feature was his nose. It was fine and aquiline in shape, the prominent bridge lending him an air of breeding, and his hair was cut and shaped to his head and shone with good grooming. Our farm boys and my father's work force were all short, sturdy and very black, their faces different because there was no bridge to their noses and their long unkempt hair was often twisted into dusty ringlets. They wore cast-off European clothes, sometimes so ragged and tattered that I wondered if they gave them any protection at all.

'You kids gotter stay in the kitchen,' announced our new keeper, and as we stood shyly at the table, in came the two younger sons of the house. Jack, a tall goodlooking young man, his grey eyes kind and compassionate, smiled when he saw us. His younger brother Billy, named after my father, was a fat freckled boy, his black hair slicked down with water, his rosebud mouth in his podgy face belying his mean and bullying nature.

'So you're Uncle Bill's kids then?' he asked. 'No wonder your ma cleared off,' but he was interrupted by his brother who rounded on him. 'It's not their fault, they're only little kids,' he said very sharply. Undaunted, Billy continued, 'those two look coloured to me,' and he pointed to Tom and me who were standing as close together as we could. We did not know what he meant by 'coloured'. Annie pushed him towards the door saying 'Gertsher Billy, don't tease,' but he was determined to have the last word and said, 'hope you bloody kids don't stay long, you'll mess everything up.' We were frightened by his tone and said nothing, but I turned to ask Annie. 'What's coloured?' She pretended not to hear and it was Billy who replied 'Your dad's a white man, but you ma's a kaffir', and with that he was gone, the back screen door banging as he made his exit.

His remark puzzled me but was soon eclipsed by misery as I stood there wrapped in it as though in a suffocating blanket, frightened of everyone in this household, not knowing where to turn for a word of comfort or an assurance that our mother would come back to take us home.

The pressure of the past days, the strangers who had come into our lives, the departure of those whom we knew and who had cared for us, the coldness and indifference of the aliens we now found ourselves dependent upon, my father's distress and sickness and the fear I felt overcame me and I put my head down and cried. Again I saw that terrifying afternoon, the fight between my father and his brother when he had rushed across the yard to tear my mother from Uncle Bob's side, screaming obscenities whilst they lunged and punched each other, falling to the ground cursing and shouting, their bodies entwined in the dust as they gouged, kicked, struggled and hit out, the blood on my father's face and my mother standing there looking on, her face white and afraid, holding the baby wrapped in his shawl but saying not a word. My sister, my brother and I bewildered, crouched close to my mother begging her to make them stop it, and crying in terror at the dreadful scene before our eyes.

I felt a sympathetic hand on my shoulder and looked up into the face of the servant Vinyu. He patted me gently and picking Tom up he said 'Come and see the herd boys, they are bringing in the cattle for milking.' He led us out of the kitchen, across the yard, through the pomegranate hedge and into the yard where the cows with their calves at foot were being tethered. Herd boys were washing their hands and arms in buckets of water before they sat down to their task, and we stood and watched as the milk spurted and splashed into the milk buckets, foaming and white.

I thought of my grandmother as I stood watching the calves butting their mothers, heard the herd boys shouting and joking, smelled the manure and the clouds of dust rising from stamping hooves, and gradually the feeling of desolation left me and I followed Vinyu and Tom back into the house. But I wondered who else belonged to this household and what more would be asked or said to us, what questions we would have to answer. It was our fault, I concluded, that our mother had run away and left us.

We had fallen asleep and been carried off to bed by Vinyu and Annie, and now, next morning, we sat at the kitchen table eagerly eating porridge, the terrors of yesterday already fading, but I was still too frightened to speak to anyone but the servant. I looked up and saw my aunt standing by the kitchen door pulling on her pale beige driving gloves. We jumped off our chairs and stood by the table nervously waiting for her to speak. Stella went to stand next to her and put out her hand to touch the softness of the gloved hand, stroking it gently and looking up with big eyes. Aunty Betty smiled at her and then said 'You kids must get washed and changed as soon as you've finished, your ma is coming to say goodbye to you, so wait by the little gate and come in back when she's gone.' No further explanation, but many questions raced through my mind. I could not put them in to words, nor could I understand the significance of what had been said.

We were taken to the small bathroom to be washed and to have our hair tidied. This was not the proper bathroom the family used, but a small addition tacked on to the end of the kitchen where the servants washed their hands, their clothes and their cooking pots and where they sat on rainy days smoking and chatting, waiting for the weather to clear so that washing could be hung out to dry.

Annie giggled and hummed to herself, repeating the same words over and over again. She blinked her eyes and hunching her shoulders, she did a shuffling dance, backing away and then advancing to flick at our legs with the towel she had draped over her shoulders. 'My,' she exclaimed, 'you ain't 'arf a lot o' mucky kids,' and abandoning us for a moment, she ran outside to rub the cake of soap in the sand of the yard and returned to scrub away at our knees, taking little bits of skin off and making the blood flow. I dared not struggle to get away, she held me in a vice-like grip, her eyes shone and she smiled to herself.

At last we were clean and dressed. There had been a scandalised conversation the previous evening when it was discovered that we had come in only our khaki dresses, nothing on underneath. Quickly my father had sat down and written an urgent note to a near neightbour, Vinyu was summoned and told to hurry back, and now we waited in the mid-morning heat, our faces and hands clean, our hair brushed and free of knots, our legs and knees still smarting from the abrasive soap, excited but a little frightened, thoroughly confused but decent in some one else's pretty dress and knickers.

Annie left us, giggling and grinning, but not before she had turned to look up the road, shading her eyes to peer into the distance. I followed her gaze to see coming towards us, the heat waves magnifying and blurring the outlines of the billowing white dress and the big hat, the rapidly enlarging picture of my mother on her bicycle. As she drew close to us, I could see her face, composed and serene, and she smiled. Carefully she dismounted from her cycle and stood it against the gatepost, and she then knelt down to take us each in turn into her arms, saying nothing, just holding us. When she turned away there were tears in her eyes, and she got on her cycle and rode away. There was no backward glance, no calling out goodbye, no explanation about what was to become of us or her, and no promise to come back and take us home.

Completely puzzled, I turned to ask Stella where was the baby, but the only sound I heard was her bitter crying and then I saw Annie skipping between the flower beds towards us, calling 'Come to Annie'. Only Stella ran towards her. Tom and I stood and watched the figure of our mother getting smaller and smaller and I wondered if she too, was crying and where was she going and when would she return. When I could see her no more, I took Tom's hand and went back to the house to take off the pretty dress and put on my khaki dress.

But I could not believe that I would not see our mother again and I felt certain that she would come back one day and take us home where we would find Jim sitting at the back door, peeling potatoes and singing quietly to himself as he had done the first time I had seen him.

The days passed, I spoke to no one, did what I was told and as soon as I could, I ran to sit and wait by the little gate. Here Tom joined me but he could not understand what had happened and was content to play with me as we made patterns with the flowers which had fallen from the hedge, and we were united only by our unhappiness and bewilderment. Whenever we heard the sound of cycle wheels on the road or the tinkle of a bell, we rushed to look through the bars of the gate hoping to see her white clad figure, but it was never our mother.

For a long time we sat there, going into the kitchen only when summoned by Vinyu for the midday meal or when it grew dark and we were called in for bed. Stella had abandoned us and trailed around with Annie, sharing the sticky sweets Annie used to seduce her away from us, and it was near the gate that Billy found us at last. 'What are you kids doing here?' he asked. 'I've been looking for you,' and he kicked my legs. 'Get up you, and go and get a rag and some water to clean my bike.' He slouched off to lean against the gate, waiting for his answer. I was too frightened to speak, so he asked again, 'What are you sitting here for?' I looked up at him, moving away so that he could not kick me again. 'I'm waiting for my mother to come and take us home,' I said at last, the words coming out with a rush. He burst out laughing. 'You've got a long wait then,' he said. 'She's not coming back, she's run away, she got sick of you bloody kids and ran away and now she's dead, she's never coming back.'

Briefly I felt the shock of his announcement as I saw in my mind's eye my mother dead, lying on the ground in her pretty dress, dead like the kudu cow my grandfather had shot, like the monkeys spread-eagled on the chicken house fence, like the dead cow floating down the flooded river and like the tribesman who had been brought to the farm, his head smashed in by a knobkerrie during a beer drink in the Mashona kraal.

'She's not dead, she's not, she's coming back tomorrow,' I screamed as I hurled myself at my tormentor, flailing at him with my fists, kicking and crying. 'Oh yes,' he sneered as he held me away. 'How can she, she's dead, she's never, never coming back, I heard my mother say so.' He turned away, taking his bicycle with him and calling for the garden boy. 'Cheeky bloody kids,' he muttered as he kicked at the sand.

For a long time I cried as I sat under the hedge, disregarding all Vinyu's pleas to come out, all Annie's threats as to what would happen if I didn't, but at last, as it grew dark and I saw the long shadows falling across the garden and heard the night-jars mewing and crying as they fluttered through the peach trees, I slowly made my way back to the kitchen. Vinyu was sitting on his stool in the corner by the stove, waiting to be called to serve the meal, and he looked up as I stood blinking in the doorway. 'Miss Annie is looking for you,' he said and he reached into his apron pocket and took out a squashed soft toffee and carefully removing the paper, he handed it to me saying, 'I've kept this for you, here take it,' and he guided me to the small bathroom where I found Annie singing away and happily scrubbing Tom's legs.

After the family had eaten their evening meal, we were called in from the kitchen to the sitting room. Thick patterned rugs lay on the polished wooden floor, sofas and fat armchairs stood about, bowls of flowers graced the mantlepiece and a clock chimed softly from the corner where it stood on a glass fronted cabinet. Pictures of country lanes, of villages in distant lands and mountain views, hung on the walls and the lamp with its red beaded shade cast a mellow light over the family as they sat listening to a gramophone. An arm reached out to draw me to his side and I realised that this must be our Uncle George, father of the three cousins, husband of Aunty Betty and master of the household.

He was a small neat man, always clean and immaculately dressed. He smelled of tobacco and his moustaches were stained and yellow from the cigarettes he smoked. He was very short sighted – almost blind – and he peered at me through his milky blue eyes and asked gently, 'Are you the naughty girl who's been sitting in the hedge all day?' but I was too frightened to speak and merely nodded. 'You ain't got much to say, 'ave yer?' he asked as he seated me on his lap. 'She's a liar and sulks,' said my father who was sitting nearby with Stella beside him, 'and if there's anything I can't abide, it's a sulker.' 'She's a poor little bleeder,' said my uncle, 'ain't she small for her age?' 'Nah,' said my father, 'she's got a bad chest and corfs all night and sulks all day and cries if you look at 'er. Can't even speak proper neether, gabbles away with the niggers whenever she can. I don't know what I've done to deserve all this,' and he sniffed and his eyes watered and he got up to stand by the glass door, looking out into the night where the lightning flashed and the distant rumble of thunder was heard.

'You come to me if you're in trouble,' whispered Uncle George as I watched my father, and for a moment I felt a surge of well-being, but my aunt's voice from the passage door drew my attention. 'What are you two whispering about?' she asked. 'Nothing Tot,' mumbled my uncle as he put me off his lap, and I scurried from the room, only to be called back. 'It's time you went to bed,' said Aunty Betty, 'but first, I want to talk to you,' and she pushed me into the passage in the direction of her bedroom.

I found myself in a room of such unparallelled luxury that I looked about in wonder. Heavy lace curtains were looped up with satin ribbon and hung from the windows and doors, thick white rugs were scattered over the polished floor, vases of bright flowers stood on the dressing table amidst cut glass bottles and bowls and silver brushes, and on a desk in the corner among papers and letters and a softly glowing lamp, stood family pictures in silver frames. Foremost among these was one of my father in his wartime uniform of a sergeant in the Machine Gun Corps. He stood leaning against a marble pillar, in full uniform, his cap in hand, his putteed legs crossed. He had served in the latter part of the East African Campaign against the German commander von Lettow-Vorbeck, and he never tired of re-living his exploits and telling stories of what he had done. Some of his tales were true, but others changed from time to time and sounded different as he re-told them.

My glance shifted around the room to the double bed in the centre. It was covered with a white lace bedspread and a number of large pillows and soft cushions were strewn about it. On the bed lay my cousin Georgie still in his dirty work clothes, fondling his dog Dingo, their faces close together on the lace covered pillow, and the remains of a bone lay on the white shaggy rug where the dog had dropped it. There was a movement from the bed and Georgie rose on one elbow to ask petulantly, 'Ma, how much longer is Uncle Bill going to share my room? His clothes are all over the place and me and Dingo are getting fed up.' The dog slowly waved his tail at the sound of his name. 'I tell you Ma, I didn't mind at first, but he's been here for months now; why can't you put him and his kids on the back verandah, I don't want to share with him any longer.' My aunt sat on the side of the bed and stroked her son's hair, gently saying, 'Never mind my darling, I'll tell Vinyu to move his things tomorrow and you can have your room to yourself again.' 'Thanks Ma,' said Georgie as he got up, kissed his mother and slouched out, his dog padding silently behind him.

Aunty Betty seated herself at her dressing table and turned to me at last. 'Now what have you to say for yourself? Billy tells me you tried to fight with him this morning and you've been sulking in the garden all day. Did you?' I nodded. She reached for my arm and shook me, 'Speak to me when I ask you something.' 'Yes,' I said. 'Billy said my mother is dead and is never coming to take us away.' My aunt's face went red and she shouted at me, 'Oh, I suppose we're not good enough for you and you want to go back to live in Hatfield with only a nigger to look after you, do you?' I was too frightened to speak and we looked at each other for a few moments.

75

Plucking up courage at last, I asked, 'Is our mother really and truly dead?' She did not answer but tapped her fingers on the dressing table and then got up to stand by the door. 'Your mother has run away and she's never coming back, she just got fed up with you lot. If she had loved you, do you think she would have just left you with that nigger boy and gone away?' 'No,' I replied feeling tears in my eyes and trying not to cry. 'Your dad has no one to turn to, and I said I would have you here to live, but all I get from you is trouble, you're ungrateful and naughty and you tried to fight with your little cousin, but remember this. This is his home, so mind your tongue or I'll send you to the Children's Home. Now go to bed, but before you do, go and say sorry to Billy.' I had hardly understood most of what she had said, but her last words were very clear and I turned to go.

She turned back to her dressing table to adjust the angle of the mirror and peer at her reflection. When I got to the doorway, she called me back and when I drew near, she put her arm around me and with the other hand, she moved my hair away from my face. I thought she was going to forgive me and kiss me goodnight, but she studied my face for only a few seconds before she said, 'These will have to go, you look like a little Portugoose but you're only a little toe-rag,' and she tugged at the small sleeper earrings I had worn in my ears for as long as I could remember. In my grandmother's family it was the custom for all the girls to have their ears pierced when they were very young, it would improve our eyesight she had said. My sister had screamed and fought and run away to hide in the kopje behind the house, but I, who was always eager to please, had gladly volunteered for the operation.

Everything necessary had been assembled on the verandah table at the farm. A lighted candle, Grandad's small picture-framing hammer, the cork from his brandy bottle, a big reel of strong white cotton and Grandma's newest sewing needle. A long double thread was drawn from the reel, threaded through the needle and knotted at intervals. Obediently I put my head in her lap and holding the cork behind my ear-lobe, she quickly passed the needle through the flame of the candle, wiped it on her clean apron and in a second, had driven it through my ear lobe into the cork. Before I had been able to scream or wriggle, she had turned my head to repeat the operation on the other side and then the threads were drawn through, knotted and tied off.

My grandfather had appeared to watch and loudly applauded the performance, clapping his hands and saying not only that I was brave, but that I would undoubtedly grow up into a pretty girl. A kiss and a piece of his biltong were traded. For several days after, the cotton loop was pulled through the little hole, taking away the scab which had formed. When the cotton came away clean, it was cut away and the small gold rings which were always kept in her handkerchief case were slipped in. Proudly I ran down to the compound to show them to the umfazis and to re-tell how it was done, but they were not impressed. Their own ears had long slits in them and they had inserted pieces of reed or polished pebbles which swung as they moved about. I was glad I had only had to submit to my grandmother's sewing needle and not to a sharp knife or stone, as the native women had had to. When I showed my prize to Stella, she said it wasn't fair, she should have had the earrings being the eldest, but I reminded her she had not been prepared to have her ears pierced and the rings were of no use to her.

But now I realised that I was to lose my earrings and as I lay on the mattress with Tom, in Annie's room, I resolved to take them out and hide them, and to say I had thrown them away if I was asked. I glanced over to the bed where Annie lay with Stella enfolded in her arms, her lop-sided face clearly visible in the shadows of the room, her twisted mouth open as she snored gently. Carefully I removed the earrings and pushed them into the seam of the mattress where it had split, and as I drifted off to sleep I heard the rise and fall of voices from the living room, interspersed with bursts of laughter, the thunder growing fainter as it died away and the muffled sound of tom-toms far away in the depths of the bush. I wondered where my mother was, and would my father smile kindly at me again and not send me to the Childrens' Home. I slept.

Tom and I spent all our days together making up our own games, climbing the peach trees and exploring the small thicket which separated the servants' compound from the main house. We had no toys but we joined the picannins in their games, hiding when we heard Annie calling us. We were not to play in the compound, she had said, the niggers were dirty and we would never learn to speak properly if we spent all our time with them. But no one else spoke to us, the grown-up family were away all day, Billy played with his own friends at their houses, Vinyu was busy cleaning, washing and cooking and the garden and herd boys had their own tasks to do. My father had at last found work and left early in the morning, and Tom and I climbed the peach trees to eat the green fruit or insinuated ourselves around the servants' cooking fires to share in their midday meal of vegetables and cooked mealie meal. We had stomach aches and colds which went unnoticed and we clung together, afraid of the big cousins, and of the dog Dingo who curled his lip and growled if we came too near. Of my aunt we were quite terrified. She paid us little attention but her presence loomed over the household and her word was law.

Uncle George and his wife were first cousins and had married when still in their teens. They were both uneducated and as children had run wild through the streets, the markets and music halls in the East End of London, where they lived; but they had a great capacity for hard work and together had traded from a stall in Whitechapel, selling anything they could buy cheap. When Aunty Betty's parents had emigrated to Africa, they remained behind to take her father's place in an uncle's brickyard in Essex, promising to join the family when they had saved enough money to pay their passages to Capetown, and they had arrived two years later with their two babies. For two years they had waited to join a wagon train travelling to Rhodesia, living in the back yard of a Jewish trader, where George had been employed as the nightwatchman and Betty had helped in the store.

Their third son was born in Capetown and as soon as she had recovered Betty decided it was time to leave the Cape and to join her parents and family in the north. When they reached Salisbury, they soon started to look for a suitable site where they could set up a brickfield. They had noticed that most of the houses in the capital were built of wooden poles cut from the bush and plastered together with a mixture of clay and sand, and had thatched roofs. Few survived for more than a year or so; they collapsed during the heavy summer rains, the wood eaten away by termites, the clay melting in the tropical downpours and, very often, the thatch catching alight from over zealously stoked cooking fires.

Some of the homesteaders made their own bricks but they did not know how to fire them and their houses did not last much longer than those built of wood and clay. Betty felt that she and George had arrived at the right time and they explored the outskirts of the town in their search for clay deposits. They found a big stretch of land on the banks of the Makabusi river which was almost solid clay and here they pitched their tents and started to build huts where they would spend the next six months.

The banks of the river were cleared of trees and scrub, rough shelters were put up for the tribesmen who drifted in asking for work, and the site for a pugmill was decided upon. My father was asked to write to the uncle in Essex to send out a mill and all the necessary machinery and moulds, and at the onset of the next rainy season everything arrived from England, was unpacked and reassembled. But one very important point had been overlooked. An ox or a donkey was required to pull the driving pole around to activate the mill; despite many visits to the local market and enquiries at outlying farms, no such animal was to be had. Horse sickness had killed all the imported horses, and mules were being ridden instead, and oxen and donkeys had taken their places in the shafts of wagons, scotch carts and drays which were the only form of transport.

Quite undaunted, Betty suggested to her husband that they put two tribesmen into the harness of the driving pole and for eight hours a day, the two men trudged around, dragging the pole with them, churning up and washing the clay. Men stood by to pack it into the moulds, and the soft bricks were carefully laid out in long rows to dry in the sun and then stacked into kilns to be fired at the end of the rainy season. Axes were issued to the work force which went into the bush to cut down trees for firewood, and ox wagons and donkey carts queued for miles waiting for the loads of red ordinaries, face bricks, steel blues, fire bricks and specials, each one bearing on its indented side the initials E.S.

This brickyard was Uncle George's domain, where he ruled with a heavy hand, directed by his wife who was feared even more, even though she was a woman. The sound of her approaching motor car sent the unsophisticated tribesmen into terror and many ran towards the river, fearing that this machine was the work of a very powerful witchdoctor. One brave man had bent down to see where the devils were who made the fearful noise, but he had been too frightened to open his eyes and was thus unable to enlighten his fellow men. He was however much respected afterwards for his daring, and eventually became their spokesman in matters relating to work.

George now controlled a labour force of two hundred men who had left their families in their kraals to come and work for the white man's money and for what it could buy him. On the banks of the foetid river, they lived in shacks made from discarded wooden boxes, flattened-out tin cans which had held paraffin or petrol, or sheets of corrugated iron salvaged from the municipal rubbish dump next to the brickyard. Some of the more fortunate had found old abandoned water tanks which they dragged up to the shanty town. They slept in their crowded and decrepit huts, lying on the bare earthen floor, wrapped in their blankets, the fire burning sluggishly in the centre of the hut, and they were assailed by the fever-bearing mosquitoes which rose from the river in clouds. They shared their daily ration of mealie meal doled out at the end of each day by the Inkoos.

There was no other source of water for their use, nor were there latrines, so the river and the bush served both purposes, and often they must have wondered why they had chosen to exchange their homes and gardens in the kraals, their hunting lands and the mountains, for the dubious luxury of ten shillings a month, all found. But George had never thought to improve the lot of his workforce: after all they were only natives and he had not made a decision, voiced an opinion or entered an argument for as long as he could remember. Betty ran the home and the business, dealt with clients, bullied her family, collected money, and banked it and made all the decisions, and he was content for it to be so. Although he was not entirely happy about the three children who had come to live with them, he dared not say anything, it was not in his nature to do so and he always deferred to his wife. In me, he thought, he had seen a failure like himself and he sensed that his wife acknowledged that he was drawn to me in my unhappiness, but he could and would do nothing about it.

Now I stood on the verandah, early in the morning, as Uncle George came from the dining room after his breakfast. The garden picannin stood shivering at the doorstep, holding his bicycle ready for him, while he adjusted his trouser clips and buttoned his jacket. With a sly wink at me, he took two or three hopping little steps, leaped into the saddle and went wobbling and shaking down the rutted road which diminished into a narrow little kaffir path. Onwards he pedalled through the bush, dodging rabbit holes, kaffir-orange trees and dry ditches and at last he faded into the dark line of trees and I turned to the sound of Annie's voice calling me into the kitchen for my porridge.

'You kids gotter go to school next month,' announced Annie as we sat spooning the soft, sweet porridge into our mouths. 'He's gorn to see the nuns at the convent, to see if they'll take you.' She sniffed and slid her eyes over us. 'Gawd knows if they will,' and she went over to put her arm around my sister. Leaning down to put her face next to Stella's she asked, 'You don't wanna leave Annie do you luv?' 'No,' replied Stella, 'I want to stay with you.' Annie blew her nose noisily but I remembered Vinyu showing me my father's new suit and shirt he had pressed the evening before, and I knew now that his journey with my aunt to the town had been for an interview with the nuns at the school.

'What's nuns?' I asked. 'They're ladies who live together without any hubbies or kids and they pray all day and they'll whip you lot when

80

you're naughty.' Annie giggled as she said it and her face lit up. 'What's praying?' I asked, still not satisfied, but she jumped up from her chair and taking Stella's hand, she went off to make beds and see to her other domestic chores, saying 'You'll soon find out.' I looked up to see Vinyu and asked him the same question. 'Don't listen to her,' he said, 'she knows nothing. I am a mission boy and I know about the nuns. They are white ladies who teach us about God and church, but praying is what they're best at,' and he proceeded to tell us all about it and what it meant.

'Yes,' my father admitted, he had been to the Convent to see if the nuns would take us, but there had been a number of difficulties and he was to go for another interview in a month's time. The Mother General of the Dominican Order was making her annual tour of inspection throughout the province and would consider our case at the conclusion of her journey.

'If they take you at the Convent,' said my father, addressing my sister as I stood in the background, 'you'll have to wear the school uniform, but in the meantime, your aunty has sent for the Sammy to come and make you some clothes to wear here, but Gawd knows how I'm going to pay for them, I'm not made of bleedin' money and it don't grow on trees.' I felt guilty that my father had to suffer like this to provide us with dresses and knickers; we had never had more than two khaki dresses each and the thought of so many possessions troubled me.

'And another thing,' said my father. 'I don't want you kids playing with the picannins or speaking Shona to Vinyu, it's plain English from now on,' and he emphasised to Stella that because she was the eldest, she was to report to him if Tom or I deviated from his order. But we had no toys, no books to look at, and no one else to play with except the picannins in the compound who called us to climb trees with them, to run down to the river to play in the deep pools where they splashed and swam while we stood on the banks watching them and wishing we could swim. With them we ran through the bush looking for wild fruit, and when their mothers called them in, we were desolate and slowly made our way home to the empty house. Our efforts to entice the garden boys from their work were met with orders not to worry them, but we practised our English with Vinyu while Stella trailed around with Annie, helping her and revelling in her new found security.

In due time Vinyu was despatched to summon the Sammy, ignoring my pleas to go with him. He set off in the direction of the river bank, returning later to say that the Sammy would arrive early tomorrow morning before Madam had left for the brickfields; we were to have two new dresses each, said my aunt, Stella was to choose the colours, and petticoats, knickers and bodices were also to be made and if we dirtied or tore them, we would be thrashed and sent to bed.

'The Sammy' was Mr V.J. Lalloo, a sad-faced Bengali who had left his native India when he was fourteen years old and had travelled with his parents to Natal in South Africa as an indentured labourer on the vast sugar plantations owned and managed by white English planters. With his parents, his brothers and his sister he cut cane from dawn to dusk six days a week, earning a pittance and living in the barrack-like huts on the plantation, but the harsh conditions, the low pay and the inadequate living drove him to seek something better.

With his savings he bought a bicycle and rode around the affluent white suburbs of Durban, offering to mend or sew for the white ladies who lived in their handsome bungalows built on the brow of the hill overlooking the sparkling waters of the bay. His grandfather had taught him well in the old days in India, and now he sat cross-legged on the back verandah of his white employers' houses, diligently mending shirts and trousers and household linens, sewing on buttons, altering dresses, darning socks and threading elastic through the soft satin underwear of the ladies of the house. Very rarely madam would allow him to use her Singer sewing machine, and he cut out and sewed sheets, pillowcases, dresses, trousers and jackets.

'Sammy's so cheap and quick,' the ladies told each other as they sat on their spacious verandahs, drinking tea and gossiping the morning away, but when he took his money for his day's labour, bowing low and touching his brow, he despised them for their indolence, their insensitivity and their brashness. 'What's your real name?' one of the more friendly ladies had asked him. She prided herself that she was liberal in her outlook and was even prepared to address him as 'Mister', but when he replied 'Weejay Lalloo, madam,' she had laughed and replied, 'I think I'll just stick to Sammy, like the rest do.' He had felt embarrassed and bowed low saying, 'Thank you madam, thank you.'

When he turned twenty, he sent for his wife whom he'd married when he was twelve years old; she had continued to live with her parents on the sugar plantation where they were labourers, just as his parents had been, but with the increasing demand on him for his tailoring services, he decided Aisha would help him expand his business. He had bought a barrow on the market and now Aisha pushed it through the streets as he rode ahead on his bicycle, touting for work. Rolls of strong white calico, terry towelling and sheeting were piled high, together with rolls of crepe de chine, georgette, Moygashel Linen, cottons and voiles.

But one day Sammy had disappeared and was no longer to be seen riding slowly ahead of Aisha and her barrow. He had said nothing, but had quietly withdrawn his money from the bank, sold all his possessions and taken the train to Salisbury in the new colony to the north, where he had heard there was a great deal of money to be made. Here, he and Aisha had rented a room in the area designated for coloured people to the west of the city. But the people in his street resented them and they had left the city and gone to the outskirts and had come to a deserted shed on the river bank. The roof had fallen in, weeds and grass grew through the floor in its two rooms, and in one they found a pile of manure, left there by the goats which grazed along the river bank and which seemed to belong to no one.

As soon as they had cleaned and repaired the shack, Sammy got on his cycle and visited the homesteaders, but it was the white woman who owned the brickyard who kept him fully occupied for the first few months before the rains came. He mended and darned, cut and sewed, for the family of three boys and their parents; and for the house servant he made white uniforms such as he'd seen in the homes of the white families he had visited in India with his grandfather. Soon Aisha joined him, pushing the barrow piled high with lustrous silks and satins, homely cottons and calico, and when the dry, cold weather came, woollens and worsteds specially imported from England.

Now Sammy stood respectfully at the back door, his cap in hand, waiting for his orders. His wife leant against the heavy barrow and we looked at her, curious about her clothes, her long glossy hair tied up in a large knot at the back of her neck, her tinkling bracelets and the red mark in the centre of her forehead. But my eyes were rivetted particularly to the jewel in her nose; for many moments I wondered how it had been inserted and then I heard my aunt's footsteps coming down the passage.

Although he bowed low and wished her good morning, my aunt ignored him and said sharply, 'These two girls need two cotton dresses each Sammy. I want you to make them a set of underwear each and I want it all done before you leave tonight. Now show me what you've got, I'm in a hurry. Nothing too expensive please, I know you think I'm made of money, but I ain't.' Sammy beckoned to Aisha and together they unwrapped the rolls of material and laid them carefully on the verandah floor and we all stood back to admire them.

Stella came forward and was told that she could choose, but I had lost interest because I knew that what she liked would not suit me; she was small and blonde, with pale yellow hair and almond shaped green eyes which would show to advantage against the royal blue and deep plum coloured material she was fingering; my dark brown hair and olive skin, still tinged with yellow from our frequent attacks of malaria, cried out for something lighter and prettier, but the decision was made. A price was agreed upon, the lengths of material cut from the rolls, calico chosen for our underwear and Sammy and his wife retreated to the far end of the verandah to start work.

Carefully he undid his machine from the back of his bicycle, looping the string which had held it securely, and stowing it carefully in his breast pocket. A tape measure was produced and one by one we were measured while Annie stood by to supervise. All day Sammy cut and sewed, calling us at intervals from our games by the hedge to see if the measurements were correct, and by evening, as my aunt drove in to the yard, he was packing up his sewing machine and Aisha was re-loading her barrow. The garments were all scrutinised and paid for and he was asked to return at the month's end as it was likely school uniforms would have to be made. 'Which school?' he asked. 'I will have to get material for the gym slips if it's the Girls High or the Convent,' he said, 'but not for the public school, the children wear their own clothes there they are all very poor people, like me, who send their children to that school.'

'You've got a nerve Sammy,' said my aunt. 'You know very well that you can't send your kids to any of our schools, they don't take Coloured or Indians.'

Sammy's smile widened even further and he looked ingratiatingly at my aunt. 'You misunderstand me madam, I meant the parents were poor like me, not that I would send my children, if I had any, to a European school.'

'Well mind your tongue then,' said my aunt, 'the schools are for the white people not for the likes of you. Stick to your tailoring and sewing and don't forget you're only an Indian.'

If Sammy felt he was insulted, he never showed it. He bowed low, clasping his hands together and touching them to his forehead as he bade my aunt good night and thanked her for her custom. 'Cheeky bloody Indian,' she remarked as the couple walked to the gate where he took the barrow from Aisha and followed her into the gloom of the evening as she pushed his cycle. They spoke quietly to each other and as she turned to smile at me when I followed them to the fence, I saw her eyes flash and heard her sharp retort to something he had said. I decided I would wait until I knew them better before asking Aisha how she had got that jewel into her nostril.

It was many weeks later that my father paid another visit to the Dominican Convent. His suit was pressed and he told the garden boy to polish his shoes and clean up his bicycle, and he rode off towards the town. We were afraid, wondering if we were to be uprooted again and – worse – if my brother and I would be separated. With a lot of giggling and chuckling, Annie had told us that boys could only stay at the Convent with their big sisters until they were eight years old and after that it was the Jesuit College on the northern outskirts of the city for bigger boys. 'The monks there walk about with a cane in their hands and they thrash you if you don't kneel down when they walk past, and on some days you don't get any food at all.' My brother Tom cried at the prospect awaiting him, but when we asked Vinyu if it was true, he sucked in his breath and scornfully asked 'Why do you listen to such stories? I have told you, I am a mission boy and I was only beaten once for being cheeky.' We were too afraid to ask my aunt and neither my father or any of the household bothered to enlighten us.

Once more Sammy was sent for and this time he came bringing with him a roll of navy serge and another of white calico. Gym slips and shirts were hastily made, sheets hemmed and pillow cases put together and we sat on the back verandah with Annie who was writing our names on everything and sewing tapes on hair brushes and toothbrushes – the function of which had not yet been explained to us; Stella and she sniffled in between wiping their eyes and looking for the marking pencil. A cabin trunk was brought in from the store room and all our new clothes and linen were packed; my father put on his new suit and stood back to look us over in our new black shoes, black socks and navy serge gym frocks, but his gaze strayed back to the wall mirror and he carefully adjusted his bowtie and smoothed down his hair. A rickshaw had been summoned from the city and we were loaded into it and borne away.

We sat crowded together on the one seat with the trunk balanced behind us, a little excited but quite frightened of what lay ahead of us. We watched the native pulling our rickshaw as he bobbed and sweated along the road, only stopping where the road grew steep, to wipe his head and face with an old rag he drew from his shirt. Now and then he had to stop for a rest and we got out to stretch our legs while he sat sweating and puffing in the midday heat. At last we drew up to the front door of the Convent, the bell was rung and we were shown into the parlour to wait for the Mother Prioress.

'These are my three children,' my father said, naming us in turn, and then he drew from his inner jacket pocket an envelope he passed to the nun. We sat with our mouths open, uncomfortable in our new clothes, dreading the moment when we would be left and hoping that my father would be told that they had changed their minds and that we could not be accepted so that we would return to my aunt's home where Vinyu would be waiting, clicking his teeth and grinning at us in these unfamiliar garments.

'You are very generous,' said Mother Prioress when she had glanced at the amount written on my aunt's cheque which my father passed to her. 'I will see that some of this goes to our Mission Fund,' and she tucked it away in her skirt pocket before adding, 'have the children been to school before?' 'Yes,' he replied and proceeded to tell her that we had been to a small private school in Salisbury before he had decided to send us as boarders. 'When their dear mother died, I could not look after them myself,' and here he took his handkerchief from his pocket and blew his nose long and loudly, then wiped his eyes and continued, 'and my sister has a business to run, you will see it is her cheque, but she agreed with me that this would be the best thing for them. Here I know you will give them all the love and kindness little kiddies deserve and I only want the best for my children.' He looked at us fondly and then looked away to blow his nose once again, and then he went on, 'we have been a happy little family until my dear wife died and they have wanted for nothing. I know you will take great care of them and make allowances for them.' And then he turned to look at me and said: 'My younger daughter is not very strong and spent a lot of time in bed sick, so if she tells you anything, don't believe it all, she has a very vivid imagination and loves to tell us her little stories.'

I was dumbfounded at the proceedings. I had never heard my father speak in such a carefully controlled voice; neither had he used the words he used to us every day – words like ain't, bleedin', bloody, strewth or Gawd Almighty – and I knew he had made a mistake saying we had been to school in the town, when in reality we had been to what amounted to a dame school run by two well-meaning ladies for the benefit of the ragged children in the poor section of the city environs. And what had he said about our happy little family?

86

My father's assertion that our mother had died was a lie I knew, but when I saw the sympathy it elicited from the Mother Prioress, that was the moment I released my mother from my mind and accepted the fact that to me, she really and truly was dead. And I knew too, that the only constancy in my life was the black man, whoever he had been; the boss-boy on the farm, my father's garden boys, Jim, and now Vinyu. They had taken care of us, they had been kind and patient, they told us stories and taught us their language, they had protected us and they had always been there.

I felt the tears in my eyes as I thought about them all but I resolved then that I would never again recall the past nor those whom I had trusted and loved. I was lost in my thoughts but looked up when I heard my father rise to his feet and I saw him hold out his hand to the Mother Prioress. She patted Stella on her blonde head and asked, 'They are Protestant I believe?' For a moment my father looked puzzled, but then he smiled and laughingly said, 'Oh yes, does it matter?' 'Not at all,' said the nun, 'we have quite a number of girls here who go to other churches. The Church of England nuns come here twice a week to give those of their faith instruction, and on Sundays they go to their Cathedral. We have a few Jewish girls and two from the Greek Orthodox, but we have no Dutch Reformed, there are so few of them in this country and I believe they go mainly to the public school.'

At this remark, my father smiled, but the nun had not done with him. 'Your little son will have to go in with the babies, you understand, and can only remain with us until he turns eight, but that is a long time away. We are in God's hands Mr Sadler, and will speak about that matter later. But have no fear that we will try and convert your little ones; we will offer up prayers for your dear departed wife and we will pray for your children.' We walked with my father to the gate where the rickshaw boy was still waiting, lying in the shade of a msasa tree, fast asleep, his sweaty rag over his face to keep the flies off; my father bent down to kiss us goodbye, saying 'Ta-ta then you kids, I'd better be off.' To me he added, 'Watch your step miss, or you'll cop it,' and then he was through the gate, kicking the rickshaw boy in the ribs, and shouting, 'Wake up you lazy bleedin' kaffir, let's go.'

My sister and I found ourselves in the same class. We sat closely side by side, afraid to speak, overcome by the sight of so many other girls, and hoping that the teacher would not notice us, but we were objects of great curiosity. 'Sister told us you are two poor little orphans,' said one of our temporary guardians. 'What did you mother die of?' 'Don't know,' said my sister. 'Of the flu,' I volunteered, glad that we had achieved some sort of status and realising that capital could be gained from my motherless state. 'You poor little kids,' said the other guardian. 'But you'll like it here and the nuns are very nice. If anyone's nasty to you, come to the Senior study and ask for Di or me – my name's Sybil – and we'll fix them.'

PART THREE

After the first few days, I began to fit in to the regulated life of the convent, and slowly I lost my fear of everyone about me. I regained a little confidence, stopped crying and gradually began to enjoy the lessons and the companionship of the other children. The food was plain and frugal but if one of the boarders did not eat her share I happily cleaned up her plate for her; my eyes and skin lost their yellow tinge from the malaria attacks, my coughs and colds vanished, I found English easier to speak and many friends were made. I sometimes recalled the conversation in the rickshaw, my father moving forward in his seat so as to emphasise what he was about to say. 'Yer both old enough now to go to a proper school where they'll teach you to read, write and add up proper. Yer don't want to be like the niggers and them Afrikaners, ignorant and stupid. Yer don't know how lucky yer are. Look at me, did I get the chance you're both getting? No, I had to leave school when I was twelve. Had to help me dad keep the family. There was no posh school for me, a trunk full of noo clothes and three square meals a day.' He was silent for a few minutes as he waited for his words to sink in, and then he continued. 'Yer'll have to work hard if yer want to amount to anything. Yer'll have to pass tests or yer'll be chucked out. Then where will yer go? It will have to be the public school with all them Afrikaans kids. It's up to you.' Momentarily I had envied those luckless children their lack of opportunity and I had asked, 'Did Aunty Betty have to go to school?' 'Don't be so bleedin' cheeky,' he retorted. 'She uses her brains, works 'ard and ain't nobody's fool.' Chastened and silent, I had agreed. 'Yer want to count yer blessings my girl, and be thankful I got yer into a decent school,' he said, and we nodded in bewildered agreement.

Vinyu had agreed with my father. 'You must listen to the sisters,' he told me, 'and you must work hard. There are many who would wish for a chance such as yours to learn to read books, write letters and

91

understand money. Look at me. I was nearly a grown man, almost twice your age when I went to the Mission school. It was hard for me to learn at that age.' 'You are a native,' I reminded him. 'You didn't have to go to school.' 'No,' he replied, 'what you say is true. But if I had not, I would be still living in the bush, ploughing my father's land, eating his food and with no money in my hand.'

His words had been like a goad. I was ashamed at the way my father spoke, swearing and cursing to lend weight to his words and I did not want to be like my aunt who could not read and only wrote her name with difficulty. Nor would I be like Vinyu, wasting away the years. I wanted to know what everything meant, to be able to read my school books, to understand the dreaded tests, to have some distinction which would give me status, to win acknowledgement and even some admiration, but most of all I wanted to be better than those about me.

But my sister was in the depths of misery and spent all her free time huddled against me or looking for me so that she could cry and snivel, saying 'I want to go home, I don't like it here, I want Annie'. In class she spent so much time crying quietly into her handkerchief that I was obliged to help her with her lessons, and it was only the realisation that the first term was drawing to a close and soon we would all be dispersed for the holidays, which restored her to normal life in the convent.

We knew our aunt would fetch us in her motor car and I was excited at the prospect of the car ride back to her home, but the thought of the big cousins, of my father's indifference and our aunt's coldness did little to make the prospect of school holidays inviting, and it was my turn to cry when we were summoned to the parlour and found my father waiting. He barely glanced at me when we greeted him so did not comment on my distress when I saw the same rickshaw boy squatting under the trees. 'I thought Aunty Betty was coming to fetch us in her motor car' I said. 'Nah,' he said. 'She asked me to come for you, she's got other things to do, but ain't you kids pleased to see your old dad?' 'Yes,' we said dubiously, and we climbed into the rickshaw.

The journey took over an hour and when my father paid the boy his fare of half a crown, he threw the money to the ground for the man to find in the sand. 'Never hand a kaffir anything, even money,' he said. 'He'll think he's your equal, but we know, don't we, that he's only a baboon.' I felt ashamed for him, but did not have the courage nor the words to argue with him. I wondered why they were brought into our homes to wash, clean, cook, look after small children and attend to all our needs, if they were considered savages to be compared with baboons.

Many things had changed when we returned for those first school holidays. Annie had persuaded her sister to allow her to curl her hair and she wore a pretty red ribbon in it and face powder and rouge on her face. She looked well pleased with herself and less afraid of her sister and brother-in-law. She wore a more fashionable dress which my aunt had passed on to her, and she smiled at us and remarked 'My, ain't you growed!' She took Stella's hand, saying 'Come on me darling, let's go for a walk', and they strolled out of the gate and took the narrow path which led into the bush away from the house.

Dingo lay alone on his divan, his head sunk onto his paws, his eyes fixed on the gate at the end of the garden, his food untouched in its bowl on the floor. All the fine furnishings, the cushions and rugs had gone from the verandah and only the birdcage with its lovebirds and canaries was still in its corner. There was no evidence of our cousins and my aunt and uncle were nowhere to be seen, so I went in search of Vinyu who I found sitting under the plum tree in the backyard, cleaning and sharpening the table knives.

He sprinkled powder on the knife board, rubbed the knives up and down, and when satisfied, placed them carefully in their box. 'I have to do this at school', I said, 'we all have to help,' and I left him to climb the pamplemousse tree where I hung upside down by my legs. The conversation continued.

'We have to make our own beds too,' I added, hoping to gain his approval, but he looked at me for a few moments before asking 'and I suppose you spend a lot of time praying too?' 'No,' I replied, 'only on Sundays when we go to church.' 'You don't pray all day? Do you have lots of time to read your books and practise your writing?' 'Yes,' I said, wondering where this was leading to. Uppermost in my mind was the change which had come over the house, so I asked again: 'Why is everything different from when we were here before? Where is the madam?'

He laughed, picked up the knife box and led the way back to the kitchen. 'Wait here,' he said. 'I'll get the milk bucket and I'll tell you as we go for the milk.' I held his hand and we spoke in Shona and he told me what had happened soon after we had been taken to school.

A wandering Jehovah's Witness had called at the house and had been made welcome. He had knelt down to say prayers for the family when they returned from work, and had stayed for dinner, eating only the vegetables and pushing the meat to the side of his plate; a glass of water was asked for, the tea and pudding kindly but firmly refused. Then he had spent a long time on the back verandah talking earnestly to my aunt and uncle, casting his eyes over the fine furnishings and elegant surroundings and the evidence of the good living spread about him. The world was about to end, he said, and the sinners and idolators would be cast into hell fire.

Emphasising his message with long passages from the Bible, he urged them to give up the pleasures and trappings of their life, to go down on their knees and spend all their time in prayer each day, to beg the Lord for forgiveness for their evil and selfish ways, to love their neighbours, little children and heathens, and to share their wealth with those who had nothing. Beginning, of course, with his church – and my aunt sat down at her desk and wrote out a cheque for a considerable sum of money. 'Make it out to me please,' he had asked, 'I have not yet opened a bank account for my beloved church, I have only recently arrived in this country, but these are my credentials,' and he passed some pamphlets to my aunt. Pride still lurked within her breast however, and she could not bring herself to admit she could not read nor would she summon one of her sons to read the leaflets for her.

'How do you know all this?' I asked Vinyu. 'I was sorting the washing on the table by her bedroom and the door was open,' he replied. Everything the man had told them was sincerely believed and at once there had been changes. Pictures and ornaments had been packed away and were destined for the store room, the silver and cut-glass from her bedroom and the sitting room were stowed away in the boxes they had originally arrived in when purchased at a household sale in Salisbury; thick enamel plates replaced the fine china on the dining table, tea and coffee were banished and they drank water from enamel mugs. Vinyu boiled rice or potatoes for their midday meal, sandwiches with egg or lettuce were offered for dinner at night and the only sound heard in the house was the hum of earnest voices as my aunt and uncle knelt by their beds, waiting for the world to end and praying for their souls.

'But what about the cousins?' I asked. Georgie, he told me, was working in town and was looking for a wife; but he had not saved enough for the lobola, the bride price which was the common practice with all African tribes. Vinyu said he thought Georgie would have to work for a long time to buy sufficient cattle to pay for the wife, but if she was from a Dutch family, as the family suspected, goats or even a few donkeys would do. Cousin Jack was looking after the office at the brickfields and slept at a friends house because when he had complained about the food in his own home he had been told there would be no change. Cousin Billy, being still only an umfaan, said Vinyu, was with his mother and father praying. He had stayed away from school and no longer played at his friends house.

I was frightened at this turn of events and asked Vinyu if he knew what would happen to us. He put the milk bucket down and leaned against the fence, sucked at his teeth, and then said 'They are foolish to listen to that man who came here. They know nothing of him and believed all he said but I have heard of the likes of that man before. When I was at the mission school, we were told of such people, but I have not questioned madam's orders because I am only the servant.'

I kept out of the way, spending all the next day playing with Tom or hanging around Vinyu in the kitchen on the pretext that I was helping him. Later, as I stood by the back door, I noticed a servant by the gap in the pomegranate hedge. 'What do you want?' I called, then recognised him as the cook from the house about a quarter of a mile away where the Smith family lived. 'Can I see your cook please,' he said, and presently Vinyu joined him and they stood chatting and glancing towards the bedroom wing of the house. They shook hands, grinning as they did so and Vinyu returned to the kitchen. He raised his eyebrows and laughed at me saying, 'I have learned something very strange from my brother, Mrs Smith's cook,' but he would not tell me. 'It is not time, but ask if you can come with me for the vegetables and I will tell you then.'

Timidly I knocked on my aunt's bedroom door which was opened only a few inches. I could see it was still dark inside and she stood before me in her long nightgown, her feet bare, her long black hair hanging down her back. She sighed as she asked wearily 'What do you want?' I explained that the cook wanted some money for vegetables and could I go along with him? I also remembered to ask how she was and said I was pleased to be back for the holidays. She rummaged in her handbag and then held out a two shilling piece, saying 'Tell Vinyu to get just enough for today, I don't know about tomorrow.' Before she shut the door I heard my uncle's voice, and then Billy's which sounded as though it came from the bed, and I realised that I had seen nothing of him yet.

I trotted alongside Vinyu who carried the basket, grinning and smiling to himself. Now and then, he looked up and slapped his knees and burst out laughing. 'Did you pray this morning?' he asked. 'No,' I said, 'I'm on holiday, I don't pray every day like my aunty does.' He stopped laughing and then asked, 'Do you want to know what Mrs Smith's cook told me?' 'Yes, of course,' I said, and we sat down at the side of the road in the shade of the msasa trees. As he was about to serve Mr Smith his porridge that morning, the cook had glanced at the picture on the front page of the newspaper which lay beside his plate. It was of a white man, hand-cuffed to a policeman, and the cook recognised the man as the same who had called at the Smith household after visiting my aunt. Mr Smith had forbidden his wife to speak to the visitor and had ordered him to leave the property. The Smith's cook understood English very well, although he never spoke it, and eagerly he listened to the conversation as he pretended to search for some article in the sideboard. When he turned to go to the kitchen, he saw the looks of astonishment on his employers' faces and then heard their hilarious outbursts of laughter.

'That man', said Vinyu, 'is not a priest or a holy man as he told madam. He used to be a guard on the railways but was sacked because he was always drunk. He has taken money from a lot of people, but he only visits those who live out of the town away from the police station. He has cheated many, many people.' Vinyu's eyes twinkled and for a moment I wondered how grown-up people who were as rich and clever as my aunt could be so foolish as to believe such a man. 'Will you tell madam when we get home?' I asked. 'No,' replied Vinyu 'but I think Mrs Smith will.'

We came in sight of the vegetable gardens laid out in rows along the banks of the river. They were owned and cared for by the coolie, not to be confused with Sammy, but an Indian like him. They were not friends and never spoke although they lived only a few yards apart. It was something to do with caste said Vinyu, but neither of us knew what this could be. 'Do you think it's a sickness like malaria?' I asked. 'No,' said Vinyu, 'it's something to do with his grandmother. I heard madam say he prayed to his dead grandmother who was a cow.' He looked puzzled as he said it, and it sounded too silly to believe, so we did not discuss it any further. The coolie wore only a dhoti gathered up between his legs and tucked into his waistband and his teeth were stained red and were divided by large gaps. He was completely bald and appeared to have no wife or children, only two young picannins who helped him bring the water up from the river in buckets and who hoed and weeded his little garden.

Vinyu held out his hand to greet the gardener and then stood back to look at his little house. It was painted a delicate shade of mauve, the stones and bricks which lined the garden paths were whitewashed, and everything was spick and span. 'So, it is finished then?' he asked and the coolie bowed low and held out his hand to show us in, but Vinyu declined, saying we had to get back for lunch and could he have shilling potatoes, sixpence tomatoes, tickey lettuce and tickey beans. The florin was passed over and the basket filled with the order. I realised Vinyu wanted to get home as soon as we could; he wanted to be there when Mrs Smith called.

Two days later, big, fat, beautiful Mrs Smith knocked on the back door and asked if madam was in. 'Yes,' I said, 'she's on the front verandah,' and I walked with her to where my aunt sat, staring into the distance. Her long black hair had lost its sheen and hung straight and lank to her waist. She wore a long white overall, the sleeves buttoned to her wrist, the collar almost reaching her ears. She wore no make-up and she looked dispirited and tired.

'Thought you ought to see this, Bet,' said Mrs Smith, opening her handbag and taking out a sheet of newspaper. 'Read it to me, there's a dear,' asked my aunt. Mrs Smith sat down, smoothed out the page and pointed to the picture. The headlines screamed 'Confidence Trickster Jailed for five Years'. My aunt's mouth fell open as she stared at the photograph of the erstwhile Jehovah's Witness, and when Mrs Smith had finished reading the account of the charges, the trial and the sentence, my aunt put her head down on the table and cried. 'There, there dear,' said comfortable Mrs Smith. 'I don't really know why you people don't get the daily papers, it's all in here, you know, everything that goes on,' and complacently, smiling only very slightly, she gathered up her handbag and left my aunt crying by herself at the verandah table.

'Back from school already?' she asked me as she made her stately progress down the garden path, homeward bound. 'Do you like it there?' 'Yes I do,' I said, 'I like it very much and the nuns are nice to us.' 'I must ask your aunty if you can come and spend a day with us soon, I've got a little girl called Roma about your age and she's got lots of dolls and I'm sure she'll let you play with them.' 'I don't have any dolls,' I replied, 'but I'd like to come and see you and Roma. Can my sister come? She's older than me and she's got a doll with yellow hair like hers. I had a dollie but I washed its face and it all came off and its hair fell out too.' She laughed at my remark and said she would soon arrange it all with my aunt.

For the next week, we carried boxes and packages from the storeroom

97

and garage to the back verandah where all the pictures, ornaments, rugs, mats, cushions and bric-a-brac were unpacked, washed and dried and returned to their original places. Gradually the house assumed its former air of luxury and comfort, and my aunt emerged early each morning dressed and made-up and smelling of violets. Uncle George, still looking a little bewildered, donned his freshly ironed tussore suit, leaped on his bicycle and pedalled off to the brickfields and Georgie and Jack returned to the fold. Dingo wagged his tail and panted happily after his master, and cousin Billy invited his friends to play at his house, explaining our presence as 'these are my Uncle Bill's kids, they're just here for the holidays.' Life went on as before.

Annie suddenly bloomed and starting singing around the house, but she no longer took Stella when she went for long walks into the thick bush. 'Why don't you go with her?' I asked. 'She said I mustn't tell,' said Stella. 'Mind your own business.' And she picked up her dolls and flounced away.

My aunt's emergence from her temporary exile was celebrated on the last day of the holidays when my father had returned home. I heard him telling my aunt that he'd not had any luck in Jo'burg, and then he said he would be seeing a solicitor after we'd gone back to school. I did not know what he meant and even Vinyu did not know the meaning of the word so although it sounded ominous I put it from my mind.

'What shall I cook for dinner?' asked Vinyu, standing in the doorway. The whole family had congregated on their return from their various offices and places of work and were sitting on the verandah. 'Steak,' cried my aunt, 'steak for everyone,' and she laughed as she caught my eye, 'even for the toe-rags before they go back to school,' and she seized my hands and danced around the furniture as the cousins laughed and clapped their hands. Everyone rollicked about, glasses were filled with beer and they slapped each other on the back as though a great victory had been won, when in fact it had been a defeat for both parties. My aunt's home had been reduced to a travesty of its former state, business had been lost when builders had found their orders for bricks unfulfilled because Jack could not and would not drive the labourers to work twelve hours a day, her bank balance had been depleted – but for us three children, it was a turning point.

Somewhere in those exhortations to throw off the trappings of worldly living, and the subsequent entreaties for forgiveness and pleas for heavenly guidance, there had crept a feeling of tolerance and pity for us, and attitudes slowly changed. No longer were we held responsible for our delinquent mother's shortcomings or sins, allowances began to be made for our ages and for the loss of our home, and we were granted a small degree of status in the family. Stella helped tidy bedrooms, I was left to my own devices and Tom joined my cousin in his games and adventures with his friends. But cousin Billy kept us in check, refusing to admit us to his own family circle, reminding us not to get above ourselves, passing us off as 'just here for the school holidays' and always blaming Tom or me for his own misdeeds when found out. I felt it was a fair price to pay and secretly I thanked the white convict in the city jail for his visit to my aunt's home.

When I went back to school, I found I had left my sister behind me in class. I moved up but she remained with girls much younger than she was, and sat stubbornly at the back of her class, doing only the minimum of work. 'What is the matter with your sister?' asked Sister Rose, her class teacher. 'She's always like that,' I said, 'I think she's homesick,' but this did not satisfy the nun and when at last my aunt drove up to the front gates of the Convent to fetch us home for the next holidays, she was called into the parlour to have a long talk with the Head of Studies. 'There is some deep-seated unhappiness there,' said Mother Frances, and asked if my aunt knew anything about it. Again the story of my mother's supposed death was related but the nun reminded Aunty Betty that that was many months ago and she thought it was something more recent.

When we got home, she took Stella into her room and sat down beside her on the satin covered bed, took her hand and kissed her gently. 'Now tell your aunty why you cry so much at school, sister is worried about you and so am I.' My sister sat there dumbly, then said: 'I hate Annie, she was nasty to me.' 'But surely,' said Aunty Betty, 'you haven't been thinking of that for the whole term? What did she say or do?' She turned Stella to face her, and the whole awful story came out.

On her daily walks with Annie, she had been told that my father had had a letter from Grandma Williams in Rusape. Grandma had written to say that they wanted us to live with them if we were to be boarders at the Convent. After all it would entail only a train journey at the beginning and end of each term, a journey which either she or Grandpa would be only too happy to make, and as we were her daughter's children, they felt they had more right to us. My father had been furious and had written back to tell them he wished to have nothing to do with the

Williams family and that included Charlotte, their daughter and there the matter had ended. 'But I still don't know why you have been crying so much,' said Aunty Betty, wondering just what went on in her younger sister's mind and for what reason she had told the child about something she could not understand. 'Is that all?' she asked, and Stella started to cry and flung herself down on the bed. 'It was that man who came when we were talking,' she sobbed, 'and he told me to stay where I was and not to move. Annie was glad to see him and put her arms around his neck and they walked away and I just sat there.' She hiccuped and would not look up at my aunt's white, astounded face. 'And?' she asked 'how long did you sit there?' 'For a long time, and then I went to look for them and I saw them lying on the ground and he was . . .' but she wouldn't say more and begged my aunt not to ask and please not to tell Annie what she had told her. 'Annie said if I told you that she let that man kiss her she would ask you to send us back to Grandma Williams, and I don't want to go.' Aunty Betty's face was grim, but she leaned down to take Stella in her arms, saying gently, 'You are staying with me, no one can send you away, so don't cry and don't say another word to anyone about what you've told me. I'll sort Miss Annie out, so you stay there and I'll send Vinyu in with your supper later,' and she covered Stella with the counterpane and left the room.

The sound of doors banging and scurrying feet echoed through the quiet house. Tom and I sat in our accustomed places at the kitchen table, playing with some fragments of left-over dough, Vinyu was called, and despatched to the brickfields on Uncle George's bicycle with a note, to summon my father who was giving Jack a hand. Presently the whole family was assembled in the front verandah room among the flowering plants, the opulent furnishings and the singing birds.

Georgie fondled his dog's ears, Uncle George looked embarrassed and worried, my father sat rubbing his chin and sniffing and cousin Billy stood hidden in the folds of the curtain at the doorway, listening and watching everything that went on. Annie asked 'Dinner ready yet?' 'Sit down Ann,' said Aunty Betty, 'I've got something to ask you and I want the truth, d'ye hear?' Annie looked around, her face reddening as she realised she was the focus of attention. 'These long walks you take every day,' began my aunt, 'where do you go?' 'I just walk along the bush road,' said Annie, and she smiled anxiously at her sister. 'And why don't you take Stella with you any more?' Annie laughed self-consciously and shrugged her shoulders. 'She don't always want to come,' she said, and then she looked around at the hostile faces and asked, 'What's this all

100

about? What have I done?' 'You know very well what you've been up to and so do I,' said my aunt. 'You've been meeting a man and carrying on with him, haven't you?'

Annie leapt up, bursting into tears as she did so and cried, 'You don't want me to have a friend of my own, do you? You just want me to work like a nigger all day and never to have any fun.' 'I'm glad you call it fun,' said Aunty Betty, and realising that Annie was becoming hysterical, she spoke more softly saying, 'We don't mind if you have a friend, but tell us who he is?' 'Shan't,' said Annie. 'Well then,' said my aunt, 'tell us what sort of fun you have?' 'No,' said her younger sister, 'and you can't make me,' and she put her head down on her knees and cried.

'Come on,' said Aunty Betty, 'tell us what you were doing with your man friend in the bush?' 'Shan't,' shouted Annie, tears coursing down her reddened face, her mouth drawn into an ugly shape as she looked at her assembled relations. 'Shan't,' she yelled as she rose to her feet. My aunt realised she had made a mistake, confronting her sister before the whole family, so she went over and took her hand. 'Don't cry dear, and don't shout like that, we only want to know who he is.' But her sister would not be mollified and snatched her hand away. 'Leave me alone,' she cried, 'I don't want any dinner, leave me alone,' and she went towards the door, but as the two sisters drew level and looked at each other, the truth struck Aunty Betty like a blow between the eyes.

The curled hair, the request for a cast-off dress, the clumsy application of powder and rouge ... but worse was the bloom and the roundness of her sister who had always been pale, colourless and angular, and the radiance in her eyes. It told my aunt everything she had dreaded to know.

She controlled her disquiet, saying, 'Well, we'll have dinner even if you don't want any,' and she led her men folk into the dining room; she knew that Annie had been close to hysteria and that the men had been deeply embarrassed at her revelations, but she was determined to get to the bottom of the affair.

When the men had gone to the verandah to smoke and ponder and conjecture the seriousness of what they had learnt, my aunt again confronted her sister in her bedroom. We heard their raised voices, Annie's screams, my aunt's voice shouting, then a series of slaps and blows and a sudden silence. Grim-faced, our aunt came to the bedroom door and called her sons and Vinyu, and as we stood open-mouthed by the kitchen door, we saw the men carrying our beds and bedding out onto the back verandah. 'You needn't have hit her so hard,' Jack reproached his mother, but she was too angry to reply. She locked the bedroom and said to us, 'You kids'd better sleep on the verandah for the time being, Annie ain't too well.' She turned and went into her bedroom, slamming the door behind her.

An uneasy quiet settled over the house, but as it did not seem to change the tempo of everyday life, I hardly noticed Annie's absence. We knew she was still locked in her bedroom but we did not know why she was being punished, in spite of Billy's lurid description of what had taken place on the verandah. Stella was afraid to be left at home and spent most of her time playing with her dolls under the syringa trees at the brickfields office, going back and forth with my aunt in her motor car. Even Vinyu, with whom I spent all my day, admitted he knew nothing, although he often sucked through his teeth, saying 'my weh' several times and shaking his head.

The school holidays were very short and when we returned to school, my father asked for an interview with the Mother Prioress; I stood with my sister and brother looking out into the grass covered courtyard at the back of the parlour, watching the sparkling fountain as the water rose and fell into the small pool, and then I heard my father ask 'Can the children possibly stay here during the next holidays? My young sister who normally takes care of them has been very ill, and I think it would be better for her to recover completely before they come home again.' After some deliberation, it was decided that we would go to the school farm some miles out in the bush and I heard my father saying that we would be quite willing to work.

As he said his goodbyes, he said we were to do as we were told and to help the nuns on their farm and that he would try to come and see us: Stella cried bitterly, but Tom and I were quite satisfied with my father's order and happily returned to our classes and friends. 'It's not fair,' wailed Stella, 'if it wasn't for you two, I could go home to Aunty Betty, I don't want to spend the holidays with a lot of old nuns. Why should we have to work when all the others are with their parents at home?' I felt sorry for her but was quite happy at the prospect of six weeks of freedom with the nuns.

We were put to work in the convent garden where we sorted out potatoes with the children from the Catholic orphanage which stood on a hill overlooking the farm. Every day was full of laughter and games, and on Sundays after church we were issued with tennis racquets and balls, the nuns hiked up their long white serge skirts and we played tennis on a clearing in the bush. It was winter, and slowly the bush died, the grass turned brown and the pools in the river dried up; frosts turned everything in the garden slimy black, and veldt fires raged on the skyline. We leaned out of our windows in the dormitory, watching the nuns and the garden boys trying to beat out the flames with wet sacks.

I had no cares and was happy for the first time. The nuns read us stories at night when we went to bed and by day we did our allotted tasks and were then free to read or play. Expeditions to the town were planned and visits to the Convent to see the nuns who had befriended us, but soon it was time to return to school and to await the next holidays at my aunt's house.

Slowly I made more friends at school and a small group of us spent our spare time playing in the recreation ground which was built on a big piece of land across the road from the school. Here we were allowed to do as we pleased. We listened to records on an old gramophone, swung from the rafters or talked about ourselves; tennis fours were organised and played, games of hockey were fought out with other small cliques, and we quite unashamedly robbed the day girls of their lunches with promises to help them with their homework. Two nuns always patrolled the grounds, reading their Office for the day, apparently oblivious to the yelling, shouting, screams and cries of many small girls.

I hardly ever saw Tom, but he was six years old now and had his own friends. Some days he waited by the door to ask me about future holidays, or to ask whether I knew if our father was coming to see us, but gradually we drifted apart and became more self-reliant.

I never spoke about my aunt's home or my father, and my mother was never mentioned. She had faded from my mind, and if I ever thought about her, it was to wonder how she had died. I reasoned that if she was alive, she would surely have come to see us. In my immature mind, I realised too that I was more free than my contemporaries; I had no emotional ties with an older woman, I could never be hurt or have demands made on me; but I knew too that there was a void in my life. Thoughts like these rarely surfaced; they were pushed firmly out of my mind and I was happy and glad about everything around me.

It was nearly a year before we were summoned to the parlour at the end of term. I barely recognised my aunt when I first saw her. She was sitting in the hard, straight-backed chair, whilst an embarrassed nun sat

103

opposite hardly daring to look at her. Her long black hair was gone. Now she wore a short style called an Eton Crop, the hair appearing to be painted on to her skull, and coming forward in two big kiss curls on her rouged cheeks. Heavy make-up, long bead necklaces and a dress which came above her knees and which appeared to have no waist, pink silk stockings and patent black shoes completed the bizarre picture, and when she rose, she tapped her long black cigarette holder into the pot of ferns to discard the ash. She smiled brightly at us and asked 'How do you like it?' as she twirled around, sending the points of her short skirt swirling into the air, and showing us her lace-edged knickers. Sister Amata blushed deeply and excused herself, only pausing to say a shocked goodbye as she scurried back to the safety of the school office.

Many things had changed when we finally arrived at her house. Aunt Annie was no longer at the gate waiting for her charges and we learned she had gone with her mother back to England. Although we had been unaware of their presence, our English grandparents had lived in a little house the other side of the brickworks and there my grandfather had recently died. No more was said about Annie's punishment. Vinyu winked knowingly when I asked him, and said 'Ask Billy, he was there, he'll tell you everything.'

My sister transferred her affections to my aunt. If there was any shopping to be done in the town, she climbed into the car and obediently sat beside Aunty Betty, and gradually she assumed the position of daughter of the household and blossomed in her new found security. My brother ran around with Billy's friends and I drifted along on the boundaries of everyone else's life, quite content for it to be so, my only anxiety that I might do something that would draw attention to myself.

Cousin Georgie spent little time in his home; a new cotton ginnery was being built in the town, and he was employed there with some thirty other white men as a bricklayer. When the five o'clock hooter blew, he washed and tidied himself up, mounted his bicycle and rode off some four miles to visit the Marnewicj family. The object of his visit was the eldest daughter, Claudine, a pretty little dark-haired girl who made herself charming dresses on her mother's sewing machine and who seemed to have a number of ardent admirers.

'Georgie is going to ask Ma if he can marry Claudine,' announced Billy as we sat in the back yard, playing with his white mice, but he did not hold out much hope for her consent. He said his mother objected to the Marnewicj family 'because they're Dutch'. I had seen Georgie speaking earnestly to his mother, and she had cried and there was tension between them; but the engagement was eventually announced and plans for the wedding went ahead. My father was elected to be best man.

Dingo forsook the divan on the verandah and now lay on his master's bed, looking at the doorway and whining softly to himself. He ignored his food and grew thinner, but when I approached him and twitched my fingers at him, he growled and showed me his teeth, longing only for the moment when he would hear his master's footsteps on the verandah. 'That bleedin' dog will have to go,' announced my aunt, and some days before the wedding I saw two of the herdboys carrying a heavy mealie meal sack and going in the direction of the river. I did not see Dingo again and Georgie appeared not to miss his faithful friend. He duly married his Claudine and went to live in a little house in the town.

Jack worked in the brickyard office, taking a lot of the administration from his mother's shoulders, but that year brick-making ran into trouble. The rains had started early, the river rose and flooded the brickyard and the pugmill leaned dangerously because its foundations became undermined. Bricks drying in the sun were washed away or slowly dissolved as the rain pelted down, huts collapsed and most of the workmen succumbed to malaria and lay wet and shivering quietly in their shacks. No one thought to call a doctor or to issue quinine and many of the men died in the night. The bodies were piled into oxwagons and trundled off to the native burial grounds on the outskirts of the native locations.

As soon as the rain stopped and the river receded to its former level, the pugmill was righted and work re-started. Bricks of all kinds were laid out to dry and then built into kilns to be burned; orders were piling up and my aunt went to the market where she bought a span of four oxen, so the work went on faster than before, and at the start of the very cold winter, the kilns were fired. A blue smoky haze hung over the brickfields as the fires burned fiercely non-stop and at night many of the tribesmen crept out of their huts with their blankets and climbed to the top of the kilns to enjoy the warmth. But the next morning their fellows pulled their bodies down from where they had died, killed by the gases given off by the fires. The police had to be notified and soon convicts from the prison arrived pushing covered stretchers onto which the bodies were loaded, to be carried away to a communal grave. Soon more tribesmen arrived to take their jobs and despite all the warnings, many of them joined their kinsmen in death.

Aunty Betty no longer spent all her days at the brickyard but every afternoon she drove over in her car, through the bush, over scrub bushes and antbear holes, bumping and swaying through the trees, and arrived at the office, cool and unruffled. One day I had been invited to accompany her and heard her ask Jack 'How many?' I thought she was asking how many dead kaffirs had been taken off the kilns, only to learn that she meant how many thousands of bricks had gone out to the city that day. Tallies were scrutinised, figures checked and balanced, letters collected to be dealt with at home by my father, customers placated and sometimes, police answered. But the fact that men had died on the kilns during the night was hardly commented on and appeared to be of no significance at all.

We were back for long school holidays and I was nearly eight years old and in love with cousin Jack. But he was courting, said Vinyu, and this we took to be visiting a girl in the town. Her name was Hilda Maas, and every Saturday evening Jack put on his best flannels and sports coat and rode off on his cycle to see her and her family who lived in the Railway Married Quarters. I was mystified as to why he cycled that distance just to see a girl, and asked Vinyu if he knew what they did. 'Do they play about in the dark?' I asked, but he tsk-ed through his teeth and flicked at my legs with a dish towel, saying 'You white people have very strange customs, ask him yourself, what it is they do.' But I was too shy to speak so boldly to my big cousin, although he was always kind to me.

I squatted on my heels, holding the oil can and quite embarrassed at being asked to help Jack. He was cleaning the lamp which clipped on to the front handlebars of his bicycle. It was a carbide lamp, he explained, as he measured out the water carefully and filled the tank behind the saddle. It would drip on to the carbide and the gas would be lit with a match. It gave off a sour, smokey smell and made just enough light to throw a soft aura on to the immediate surroundings, but it was sufficient to light the way to Hilda Maas's home in the Railways Married Quarters. Feeling a little braver I asked 'What do you do when you go and see your girl friend? Do you play in the garden?' He looked at me for a moment and then burst out laughing and said 'Wait until you're grown up, you'll find out then.' Still chuckling to himself, he adjusted the lamp wick and with a wave he rode off into the darkening night.

Hilda Maas had a small brother called Brewerie who was Billy's newest, special friend. He was coming to spend the day with our cousin and we liked him; he allowed us to hang on to the fringes of his friendship with Billy, who was always ready to remind us that we were only in his home for the holidays. We questioned Brewerie about his family and he told us that his father used to be an engine driver in Amsterdam. Where was that? we asked. 'In Holland of course,' sneered our all-knowing cousin, but I was puzzled because the Maas family always spoke English and therefore could not be Dutch like those people who lived in the south and who had fought against our king during the Boer War. Those people we were constantly being reminded, only deserved our hatred and contempt for their actions. 'Bloody Boers' said Uncle George.

Now we hung around the gate by the cattle shed and presently we saw Brewerie sitting on the bar of his father's bicycle. He was carrying his new air rifle which had been given him for doing well in school. His father added that he knew how to use it and had been warned never to point it at anyone and that he hoped the boys would have some luck in their shooting expedition. They had planned to search for rabbits and dassies some distance away through the bush.

'You kids can come with us,' cried our cousin and we left the grown-ups sitting on the verandah, drinking tea with Mr Maas. He could not stay long, he had said, he was due to take the 152 up to Umtali later that evening but would come back to take his son home later in the day. We ran through the bush barefoot, dodging the three-pronged thorns lying hidden along the path, and watching out carefully for snakes which often lay basking in the sun, torpid in the morning heat. We came suddenly to the granite kopjes and heard the dassies barking in alarm as they stood on their hind legs peering through the undergrowth, twitching their noses and making ready to bolt. The bush thinned out into savannah as we drew nearer to the rocks, and searching about, we soon found a cave at the bottom of a small kopje where the two boys proceeded to remove all their clothes, saying they were pretending to be kaffirs hunting for lion. We took off our clothes too and then we all climbed up into the trees which grew amongst the boulders. We halooed and shouted and we heard the scrabbling of little feet as the dassies fled to their hiding places, but soon Tom and I found we were in a wild fig tree which was twined around the cleft of the rock from which it grew, the roots splitting the surface, and through the big glossy leaves, we could see ripe figs. We picked and ate them although we had been told by the garden boys that they were full of worms. They were sweet and juicy, so we gave no thought to the grubs amongst the seeds. Wild violet

107

trees grew beneath our feet amongst the msasa trees and we sniffed at the purple flowers, enjoying their spicy perfume.

Sometimes we found kaffir oranges lying in between the boulders, some split open by the monkeys who lived in the dark caves higher up, and Tom and I cracked the oranges open with a stone and ate the slippery, pungent fruit. We knew we would be punished if we told our cousin we had eaten the oranges; only kaffirs and baboons ate them so we were careful to wipe all traces from our mouths.

The two older boys had long since left us and we heard their voices fading in the distance as they went on their hunt for the dassies. Suddenly we heard a shot and rose to our feet and started our descent down the boulder, slipping and slithering as we groped for footholds. Then we heard shouting and screaming and Billy appeared through the long grass, shouting 'Run home and fetch Jorbey, I've shot Brewerie by mistake. Hurry and run as fast as you can!'

Quickly I pulled on my dress, and freeing myself from the terrified cries of my little brother I set off while Billy shouted after me 'Just fetch the garden boy, don't tell my mommy, and run as fast as you can.' Not pausing to ask if his friend was dead, I ran off, crying and sobbing, falling over roots, bumping into small trees, scraping my hands and knees and being caught by thorn bushes. After a long time I saw the house in the distance, everything quiet and tranquil and I ran around to the servants quarters, calling for Jorbey. He was a young man from Fort Jameson in Nyasaland who worked as the garden boy and spent from early morning to late afternoon digging, watering and weeding. He cleaned the car, polished the verandahs and did any odd job that no one else would do and he also cooked the midday meal for the servants.

As I drew near I saw him scouring out the large black pot he cooked the mealie meal in, whistling tunelessly to himself as he scrubbed at the inside with a handful of ashes. He looked puzzled as I clutched at him, crying and saying 'Come quickly Jorbey, Billy has shot Brewerie Maas with his gun, he's dead, come quickly.' Then his bewildered look changed to understanding, he took my hand and we set off, but he soon stopped and told me to climb onto his back so that we could go more quickly.

Billy had put on his clothes and Brewerie was lying on the ground, quite white, with only his shorts pulled on and in his back a little hole, black and shiny, oozing blood which trickled and dried into the waistband of his trousers. 'Is it sore?' I asked when he turned over to look at us but he said nothing and I could see the tracks of his heels where Billy had dragged him back to the cave. Jorbey clicked his teeth, shaking his head, and then he picked up the little boy and we started back to the homestead. 'Poor Brewerie,' I said to Billy, 'is he going to die?' 'No,' he shouted, his voice rising hysterically, 'it was only a small bullet, I didn't mean it, it was his own fault, he went in front of me and I didn't see him. You're not to say it was my fault, it wasn't,' and he started to cry.

Now and then we stopped for Jorbey to put the child down and to have a rest, and at last we came out of the bush at the back of the house, near the servant's compound. Jorbey put Brewerie down against the side of his hut and after fetching some water in a clean jam tin which he used as a cup, he went off to find Vinyu. Together they lifted Brewerie and carried him to the house. Aunty Betty was standing on the verandah as we all drew near, and once again Billy burst out, before anyone could speak. 'It wasn't my fault mommy, it was his, he got in front of me.' His mother put her arm around him and drew him to her side. Brewerie had closed his eyes and lay inert and white-faced on the ground between us as we stood wondering what would happen.

The motor car was brought out of the garage and the two servants laid the child on the back seat. Vinyu climbed in beside my aunt and they drove off in the direction of the town. We sat with Jorbey in the dust, not saying anything, but our eyes were fixed on Billy. 'Brewerie's mother's going to be very cross with you,' I volunteered. 'She won't let him come and play with you again.' 'Shut up,' he cried, 'you bloody kids don't know what happened; he got in front of me, it was all his fault, you're not to say I did it.' 'But you did,' I said, suddenly feeling very brave and despising him for the bully he was, for his ability to shift blame and for the lies he told and for the many little cruelties he subjected us to. He lunged at me shouting, 'I'll tell my mother on you, you cheeky little poor-white, see if I don't.' I held my tongue, remembering the warning I had been given a long time ago about fighting and answering back, and I joined Tom and Jorbey and together we dawdled the afternoon away.

After a long time we heard the distant chugging of the car as it laboured up the hill from the river. It came to a shuddering stop in the yard and out stepped Mr and Mrs Maas, Aunty Betty and Vinyu. Brewerie's father was a large red-faced man with a shock of blond hair, and he smoked a pipe with a man's face carved on the bowl. His little wife was plain and was the first person I had seen who wore eye glasses. I could see she had been crying and my heart sank as I wondered if her little boy had died.

'Tell me what happened,' she said to Billy, who had gone to stand beside his mother, and once more he burst into tears, whining and snivelling that it wasn't his fault his friend had been shot, he had got in his way and he hadn't seen him when he pulled the trigger. Mrs Maas came towards him, her face transformed by a smile as she took him into her arms, and she said, 'If it wasn't for you, klienke, my little one might have died. You see, when they took him into the operating room, to take out the bullet, they found his appendix was on the point of bursting. If he had not had this accident, it would have burst while you were in the bush and it would have been too late to get help then. But here is the bullet, I have brought it for you,' and she held it out to him. 'It was only a small wound in the soft part of his back and did him no harm. But thank you again, my boy, you have saved my little one's life,' and she kissed him on his cheek.

We were dumbfounded at the turn of events but we looked at my cousin with different eyes, seeing him as the saviour of his friend, and I wondered if this was a miracle like the ones we had learned about at school and which the nuns constantly told us about. And I wondered what Hilda Maas would say when she heard that Billy had saved her little brother. He went to stand by his mother again and Aunty Betty looked at him proudly as she hugged him and said, 'My little darling, you only think of others,' but when I smiled at him diffidently, he put out his tongue at me.

I sat by the big tin bath, dabbling the blue bag in the clean water, waiting for Vinyu to finish rinsing the sheets, and then I asked him 'Do you know those trees on the way to the rocks? Those with stones stuck into the branches?' He pretended to be busy wringing out the sheets, so I repeated my question. 'I saw them the other day when we went to the rocks with Billy. Who puts the stones in the trees? What are they for?' Again he ignored me and picked up another bundle of washing, but I followed him and persisted: 'You do know the stones I'm talking about. Who puts them in the branches and what for?' He turned to face me, his face startled, and then he said: 'You mustn't go there again, it's not for white people, it's witchdoctor's medicine, there will be trouble if you touch them.'

'But you are a mission boy,' I reminded him. 'You're not supposed to believe in witch doctors, are you?' 'I'm a good Christian,' he said 'but in my tribe we listen to both God and N'Ganga, so don't speak to me of

110

matters you don't understand.' 'But what about the stones?' I asked again. He knew he would have no peace until he told me, so we sat down on the now upturned bath and he turned to face me. I could see he was still frightened by my questions, and after a few moments he said, 'They are curses put there by a man who has a grievance against another. He asked the N'Ganga to put the curse into the stone and then he takes it to where he knows his victim will pass, and he lodges it firmly in the branches. When the cursed man passes that way, he will feel the curse and soon he will die.' 'Is that true?' I asked. 'Do you know anyone who that has happened to?' 'Many,' he replied. 'Are any of them for you?' I asked. 'No man knows if the curse is for him,' he replied. 'How can he? But no man passes that part of the bush, knowing that many curses are there, waiting.'

'How much do you have to pay the N'Ganga?' 'Sometimes a goat or some fowls,' he replied. 'I do not know, I have not done it myself, but that is the place they took that man who used to meet Miss Annie,' he added, realising the instant the words had left his lips that he should not have uttered them. 'What man?' I asked, eager to know, 'and what did they do to him?' And because Vinyu could not evade my constant and persistent questions, he soon told me what had happened a year earlier, just after we had gone back to school.

'Miss Annie was kept in her room,' he told me, 'and Baas George, Jack and your father went into the bush and waited for the man whom she had promised to meet. They hid behind the trees and when he came cycling up to the place they ran out and caught him. They tied him to the tree, took off his clothes and they whipped him with your father's sjambok. They whipped him till the blood ran from his back and then they left him there. Early next morning a native who works in the town walked past that place and heard the man crying. He was afraid but he stopped and cut the ropes from the man's body and left him where he fell, at the bottom of the tree. His clothes were lying around and when that same native passed again that way, the white man had gone.'

'And then what happened?' I asked. 'I do not know. I did not go there but the men of this house were quiet and did not speak of the matter at the dinner table that night.' 'Do you know who he was?' I asked. 'Yes,' he replied, 'he was one of the many brothers who live in Hatfield, near where your father and mother lived. He was the youngest of the family, and I often saw him cycling to his work in the town. He passed this house many times and used to wave at Miss Annie. But he is a Dutchman,' and here Vinyu sniffed. 'But it was wrong what your

111

cousins did, they should have let him have Miss Annie, he would not have had to pay a big lobola, after all, she is no longer a young woman and sometimes she laughs too much.' He tapped his head, indicating that she was not in full possession of her wits.

'What did Annie do, did she know about the beating?' He drew in his breath and shook his head. 'Bad things were done. I do not wish to say more. You are not to speak of this matter with Stella or Tom or any one else,' and then he grinned at me, showing his yellow teeth and his eyes crinkled. 'If you say one word, I will get a very big stone from the river and pay the N'Ganga to put a curse in it for you.' He prodded me in the chest and I shivered, half believing that he would do so, and silently I prayed to my guardian angel, which Mother Frances had told me to do when in trouble. I felt guilty because I could not reconcile my fear of the witch doctor with my new-found belief in the saints and angels.

'Why did Annie go away with our English Amboya?' I asked, using the Shona word for grandmother. 'Why did they send her back to England?' 'That I do not know; they talk about these things at night after dinner when I have left the house, but I do know that another lady came to see Miss Annie late one night. She stayed for a long time and I heard them talking in the bedroom. I saw her leave as I came back from visiting my brother who works for Mrs Smith. But Miss Annie was sick for a long time and when she came out of the house to be taken to the station, she looked as though she was not yet awake.' He shook his head, saying 'my weh' several times, and then he started to gather in the freshly dried laundry.

Before we returned to school, plans were made for the family to travel to England to visit their relations; we would stay in the house and Vinyu would look after us, said my aunt, and my father would call each day to see that all was in order. He had moved out of the house and had bought a small cottage at the end of the long row of homesteads which constituted the small suburb, and had at last found permanent work with the City council. He did not say what it was but he now owned a large red Harley Davidson motorbike with a side car attached. He had difficulty controlling it and when we begged to be taken for a ride, he ignored us until, driven to exasperation, he yelled 'Shut up you bleedin' kids, d'ye think petrol's free?'

Boxes and suitcases, cabin trunks and hatboxes had been brought out of the storeroom and lay about on the verandah, all open and smelling of moth balls. Leather straps for blanket rolls were sorted, tickets had been bought and money drawn from the bank, and long overcoats were being shortened for the weather which awaited the family when they landed in England. I stood at the end of the verandah on one leg, watching the preparations and wishing I was going too, when I heard my aunt asking me to call Vinyu. He was to fetch the Sammy, she told him, and he was to hurry. This time no dresses or school uniforms were made for us; Sammy brought bales of heavy cloth for overcoats, worsteds for trousers and rolls of expensive flannel for warm shirts for the men, and soon his machine whirred and his scissors clicked where he sat at his work. Aisha no longer pushed the barrow. She had two babies to look after and he employed a young native boy to do her work. He rolled up unwanted bales of material, passed the scissors, found the tape measure and pins and shooed us away as we tried to pick up the scraps to make dolls' dresses; he trimmed seams and neatened edges and when the work was done, he packed up the materials, loaded the barrow and pushed it back to Sammy's house.

At last everything was ready. We stood on the verandah when all the trunks, suitcases and bed rolls were put into the motor car and my aunt bent down to kiss us goodbye. 'Be a good girl,' she said. 'Listen to Vinyu and I'll bring you a present when I come back.' My father drove them to the station in their car but Jorbey had had to run ahead to help them stow their luggage in the van. We went indoors to pack up our school clothes but I thought of the family who would spend three days in the train to Capetown and then three weeks on a ship to England. We had no conception of such a long journey, or what a ship looked like, and the thought of so much water in the sea frightened me sufficiently to drive any envious thoughts from my mind.

Early next morning my father came to take us back to school. He rode ahead on his motor bike, having explained to the rickshaw boy that he was to take us back to the Convent, and there he waited for us, but this time his request to have us spend our next holidays at the school farm was turned down. The nuns were going into Retreat, explained the Mother Prioress, and would fast and pray for a month, and the garden boys would have to manage as best they could under the supervision of the boss boy. We would have to return to our aunt's home.

When we did so, it was to find Vinyu's wife K'buda and his small son Patronne happily settled in the compound. Vinyu had had to pay a big lobola for his wife who still wore a skin apron and carried the little boy in a sling on her back. She was kind and gentle but would not come into the house, so we played with Patronne in the compound, carrying him about on our backs or quarrelling about him. My sister soon left me in charge of the baby, preferring to play with her dolls, saying that he smelt and dribbled and was after all, only a picannin.

Vinyu brought buckets of hot water into the forbidden bathroom and watched to see that we washed ourselves properly, then he helped us dry ourselves, brushed our hair and put us to bed. Sometimes he wanted to get away to spend time with his family and we frequently found ourselves going to bed when it was still daylight and before the herdboys had finished their milking. We heard motor cars being driven up from the river and heard the tinkle of bicycle bells as people who worked in the town returned home, but we did not wish to displease Vinyu so we sat on our beds whispering and making up stories. Sometimes I woke in the early hours of the morning and my brother and I ran out into the garden to chase each other through the flower beds, or climbed the trees, still in our nightgowns, and ate the half ripe peaches or plums. But we were careful not to make too much noise, it would carry in the still morning air before dawn and we knew there would be trouble if any of the neighbours told what we did.

I persuaded Jorbey to leave his work and we went with him during the days to explore the river banks; he made whistles for us from the reeds which grew in thick clumps and showed us how to play simple notes. He made catapults from vee-shaped sticks he cut from the trees and we had competitions shooting at empty beer bottles we found in the rubbish pile. But best of all we enjoyed finding empty termite hills where he said he was sure small mice lived in the tunnels hidden underground. He scooped up wet clay from the river bank and blocked up all but two holes in the ant hill. In the hole at the bottom, he stuffed dried grass which he lit and as the thick grey smoke billowed out of the hole at the top, we stood by, ready to catch the mice as they hurtled out.

Deftly he wrung their necks, and taking a small ember from the fire, he placed it on the mouse's stomach and we watched as the pale beige velvety skin split and curled back to expose the entrials. He scooped these out and threaded his prizes on lengths of thick grass and we carried them home for him. They would be added to the vegetable stew he was cooking for the midday meal and we were invited to join the garden boys for lunch. Vinyu ate with his wife and son but he did not approve of our presence, frowning and saying 'your father will be cross if he catches you here.' But we were unmoved and squatted around the cooking fire, waiting for the men to eat first. They washed their hands and rinsed out their mouths when they were finished and left us with the remains of the meal and some of the relish of vegetables and little mice. I had watched how they gathered up the mealie meal and now I snatched off a piece, rolled it into a small ball, dipped it into the stew and popped it into my mouth.

Later in the afternoon, when he heard the boys calling to the cattle which grazed on the outskirts of the bush, Jorbey filled the big petrol drum full of water and placed it on the cooking fire. When the water had boiled, he added handfuls of crushed mealies and when they had cooked he waited until the cattle approached the gate, then he tipped the drum over, throwing the mealies onto the sandy yard. When the cattle rushed in to eat the steaming maize, we ran, almost under their hooves and horns, to snatch up handfuls which we stuffed into our mouths, relishing every grain. We were not very hungry when Vinyu called us in for our bread and jam supper and we sat replete and happy as we watched Stella delicately cutting her bread into small squares before she ate them. 'I'll tell daddy what you two kids do,' she threatened. 'You're nothing but a pair of picannins.'

Once a week, we went with Vinyu to visit our father who lived on his property a short distance away. He did not call to see us as Aunty Betty had said, but I was secretly relieved because I knew he would complain about something I had done, making me feel that all his misfortunes were our fault. The pretty little cottage had been rented out to a policeman who held a senior position in the British South Africa Police; a big jovial man who laughed a lot and spoke with a funny English accent. 'Call me Tex,' he would guffaw at us, but we were frightened of him, more because he was an important policeman than by his large frame and bulky tweed clothes.

My father had built himself a one-roomed hut, whitewashed on the outside and roughly plastered within. There was no ceiling and spiders and scorpions ran across the timbers and thatch, flies hung caught in the webs, and crickets sang with their irritating scratching noise. The hut stood halfway down the property, screened by a hedge of syringa trees and a mound of rusting and discarded boilers, machinery, pieces of ploughs, an old motor car chassis, rolls of barbed wire and several old wheelbarrows missing their wheels. While we waited for my father we climbed the syringa trees, throwing the berries at each other or swinging wildly amongst the branches, but at the first sound of his thundering motorbike we leaped down, tidied ourselves and went to sit with Vinyu who sat chewing a piece of grass and chatting to my father's servant Reuben.

Every time my father asked the same question. 'What've you kids been up to eh?' We dared not admit we had frolicked around the garden and through the orchard in the moonlight, that we had dined with the herdboys or called Jorbey away from his work, and replied meekly 'just played', aware of Vinyu's lack of interest in our account of ourselves. My father did not seem aware of our unkempt appearance, our scratched and scabby legs and feet, of my hair which hadn't been washed for many weeks and now hung over my shoulders, or of my brother's missing front teeth which had recently been pulled out by Jorbey.

Vinyu rose and stood before him and then asked. 'When do they go back to school? I have ironed their clothes and put them away, but they are getting too small for them. They will soon need new blouses and gym dresses, they cannot wear the old ones for much longer.' My father frowned and looked us over, then spat on the ground. 'They will have to do for another term, I haven't got money to spend on new clothes for them.' 'But the Sammy can come next week sir, and you can pay him later when Madam returns. But they cannot wear their uniforms, they are too tight and hers' – and here he pointed at me – 'are worn out, they have been torn and mended by the sisters, but they are too small for her.' My father looked at me for a long time, then shook his head and opened the door into his home.

He lived in some degree of squalor, his discarded clothes lying in heaps on the cheap table and chair next to his bed; the table itself doubled as a dining table, but it was covered in many layers of old newspapers. The one in use was covered in tea stains, cigarette burns, blobs of food and gravy, shaving lather and squashed flies and when there was too much filth, a clean sheet of newspaper was spread over the gathering layers until it was inches thick. The smell from the faulty paraffin lamp hung over everything and mingled with the smell of the dirty water still standing in the wash basin which stood on an upturned petrol box. 'What is your work here?' asked Vinyu of Reuben in Shona, knowing my father would not understand the question, and his servant shifted his feet and would not meet Vinyu's eye. 'I cannot clean in here because my master locks the door when he leaves in the morning, so I wait until he returns. Soon he will go down to the river to look at his garden, and I will make the bed and clean the room and then I will make the stew for him to eat for his evening meal,' and he pointed to three bricks standing a little way off, amongst which burned a few logs of wood. The blackened pot bubbled quietly away and from it arose the smell of meat and vegetables cooking.

Scornfully Vinyu turned away. 'Many days have passed since this room was clean. You must ask your master for a good broom and some soap. You cannot call yourself a house-servant if you sit around your own fire all day while your master lives like a pig.' Reuben looked ashamed and embarrassed but I felt sorry for him, even if he was a loafer. 'Take these dirty clothes and wash them tomorrow,' said Vinyu, 'and we will come early and I will show you how to iron and fold them'; 'Ai-ee, I will do as you say,' said Reuben as he started to gather up the bundles of dirty clothes, and Vinyu left him and took my hand and once again addressed my father who was tinkering with his motorbike, and completely ignoring his children.

'Will I ask the Sammy to call tomorrow please sir?' he asked. My father stood up and looked me up and down. 'Do as you please,' he said to the servant, 'I don't know where's the money coming from, but tell him I'll pay him as soon as I can; but only one gym frock and shirt each mind, I can't afford to throw money away.' We put up our faces to be kissed as we said our goodbyes, but my father seemed anxious to return to the problems of his motor cycle and gave us only a perfunctory wave. Stella hung back to say a few words and then we all ran down the road back to Aunty Betty's house, followed by Vinyu, anxious no doubt, to be rid of us so that he could join K'Buda and the baby around their own hearth.

The Sammy was called to the house, and soon two sets of new school clothes lay on the bed, waiting to be packed into our school trunks, but Vinyu had not mentioned to my father that he had recklessly told the tailor that one uniform would not be enough. Time enough for that later, he thought, as he sorted out socks, cleaned shoes and inspected our clean underwear. 'Which day do you return to school?' he asked 'I will have to tell your father to order the rickshaw,' but we did not know and that evening we once again went with Vinyu, carrying the irons which would be heated over the fire so that Reuben could complete his laundry.

'Gawd knows why you keep asking me so many questions,' said my irritated father, as Vinyu asked when we were to return to the Convent. 'I don't bleeding' know, do I? But if you shut up, I'll find out tomorrow when I go to work,' so Vinyu had to be satisfied with that. But there were other questions, and when my father turned to go down to look at his flower garden, we all followed and Vinyu asked again 'When does madam come back from England?' 'For Gawd's sake, man, you know she gets back in a month's time,' said my father, clearly irritated by Vinyu's persistence, 'what's this all leading to?' Then I heard Vinyu say

117

'It's all finished sir, and I do not know what more to do.' 'You've got them bleedin' sweet potatoes, haven't you?' said my father 'There were three bags of them in the storeroom when I last looked.' 'They have eaten those long ago,' said Vinyu, 'and the money Madam gave me for food is now finished. What can I do?' and he looked worried as he glanced away. 'Give them some of your own meal, they're used to that,' said my father, turning away and thus dismissing the servant.

We trotted home with Vinyu, not really understanding what had been said and when he brought us a dish full of freshly cooked mealie meal that evening we were not allowed to eat it with our hands, but had to use spoons. My sister pushed her plate away saying she didn't like it, but I knew she did not want to put herself into our category of 'Pincannins'.

The next day Vinyu took a milk jug and went over to Mrs Smith's house and was there for a long time, then returned with a plate of small cakes and two loaves of newly baked bread, steaming hot, the crust brown and crisp; 'Mrs Smith says you are to go there for food tomorrow,' he informed us and when I carried back the plates and we stood on the back verandah, waiting for her to answer my knock, she appeared, smiling and wiping her hands on her apron.

'Did you children enjoy the soup I sent over last night?' she asked as I handed back her jug and plates. 'I thought you'd like it as a change from all that milk your cookboy gives you,' and she looked us over keenly and then addressed me. 'I'll cut your hair for you if you like, it's getting very long.' When she combed out my hair, she peered at my scalp for a long time and then asked 'Does it hurt when I press?' and she ran her hand over my head.

There were maggot-fly eggs under the skin, and because they itched a lot I had been unable to stop scratching and here and there were raw, bleeding patches which I had hoped she would not see. Hot water liberally laced with the ubiquitous Jeyes Fluid was applied, and then she ran her thumb nail across my scalp, squirting out the white wriggling worms. She curled her lip in disgust but did not stop until she had removed all the parasites. 'Go into the bathroom and undress, and we'll see if there are any more,' she said with a smile, but there were none. No more was said, but I cried, not from what I'd undergone but for shame at what I had nurtured on my head. I felt unclean, noting my sister's look of mingled pity and disgust, but Mrs Smith smiled at me kindly, saying, 'Never mind, they're all out now.' She cut my hair short like Tom's and said we were to stay for the midday meal and that she would send her servant to take us home later.

The invitation to spend an afternoon in someone else's home was so unusual and gratifying that I cheered up and sat on the verandah watching Stella and Roma Smith playing with their dolls. They did not ask me to join them. Roma ran to sit next to her father when he had been summoned to the table. She patted the seat next to her indicating that Stella should sit there and I knew they considered I was tainted and dirty. A stool was brought from the kitchen and I found myself sitting opposite Mr Smith, a large red-faced gentleman who always wore white linen suits and a pith helmet and who was a Railway Policeman. He winked at me and signalled that I should eat.

Plates were filled, knives, forks and spoons clattered and the talk flowed over my shorn head as I gobbled up my meal. 'Do you always eat so quickly?' asked Mrs Smith and eagerly I replied, 'Yes, so that I can get what's left on the other plates.' There was a sudden silence and I saw Mrs Smith raise her eyebrows as she looked at her husband, and then she shook her head. 'What do you mean?' she asked and then I told her that when the plates came in from our dining room to the kitchen where Tom and I took all our meals, there would be tit-bits left on them which we fought for. Pieces of meat or fat, but best of all, skins from the breakfast kippers or bacon rinds and the whites of eggs.

I was stopped from any further explanation when Mr Smith leaned over and asked me to pass the gravy. Mrs Smith was quite tight-lipped, and then she asked, 'But don't you all eat together?' 'Oh no,' I said. 'Tom and I eat in the kitchen and sometimes we fight for what's left on the plates. Vinyu gets cross and says he'll tell. But my sister,' and here I looked over to Stella, 'she eats with the grown-ups, Aunty Betty says she's a proper little lady.' My sister smirked and glanced up for approval but Mrs Smith merely smiled. Presently her husband got up from the table, kissed her goodbye, patted us on our heads and went out to the verandah to mount his bicycle and ride back to work.

It was arranged that we were to spend the afternoon having a baking lesson. Stella donned the spare clean apron and stood mixing sugar and butter in a bowl but I soon became bored and when Mrs Smith was called to the back door, I took the opportunity to explore her pantry.

Rows of bottled peaches, guavas and plums stood on the upper shelves; jars of candied oranges and tangerines waited for their little written labels and on the floor were bottles of pickles and sauces. In the corner on a low table stood a large china bowl full of watermelon

119

konfyt, pale green, glistening in a pool of ginger syrup and I reached out and crammed as much as I could into my mouth when I heard Mrs Smith's footsteps coming down the passage.

I was standing next to Stella diligently watching her when Mrs Smith entered the kitchen, but the tell-tale signs were all over my face. She merely glanced at me and suggested I go out and play on the swing while the girls finished their baking. When the little cakes were taken out of the oven and shared out between us, we were sent home with a kiss and a wave and nothing was said about my sticky face. 'You must come again,' called kind, beautiful Mrs Smith as she stood on the top step of the verandah, her arm around Roma, and for one fleeting moment I envied the child. It was soon forgotten as I ran back to show Vinyu my short hair and to give him a graphic description of the eviction of the maggots.

My participation in the cooking lesson occurred only once again when I was sent home in disgrace because Stella complained that I had forgotten to wash my hands and had thus turned the dough grey, and had then eaten most of it before she could put it into the baking tins. But Stella and Roma became good friends, playing with their dolls, trying on each other's dresses and walking about, their arms across each other's shoulders. I hung on the front gate hoping to catch a glimpse of the big sister, a beautiful redhead of about eighteen whom I'd seen strolling in the garden with her father. She was tall, her long red hair looped up into an extravagant style, her green eyes and luminous skin giving her an ethereal appearance, but she gave no sign of knowing of my adoration. Every morning she rode off to town to her office, scorning the admiring glances of my big cousins and lifting her head high in the air when they whistled and called after her. But once she did speak to me, calling out 'Have you seen Mortimer?' 'Who is he?' I asked. 'Does he live here?' 'No child,' she said coming closer. 'My chameleon, he's called Mortimer H. Smith and I left him on the rose-bush a minute ago. Now he's gone,' and her lip trembled and tears came into her eyes. 'Shall I call Jorbey to come and help find him?' I asked but she shook her head, saying it was no use, Mortimer changed colour so frequently and it was getting dark. She would ask her garden boy to look again tomorrow. 'What's your name?' I asked greatly daring, wishing I could come running to her bedroom window in the middle of the night with the absconding Mortimer precariously balanced on my fore-finger, safely restored to his normal bright green and eager to see his owner. 'You can call me Reenie,' she said. 'Aren't you one of Mrs Stotter's little nieces?' I was not sure what she meant and replied 'No, I'm Mr Sadler's daughter.' She laughed and remarked that it was time I went home, it was getting dark.

'Madam will be back at the end of next week,' announced Vinyu as Tom and I sat with him on the kitchen verandah, watching Jorbey watering the flower tubs. 'Soon it will be time for you to return to school. Your father will have to tell the rickshaw boy to fetch you but you will see madam before that time.' He had brought his shy wife into the house to help him polish and clean and the day before the family arrived, we stayed in bed so that our clothes could be washed.

We stood on the verandah as my father brought the car to a stop with a flourish and the family dismounted. They looked rich and well-fed, and their clothes had a more sophisticated air about them. They all spoke at once to each other as the suitcases, trunks, coats and packages were unloaded, and they compared everything about them with 'back home'. We stood watching them and I looked at my aunt to see she now wore many dangling, brilliant necklaces around her neck, but my eyes were drawn to the fur collar of her smart tweed coat which I longed to touch. She pushed my hand aside saying 'Those hands haven't seen water for a long time,' but I was too shy to speak and looked again at the collar of her coat.

At last everything was unpacked, the house and garden inspected, the cattle looked over and after their evening meal, Vinyu was called in to the sitting room to give an account of himself. For a long time their voices surged back and forth, then I heard loud shouting, Mrs Smith's name mentioned, doors slammed and a very angry but chastened Vinyu came out and stalked off to the compound.

My father was drawn into the argument and more shouting and quarrelling was heard; and then, quite clearly, from where I stood by the kitchen door, I heard Aunty Betty say to my father in her angry voice 'One was all I wanted, not three,' and he replied, 'But you know Bet, I couldn't separate them nor could I have looked after them.' Their voices faded and as I made my way to my mattress on the verandah, I passed the steamer trunks in the passage outside my aunt's bedroom. I leaned down to look again at her new coat which had been thrown carelessly down and I moved it carefully, so that I could look again at the fur collar. There were three little fox faces, their bodies joined together to make the collar and the three sets of little paws dangled over the shoulder. I wondered why my father and his sister had quarrelled about

121

it, and why he had said they could not be separated; quite clearly I could see the delicate little stitches and I went to bed wondering if Sammy would be summoned to put the matter right.

The next morning Stella was called to Aunt Betty's bedroom and handed a small box wrapped in red tissue paper. When she opened it, there was a pair of blue silky pyjamas lying in the paper. They were called beach pyjamas, said Billy, made of celanese, the very latest thing for ladies underclothes, but these were meant to be worn on the beach or for lounging around in. All the girls in England wore them when they went to the seaside, he added with the air of a much travelled youth. Tom and I stood waiting to see what had been brought for us when my aunt opened her handbag and after some minutes searching, handed me a half-crown saying 'You two can share this'.

We ran off to show Vinyu our prize and when I looked up for his reaction, he smiled kindly and said 'Look, it's got the King of England's head on it, you must not lose it.' We put it in a matchbox and buried it in the back garden, but soon forgot about it in the excitement of the family's return and the much longed-for appearance of my sister in her Beach Pyjamas. But she carefully folded them in their paper and hid the box under her bed, threatening her vengeance if we so much as touched them.

I had said my goodbyes to Mrs Smith and the beautiful Reenie, who had completely ignored me, and had walked around to the compound to have a last word with Vinyu's wife and the garden boys. K'buda clapped her hands in greeting and called Patronne away from the fire. All her belongings lay in a tidy pile by the door of her hut and amongst them I saw Vinyu's blanket roll and his few clothes tied into a bundle. As I picked Patronne up and balanced him carefully on my hip I asked 'Why are you taking your husband's things with you?' 'The Inkossikaas is angry with him, but he has done no wrong, so he does not wish to remain here. He feels he is not trusted and many bad things have been said,' she replied. 'He will come with me to our home and will speak to our headman and seek his advice. But, my little friend, he needs the money the Inkossikaas pays him for we have to buy seeds and tools to take home and next year I shall have to buy an ox for the ploughing.' She shook her head and spat through her front teeth but she reached out her hand to mine, grasping my wrist in the traditional way as we said our farewells.

I did not see Vinyu nor his wife again before they set off to walk those many miles to their home in Tete in far away Nyasaland. They walked down the road, he several yards ahead of K'buda, carrying only his stick in his hand; she trotted behind, Patronne secure in the sling on her back, the bundle and bedroll carefully balanced on her head. She turned and raised her free arm, and then they disappeared towards the crossing by the river and disappeared from view. I felt sad, feeling somehow that their departure was linked with my aunt's quarrel with Mrs Smith when the family had returned from England and that indirectly, we three children were to blame.

'Vinyu's gone home to Nyasaland,' I told my father when I saw him some days later. 'How long will it take him to get there?' He was sitting on an old motor car seat he had salvaged from someone's back yard, and he spat on the ground before answering. 'Bloody good job too, hope he never comes back.' 'How long will it take him, he's got to walk all the way?' I asked. 'A month or two, if he don't get the fever or if lion don't find him at night.' He spoke laconically, as if the matter was of no importance and I thought of Vinyu walking all those miles with K'buda trotting silently beside him, listening for strange sounds in the forest, wondering where they could stop safely by nightfall for a meal and a few hours rest and hoping that the bands of wandering natives they might meet would be of their tribe and thus, friendly.

'That nigger was too bleedin' big for his boots,' continued my father. 'He's caused no end of trouble between us and the Smiths and I was getting sick and tired of him coming here with you kids. Ain't you big enough to walk here on yer own? It's only a bleeding mile or so. When I was your age I thought nothing of walking twice that distance, and in the freezing bloody snow, back 'ome. You're soft, you lot.' I thought he wished me to be gone but he rose from his seat to walk into his shack and then turned to add, 'And another thing, before that sod left, he brought me this bill from the Sammy. Cheeky bleedin' Indian, who does he think he is, sending a white man a bill?' He shook the note under my nose saying querulously, 'As Gawd Almighty's my judge, I never said nothing about all these clothes that Sammy made for you, he can whistle for his money, I ain't paying and that's that.' He screwed up the bill and threw it to the floor in disgust.

Stella looked up at him, her big eyes pleading in her little face. 'On the list it says we've got to have three sets of clothes but we've only got two. Sister says we've got to have the same as the other girls but I look after my things and don't need any more.' She looked towards me and went on. 'It's her, she's always tearing her clothes and doesn't look after them. She doesn't care, even the nun says so.' Before I could get out of his reach, my father turned and gave me a blow across my head. 'Get orf home you little perisher and don't bleedin' come back.' As I turned to run, he seized me by the sleeve of my dress and shouted 'You think I'm made of bleedin' money, don't you? Well I ain't, now bugger orf.' I turned and ran, only pausing to make sure my brother was following. The guilt for my father's plight overwhelmed me once again and for many reasons I could not define, I cried and hiccuped as I made my way down the sandy road to Aunty Betty's house.

When I drew near to Mrs Smith's gate, I dawdled, hoping to catch sight of Reenie, and then I saw her coming towards me from the direction of their rose garden. Standing on her shoulder, swaying on his bent legs against her lustrous red hair, stood Mortimer H. Smith. His eyes swivelled in different directions and his pale green spikey body slowly turned from a muddy shade to light brown and then to russet to match those flawless golden tresses. 'I found him amongst the flowers there,' she cried joyously as she carefully dislodged him on to her forefinger. 'Isn't he pretty? Naughty Mortimer, giving his mommy such a fright,' and she wagged her finger at him. His eyes changed direction, one flickering over my face and the other casting about behind his tail as I looked at him with revulsion. How could she tell, I wondered, if he was the same chameleon she had lost? They all looked alike and were to be found everywhere during the rainy season.

'Have you been crying again?' she suddenly asked, looking more closely at me. I told her my father had hit me because I was the cause of all his troubles and that he'd said he didn't want to see me again. 'There, there,' she said changing fingers as Mortimer suddenly found himself reaching vainly for mid-air. 'Would you like to hold him for a while?' But I declined, knowing that chameleons were bringers of bad luck. Vinyu had told me that they were messengers from the spirit world, but I could not tell Reenie that, she would not have believed me. 'I'm sure your daddy didn't really hit you, it was a smack surely?' 'No,' I replied, sniffing loudly, 'he hit me here,' and I pulled down the collar of my dress to show her the finger marks of his hand. 'Never mind child,' she said. 'Run along home and don't make such a fuss.' She patted me on the head and smiling to herself, she reached for Mortimer, running her fingers tenderly along his scaly body and along his prickly spine, and making kissing noises at him.

'Daddy says the rickshaw boy is coming for us first thing tomorrow,' announced Stella as we sat on her bed after supper. 'He will come and see us as usual on Sunday afternoon and then you can tell him you're sorry.' 'Sorry for what?' I asked. 'For being such a nuisance,' she replied. I was glad to be returning to school where I would sink into anonymity in a crowd of little girls, but I dreaded those Sunday afternoon visits, wondering how many of my misdeeds my sister had filed away in her memory to relate to my father, and sure of his continuing indifference. It was a painful moment when he came thundering up the road, grappling with the controls of his motorbike, mistaking the brake for the new-fangled clutch. The big girls stood about in groups, vastly enjoying the spectacle, laughing and giggling and calling us 'Hey you Saddleback-ies, your old man's here to see you.' I cringed with shame as he handed me a paper bag already disintegrating from the over-ripe fruit he'd wheedled from the storekeeper in town.

Every Sunday, my father gave himself up to a day of sybaritic enjoyment. He lay in his bed until almost midday, reading his old copies of *Titbits* and *The Daily Mirror* which had arrived by sea mail from England. He drank many cups of the strong hot tea Reuben brought him, and when his bath water was hot, he arose and stood in his tin bath under the syringa trees while the servant ladled the hot water over him. He had very definite ideas about sitting in a bathful of water, saying it gave you the fever, and he preferred to subject his feet only to this risky act. A thorough scrub with a bar of strong carbolic soap and a kitchen brush and then a long, luxurious rinse as the warm water was poured over him; the greying skimpy towel was passed and when the ritual was completed, he stepped delicately back into the shack to don his best clothes.

His best grey flannels, sports coat and a clean shirt completed his grooming, and carefully he angled his new trilby hat on to his slicked down hair, and was ready for the greatest moment of the day. The Harley Davidson motorbike was approached with care and he bent down to make sure there were no oil smears to soil his clean socks and shoes, and only then he seated himself in the saddle, indicating to the admiring Reuben that the rest of the day was his to do as he liked.

After some moments of fruitless kicking and swearing, his machine roared into life, belching out clouds of black smoke, and fighting to regain control of the motor cycle he shot down the path on to the main road into Salisbury town. His destination was the Criterion Café, a seedy little café and store in the midst of the city where many of his friends gathered on Sundays for their lunch. They were lonely men like himself, abandoned by their families who had returned to the more sophisticated life in South Africa, men who worked on the building sites

125

all over town and who lived in rooms in the avenues. Large notices hung in their shabby rooms requesting that all lamps and candles be put out by ten o'clock and announcing that No Cooking in Rooms was allowed. Lonely middle aged spinsters who worked in offices or behind shop counters crept into the dining room, hoping to catch the eye of an equally lonely, unattached man and eyeing warily the small family groups who were having a day out.

The store and café stood in the middle of a row of small shops, selling cheap imported clothing, shoes and furniture; a butcher shop swept and silent, a barber shop boasting a red, white and blue pole and a newly opened bakery, already doomed to failure, undercut on every possible occasion by the storekeeper who had not forgotten his own baking and breadmaking skills learned long ago in his native Cyprus and who now sold his own bread rolls, buns and gaudily iced cakes to his lunchtime clients.

Mr Vetsukis' standards were not very high, but the café was the only establishment in the growing city where a cheap meal could be had. He bought most of his fruit and vegetables from the local smallholders whose produce did not meet the standards of the large retail shop in the main street, tomatoes and lettuces from the coolie scratching out a living on the banks of the muddy river, mushrooms of dubious origin from domestic servants who gleaned them from the bush on their afternoons off, where they gathered to meet their friends. Schoolboys in shorts brought their parents' empty beer bottles and were paid the deposits their mothers and fathers had put down, and if you admitted to a bank account, cheques could be cashed.

At the back of the café was a small hatch in the wall and surreptitious bottles of whisky, brandy and beer were sold from it to the coloured men who knew prison faced them if they were found out; stale bread and left-over meat was sold to the groups of natives who squatted on their haunches in the back lane, picking their teeth or quarrelling over their games of tsoro or cards. Mongrel dogs lay panting in the shade waiting for scraps and bones, only moving to twitch their ears to dislodge the hordes of flies which swarmed over the piles of rubbish swept from the kitchen and café each morning.

Opposite the store stood the Grand Hotel, a cream-coloured two-storey building, boasting of great opulence within and patronised by the new gentry; men in well-cut suits who wore gloves and hats in public, well-dressed women accompanying their husbands who all spoke in loud English voices. The Saturday night dances at the Grand were the

126

social occasion for the white population. There were lounges for the ladies where white-suited, softly-spoken native waiters brought their drinks, dining rooms smelling of hot, appetising meals and long bars where the white hoi-polloi gathered for their beer after work. Over the revolving doors at the main entrance hung a notice declaring the Manager to have the right of admission and announcing that 'Coloured, Asiatics and Natives' would not be admitted or served.

With a flourish my father brought his machine to a gliding stop and carefully parked it at the front of the large hotel amongst the cars and traps of that genteel clientele. Then he darted across the road into the dark and gloomy store, barely sparing a glance for his host who greeted him and snapped his fingers for a waiter to escort his customer to a table. He threaded his way through bags of potatoes, baskets of onions, sacks of oranges and branches of green bananas, ignoring the thick, pale sausage rolls and pies temptingly displayed on the counter, the jars of pickled cucumbers and olives, the barrels of pickled herring for Jewish customers and the slabs of dark red meat bleeding on the tin trays. Seating himself at his regular table, he tucked the stiffly starched napkin into his shirt collar and studied the hand-written menu.

Slowly Mr Vetsukis approached him, notebook in hand and took his order. 'Mixed Grill,' said my father 'and all the trimmings.' 'Perhaps some soup first,' urged the obsequious Mr Vetsukis. 'That'll do,' said my father, hardly sparing a glance for his host, firmly dampening any overtures he might try to make and muttering to himself 'Bloody dago.' The remark remained unheard as the Greek murmered, 'And perhaps a bottle of cold beer with the meal?' 'Didn't know you had a licence,' said my father. Slyly Mr Vetsukis tapped his forefinger on his nose and leaned forward to say, 'For your ears only sir, I do not, but I have plenty of beer in my storeroom. I have no licence, but I oblige my friend Mr Braude who owns the bottle store down the road. He has no room for all his stock, so I help him out and let him put some of it in my back room.' He shrugged his shoulders. 'I square things up with Mr Braude during the coming week, we are good friends and play cards on my night off.' He winked, adjusted the table setting, picked out a dead flower from the centrepiece and scribbled on his notepad.

Waiters scurried about, their greasy aprons and smeared white suits giving the café an air of seediness. 'Get your bleedin' thumb outa me soup,' grumbled my father as the waiter slapped down several thick slices of bread and a plate of dark brown soup. Plates were changed, the napkin re-adjusted, knife and fork at the ready as Mr Vetsukis himself bore in the platter. Great mounds of limp chips, greasy fried eggs, scorched sausages, a slab of greying steak and several collapsing tomatoes lay in the dish. More rounds of buttered bread and bottles of anonymous sauces were passed and my father set to. The meal was rounded off with a cup of strong tea and a cigarette and, blissfully replete, he surveyed his fellow diners. But his thoughts were interrupted by Mr Vetsukis standing nearby and asking with head cocked to one side, 'A small glass of brandy to finish off?' 'Nah,' said my father. 'Gotter get up to the Convent to see me kids, they'll be expecting me.' And then he paused. 'But I'll take some fruit in the place of the brandy, them kids like a bit of fruit now and then.' Mr Vetsukis felt himself outsmarted by this manoeuvre and picked out three very ripe bananas, a few puckered oranges and some blackening plums, turning the latter so that the bruises could not be seen. 'Gertsha, put in a few more,' urged the erstwhile guest, but Mr Vetsukis shrugged his shoulders saying he would like to, but he was also a poor man and had to think of his overheads, and as it was, he had already given away more than the price of a tot of brandy.

'See you next week, then,' said my father jovially, feeling well pleased with the meal and his astuteness at getting the better of the Greek and enjoying what he mistook for a look of respect from the storekeeper.

'Bleedin' robber,' said my father making his way to the pay desk. 'Two and sixpence please sir,' asked the elder Vetsukis daughter, her moist eyes firmly downcast, but a smile hovered over her face. She had not known her father to be outsmarted before.

I heard the distant ringing of the parlour bell as I sat with a group of other girls on the colonnaded verandah, listening to the Sunday afternoon story. I saw the Duty Sister beckoning to Stella and I rose and followed her. 'Your father is waiting for you in the parlour. He says he expected you to be at the little gate. Have you forgotten?' We apologised for the trouble we had caused and joined my father in the parlour. 'Well, how's my girls? And where's your little brother?' he asked as he led us out and around to the side gate. I explained that Tom had gone to the school farm with the other boys to spend the weekend and would not be back until the evening. He ignored me after my explanation and sat talking quietly to Stella. 'Can I learn the piano,' she asked and after a moment's thought, he said, 'Yes of course you can, with them long fingers you'll make a good player.' Then he turned to me and asked 'And

I suppose you want something too?' 'No,' I replied, 'but sister says I have to be vaccinated, I'm the only girl in the school who isn't.' 'Tell her to take you down to the doctor's then, but Gawd knows how I'm going to pay for it.' He sighed heavily, his day clearly ruined. 'Tell her to put it on the bill and I'll pay when I can.' This was to be the pattern for many years to come, various services like visits to the dentist, shoe repairs, medical expenses, all put on the bill to be paid for when he could no longer ignore the requests to do so.

Escorted by two black-cloaked nuns I found myself the following week in Dr Harworth's office in the town. 'How old is she?' asked the doctor and when he was told I was almost ten years old, he frowned and said to me 'Why have you not been vaccinated before?' Encouraged by Sister Amata, I admitted I did not know, only to be told by him that he would have to report my parents to the police, that smallpox was endemic and that vaccination was compulsory. There followed a long discussion with Sister Amata who explained how we had come to be boarders at the school, and that we were looked after by relatives. Barely satisfied, Dr Harworth said no more and swabbed my upper arm, scratched in the vaccine and told me not to scratch when it began to itch in a few days time. Before dismissing us however, he asked me 'Do you often have malaria?' 'Yes,' I replied meekly, 'plenty of times.' He felt my spleen, looked into my eyes for the yellow tell-tale signs and then turned to the nun. 'I'll see this child again when I next call at the Convent. You can take her back now, I shan't report the vaccination.' I endured the torment of the painful arm, the pus-filled blisters and the dry brown scabs which caught on my clothes, and at last they dried and fell off, leaving large indented cirles on my upper arm which I proudly showed anyone who asked to see them.

It was many weeks later that I saw Dr Harworth again. We were at my aunt's home for the Christmas holidays and with the onset of the rains Tom and I developed boils, colds and racking coughs which left me unable to breathe and gasping frantically for relief. While I struggled for air, feeling the constriction in my chest, pains surged through me, my legs and arms ached unbearably and I became unconscious. When I opened my eyes at last, Dr Harworth was sitting on the edge of my bed which, miraculously, had been brought into Stella's room. 'She has a bad chest infection and she also has rheumatic fever and will need lots of care for a long time ahead,' he said sternly to my aunt who stood by the door, dressed and ready to go to town. Prescriptions were written, instructions given and for many days I lay in bed only aware of my surroundings when someone came in to give me a dose of medicine.

Weeks passed as I lay in bed, listening to the sounds in the quiet house. The slow tick of the sitting room clock, the thump of the flat-irons as the houseboy attended to the laundry in the kitchen, the rattle of the saucepans as the next meal was got ready, the slow murmuring of the hens as they scratched in the back yard, and as the shadows lengthened and the sun set, I heard the boys calling the cattle in from their grazing. Suddenly I was aware that someone stood in the doorway looking at me. I turned and saw Vinyu. His clothes hung on him, shabby and crumpled, hiding his thin shanks and bony chest, his skin was no longer shining black but dull and dusty, and his hair was unkempt and long. He grinned, showing his yellow teeth as he did so, and he came into the room. 'Jorbey tells me you have been sick for many weeks, that the doctor came to see you,' he said. 'How many weeks have you lain here?' 'I don't know, but for a long time I think,' I replied. 'Have you come back to work for madam?' 'I have come to see if madam will take me back. My money is finished,' he said.

I wondered what it had cost him to come back and to beg for his old job. He was signed on after the incumbent cook had been given a month's wages and told to go, but Vinyu took over the management of the house on a reduced wage and on certain conditions. He would wear his own clothes for the first six months, he would not be allowed to have his wife to stay and at the end of the year he could return to Nyasaland leaving a portion of his savings behind with my aunt, as a surety that he would return on the due date. He agreed to all, looking downcast, his hands behind his back, shuffling his bare feet in the dust of the back yard.

'Jorbey says you have missed much school,' he told me as he swept and dusted around my bed. 'You must get up and try to walk or you will not get better,' and carefully, he pulled back the bedclothes and eased his arm under my back. My sister stood in the doorway, saying she would tell my aunt that I would not listen to her, but I put my feet to the ground and took a few steps, dreading the pain in my joints, and trying not to fall down, and from then on my recovery was swift and soon I was well enough to get up every day. But the cough and shortness of breath persisted and my aunt was convinced that a good hot poultice would clear the matter up once and for all. Vinyu was instructed to bring up a bowl of freshly cooked hot meal from his cooking fire. It was hastily spread between two pieces of washed out sugar bag and slapped on to my skinny chest. When I regained consciousness, I found myself in a heavy sweat, the skin of my body red and blistered and my sister standing by my bed, smiling to herself. 'Serves you right,' was all she said.

The rain continued to pour down. All conversation was drowned by the noise of the rain on the corrugated iron roof, and the gutters which fed the water tanks overflowed. No longer did the cook go out each morning to tap the tanks, listening for the change of sound which would indicate the level of the water. During the dry season, when it had fallen below a red painted mark on the tanks, he boiled the brackish water he drew for use in the house, and laundry was taken down to the river and slapped and washed on the stones and then spread on the banks to dry. But now the river was in flood and from my perch at the top of the pamplemousse tree, I could see the ever-widening stretch of silvery water as it crept slowly up the drift where cars, cyclists, cattle and pedestrians crossed. All that remained of the narrow foot-bridge were the poles on both side of the river, standing only a few feet out of the water. Debris that had been washed down from the distant hills – trees, drowned animals and weeds – clung to the submerged cables, and groups of anxious homesteaders stood on the banks debating how much further the water would rise.

'You will not be able to go to school,' announced Vinyu as we surveyed the menacing flood. 'Madam could not get her car through the water and the rickshaw-man would not even try to cross to fetch you.' Regretfully, I agreed with him, knowing that I would miss precious time in my new class, but within a few days, as quickly as the river had risen, it subsided leaving a tide mark of mud on the road. We were bundled into the car, the trunk lashed on the mudguards and taken back to the Convent. But we were the lucky ones; many girls were still absent, marooned on their farms many miles away from the capital city, unable to cross the many rivers which flowed through the lush farm lands to the north. Some did not come back because of illness or tragedies when their parents had tried to get into town, finding themselves trapped between rivers, one receding as the other came down in flood. Prayers were said for those whose homes had been swept away, for those who had died because the doctors could not reach them when they became ill with diphtheria, meningitis, scarlet fever or appendicitis. The Portuguese girls from Beira would not return either, the Pungwe Flats had become a vast lake of water, the railway line swept away and the sugar crop inundated and ruined. We became inured to the news as it reached us and the list of names mentioned in daily prayers grew longer.

Aunty Betty's fears that the brickyard would once again be washed away were allayed; ditches had been dug around the pugmill and drying yards and the water channelled into a roaring torrent of yellow, muddy water into the flooding river. But the workmen lay in their huts shivering and sick with malaria fever and once again the wagons arrived to take the bodies away for burial. Little concern was shown, more and more men came in from their kraals to find work and the queue outside the Brickworks Office grew longer and longer.

'My, ain't you kids lucky,' said Aunty Betty, when she fetched us home for the Easter Holidays. 'Your dad and me have fixed it for you to go to the seaside for the whole holidays.' I was stunned into silence. 'Ain't you got anything to say then?' she asked. 'Are we all going, the three of us?' Stella asked. 'Nah,' my aunt replied, 'it's only for girls, Tom and Billy can't go.' Stella and I looked at each other in astonishment and then Stella said, 'I haven't got any decent clothes, what about that?' 'Sammy is coming to make you each a couple of nice dresses and you can swim in the sea in your vest and knickers. Your dad'll tell you all about it, he's coming tonight to see you.'

'Yes,' my father agreed, 'you two kids ain't 'arf lucky. The Government are sending fifty kids to the seaside near Durban and you'll go by train, day after tomorrer. There'll be ladies going with you to look after you and you'll stop in a hostel when you get there. It'll take three days in the train. Wish I was going.' And he sniffed and then smiled broadly, relishing the fact that he'd been able to convince the authorities that we were indeed, hardship cases. Sammy arrived early in the morning, we were measured, materials chosen and by the end of the day our school trunk was re-packed with the two new dresses each and the rest of our regulation school underwear. Secreted amongst vests and clean socks was the Enos Fruit Salts bottle I was taking with me to fill with sea water and sand for Tom.

Fifty small orphaned, semi-orphaned, or abandoned girls gathered on the main station platform as officials rushed about, shepherding us together, crossing off lists and sorting us into groups. Stella and I found ourselves in a sleeping compartment with four others of our own age, but she was not pleased. They were girls from the public school, poorer than we were and one, she suspected, was almost coloured. 'I'm going to ask if I can be changed to another compartment,' she grumbled as the second bell rang, and the train slowly steamed out of the station under a canopy of white smoke. Interested spectators, friends and relations, railway officials, the Mayor and his retinue stood behind the barrier waving but our excitement was so great we hardly noticed them.

On through the night the train rumbled as we lay in our made-up beds, talking softly as one by one we fell asleep. Stella had not been able to find the matron in charge and complained bitterly, feeling she had been betrayed into this holiday. 'Wish I'd stayed at home with Aunt Betty,' she whined as lights were doused and sleep overtook us.

Early in the frosty morning the train drew into Bulawayo station where waited yet another group of well-wishers who had organised this first experimental holiday for poor and deprived children. Our status did not concern me, I was lost in a fever of excitement and had made friends with the other four girls, but I felt sorry for my sister who sat in the corner by the window of our compartment, sulking and refusing to join in the conversation.

The station platform was crowded with ladies in pretty dresses and beflowered hats and as we disembarked, our names were called out and in turn one group after another was handed over to a benefactress. Only Stella and I remained on the platform with the dark suited officials and the Lady Mayoress, resplendent in her fashionable gown, smart hat and gold chain of office stretched across her large bosom. 'And you must be the Sadler girls?' she asked, smiling brightly. 'You're to spend the day with me and we'll all meet here again at six o'clock when you leave for Durban.'

At last Stella was happy as we sped off in the chauffeur driven car to Mrs Ellenbogen's home in the outer suburbs. We were made welcome by her large staff and led on to the verandah for breakfast. Floors shone, silver gleamed and everywhere stood bowls of bright flowers. The cook wore a tall white hat and white gloves and heaped my plate with scrambled egg and tomatoes, filled my cup with milky tea and passed the toast and jam, and then we were free to run around the garden. Presently we were joined by Mr Ellenbogen, a swarthy little man in a dark grey suit. 'So, you're all off to the seaside in South Africa,' he asked, smiling over his spectacles. 'Have you seen the sea before?' I shook my head and said no, I had seen pictures in books though. 'It's wonderful,' he said, 'and the beaches are beautiful and sandy and you'll find shells and other interesting things there. You must bring me some shells back,' and benignly, he patted us on our heads, kissed his wife and was driven off to his office.

'My husband would like to stay,' said our hostess, 'but today is Saturday and he has to go to schule. He never misses a service, so I hope you'll excuse him,' but it was not clear to me what she meant and I wondered why she had mispronounced school like that. I imagined Mr Ellenbogen was a schoolmaster.

'You two were the lucky ones today,' said Miss Uys, our matron, as she stood in the doorway of our compartment that night as the train steamed south. 'I heard you went to Mrs Ellenbogen's for the day, it must have been very nice, she's a very important lady in Bulawayo and her husband has that big furniture store near the station.' 'We only saw Mr Ellenbogen for a minute,' I told her, 'he had to go to school, I don't know why, but that's what he said.' Miss Uys looked at me for a moment and then burst out laughing 'Did he say school or schule?' she asked. 'He said schule, but that's wrong, isn't it?' I asked. 'His wife said he never missed a service but I don't know what she meant.' Miss Uys threw back her head and laughed. 'Schule', she echoed, 'that's just the proper name for the synagogue, the Jewish church, and Saturday is their holy day like Sundays are to us. The Ellenbogens are a good Jewish family.' 'But they can't be Jews, they were so nice to us,' I cried in my ignorance. 'Don't be silly,' replied sensible Miss Uys. 'Jews are people like the rest of us, nice or nasty and as good or bad as we are.' I found this doctrine very hard to believe, cocooned as I was in the Convent where we obeyed all the laws of Rome, joining in all the prayers and going to the daily services without any hindrance. In my mind, Jews were the cause of all the troubles in the world and had been responsible for crucifying Our Lord and were to be avoided at all costs.

My father and his sister always spoke mockingly of dagoes, Jews, Afrikaners and other foreigners, proclaiming at all times their English background and Britishness; after all the Empire was all powerful and if you looked at the Map of the World, there were red patches over most of the globe, identifying the vastness of the Empire and making us all feel proud to belong. Afrikaners came at the bottom of their scale, because they completely ignored the presence of the natives, as though they did not exist; and once again I felt ashamed, knowing that my own sense of values was distorted and realising too, that I would continue to swim with the tide.

Slowly the train puffed onwards to Mafeking, the capital of Bechuanaland, that land where so many years ago my mother and father had met. But now I was more interested in the fact that although the town governed that vast country, it stood eleven miles beyond the border in South Africa and from that point, the Colonial Office administered the territory. It was here too, that engines were uncoupled and the bigger South African Railways took over the task of pulling our train southwards towards Natal and the coast.

Gangs of small picannins in their rags swarmed up to the train as we waited for the engines to be changed, offering grotesquely carved wooden animals for sale, elephant, buck and lions with fur manes. Poker work adorned every surface of the slightly cross-eyed animals, jackal skins were held up to tempt the traveller, tanned zebra hides and lion skins were displayed in the dust. 'How much?' we called to the children but there was no answer, only a finger pointed towards their mouths and they rubbed their stomachs to indicate they wanted food. Some of us threw down the remains of our sandwich lunch and as they scrambled and fought for the half-eaten bread, we laughed at their antics.

For two more days, we sat at the open window of our carriage while the wind blew in the soot from the engine, covering our made-up beds and sifting into our hair as we watched the changing landscape, but longing for the journey to continue.

'What's the matter with your friend?' asked Letty, the noisiest of the public school girls. 'She's not my friend, she's my sister,' I replied tartly, embarrassed at Stella's sulky silences, 'and there's nothing wrong, she's just homesick.' This statement was greeted with hoots of laughter and a pained look from my sister. 'She's stuck up,' said Letty, 'that's what. Fancy being homesick when you're going for a lovely holiday like this.' She lapsed into silence but continued to stare at us both and then rose asking, 'If you're sisters, why are you so different?' 'It's none of your business,' Stella replied at last, stung into a conversation with Letty, but from then on they made her life a misery, imitating her walk, fluffing out her hair as they passed, and eventually when she ignored them, putting out their tongues. 'Common, that's what they are,' my sister said. 'If you play with them, I'll tell when we go home.'

That first glimpse of the sea, the long white, sandy beaches and the kindness of the local residents made the days we spent exploring the rock pools, paddling or playing in the waves very happy; swimming lessons were organised in the shallow lagoon, walks over the cliff tops in the late afternoons and after supper we sat in lethargic silence, as one of the matrons read to us before we went to bed. It all came to an end too soon, but there was still that train journey to savour and enjoy on our way home; Stella had made friends with Miss Uys and had been

135

allocated another place with some older girls and I continued to laugh and play with my common friends from the public school.

Back at school I gave the two shells I had kept for Mr Ellenbogen to my teacher. He had not been to the station to meet us on our return and Mrs Ellenbogen had swept up two other girls to spend the day with her. The bottle of water I had so carefully brought back for Tom had broken and stained my clothes and I pretended I had forgotten to bring it when he asked. At the end of that term, with the seaside holiday almost forgotten, reports were taken home to be scrutinised and commented on. Stella's read 'She shows no interest in class work and does not try,' which elicited the comment from my father, 'If them nuns spent less time on their knees and more teaching, she would have done well.' Tom's report suggested he was ready for admittance to the Jesuit College, and mine surprised the whole family. They were clearly sceptical and my aunt's only remark was, 'Been copying have yer?' 'Takes after her dad,' suggested Uncle George, ever my champion, and desperately seeking a family characteristic which would identify me with my much wronged father. 'She don't get it from them others, they're all bleedin' foreigners and the old grandma couldn't even speak proper English.' He blinked his milky white eyes and I felt the pressure of his hand in mine as he slipped a sixpence from his pocket.

But I was more interested in the change in the family lifestyle which had taken place in our absence. A full-size tennis court had been built on the derelict piece of land where formerly maize had been grown for the cattle and the brickworks' oxen. A grass-thatched summer house ran the whole length of the court and here on Saturday afternoons the family and their friends gathered for tennis matches.

Tom and I were appointed ball boys, Stella sat with the cousins watching them flexing their arms in their endeavours to master the overhand service and to connect with the ball, and tennis shoes were tried on amidst giggles and self-conscious efforts to appear relaxed and carefree. Cousin Georgie roared up on his motorbike, Claudine in her newest georgette dress and fashionable cloche hat, sitting precariously on the carrier, carrying her tennis shoes in one hand and desperately clutching at Jackie, her little son, with the other. Cousin Jack arrived with a new girl called Molly who was reputed to know how to score and to have been a member of the Salisbury Club.

All the grown-ups wore immaculate white clothes and stood about embarrassed as fours were made up, confessing to each other 'I feel such a fool, never played before' as they eyed their partners, hoping to see some sign of skill, but knowing there was none. 'Who knows how to score?' they asked anxiously, 'and will it be all right if I serve underhand?' Standing out in the road, open-mouthed, groups of herd-boys and house servants watched with curious eyes, the antics of the Makiwa and wondered what it was they were trying to do.

Mr and Mrs Smith had been invited, past feuds forgotten in this new lifestyle, but they did not play and sat alternately watching the bungling efforts of the players and eyeing the magnificence of the tea table. Boxes of freshly baked biscuits, small cakes, sausage rolls and jam tarts had been delivered that morning in the baker's van and Vinyu had been up since dawn to cut mounds of dainty sandwiches for the tea to be served in the Ainsley, Wedgwood and Satsuma-ware china so recently purch-ased from the grand new shop in the town.

The throbbing of my father's motorbike could be heard in the yard and he soon appeared, wearing a pair of dark tinted glasses and carrying a full-size banjo which he proceeded to unpack, and strum gently to himself as he sat in the corner of the summerhouse. Everyone felt sorry for him and paused at his side to murmur kindly and shake hands. The finalisation of his divorce, that ultimate shame, had appeared that morning in the local paper under the heading 'Decree Absolute awarded to member of local family'. He was very worried, wondering if it might have come to the notice of the Mother Superior at the Convent. He knew the views of the Catholic Church on divorce and he felt he could not bear the disgrace a divorce implied. 'Don't say nothing to them kids,' he begged, 'they think she's dead and it's better that way.'

During the week, when Uncle George and the cousins had gone to work, tea parties were held. People we'd never seen before drove up in their spanking new cars or in pony-traps, or dismounted from their bicycles. Ladies who wore artificial flowers on their hats and smelled of scent patted us on our heads as we took their cycles from them to park under the pamplemousse tree, looking us up and down and whispering to Aunty Betty 'you're a saint dear'.

Claudine had been drawn into the circle. She came with Jackie and his picannin, a child of her cook's and not more than seven years old, who would play with the baby in the garden while his mother drank tea and exchanged gossip with her new friends. Always exquisitely dressed, she passed tea cups and plates, pausing only to assess her reflection in the glass doors or to pat her freshly marcelled hair. Stella followed her

137

devotedly and was promised that as soon as she left school she could have Claudine's old dresses, 'if she'd just watch the picannin in the garden'. Tom and I ran away to climb the tall msasa tree where Jorbey had helped build the tree house. There we sat, waiting for the ladies to go and wondering if there would be any leftovers for us.

Picnics were arranged on Sundays to the Hunyani River, twelve miles out of the town. Upstream the wide river had been dammed to supply the townpeople with water, and where the level of the river below the dam had fallen, a drift had been made for cattle, pedestrians or wheeled vehicles to cross. Thick yellow sand had been dug out and piled along the water edge, making a long winding beach, and here the white population gravitated to picnic and swim on their rest days. A short distance away, on the rise of a small hill, stood the hotel where dances were held on Saturday nights and where rooms at the back could be rented by the day, week or month, no questions asked. Japanese lanterns swung in the afternoon breeze over the concrete dance floor and dispirited waiters stood about waiting for the afternoon rush when the bars would open.

Early on Sunday mornings, Vinyu could be heard whistling quietly in the kitchen as he packed up the picnic food. Thick sandwiches of cold beef or mutton, hard boiled eggs, yesterday's left-over sausage rolls and cakes and bottles of beer were packed into petrol boxes, blankets and rugs to sit on were strapped to the back bumpers, the water-bag was filled and tied to the radiator where it would slowly evaporate and cool, the gramophone and the records were handed to Uncle George to be balanced on his lap and the ice cream churn full of warm, creamy custard was entrusted to Stella's arms alone.

My father was invited to join the outing. Regretfully he had parted from his motorcycle and now possessed an old weather-beaten Ford lorry. Initially it had been a Model T sedan car but the previous owner had had the back portion cut away and had built a platform over the rear wheels. My father had seen it at the Market Square and had bid successfully for it. It was just what he wanted for his newest venture, the keeping of pigs. Every Sunday morning, as early as he could and foregoing the pleasures of a long lie-in, the weekly bath and the delights of the Criterion Café, he drove into the quiet city to collect from the two big hotels the barrels of swill which had been left in the back lanes for him. Tom and I had been told the previous day that we were to be ready and waiting for him the next morning and we now sat on the flat bed of the lorry making sure that the tubs of odious waste would not spill or fall off. As soon as the barrels were off-loaded at my father's shack, the lorry had to be scrubbed down by the reluctant Reuben who felt this was no work for a house servant, but rather that of a Zambesi boy, those men who emptied lavatory buckets for the householders in the dead of night.

Everything was at last loaded. A chair for Uncle George to sit on at the picnic spot was added and Tom and I were heaved up to balance as best we could amongst the provisions. Jorbey joined my father on the front seat, sitting as far from him as he could, for fear of offending the Inkoos by his presence, but he was sulking. He had not wanted to come, it was his only afternoon off and he'd arranged to join the Smith's garden boy for a leisurely saunter into the town to look at the White Men's shops and to discuss the goods offered for sale there.

Arrival at the banks of the river became a game of chance. Hopefully we searched for a place on the sandy bank not too far from the water, not too close to other picknickers, not on dormant ant hills, not out in the blazing sun and not too distant from the ever-beckoning hotel where the family would later gravitate for their evening drink before the perilous ride back home. Rugs were spread out, bottles of beer sunk into the cool shallows, baskets and boxes unpacked, and Stella was ensconced under a shady tree to turn the handle of the ice cream churn.

While the family lay about on rugs waiting for lunch time and Uncle George gazed disapprovingly into the distance, the gramophone was wound up, a new needle carefully inserted and presently the strains of Bert Ralston's Dixieland Singers rent the still air; feet tapped in rhythm, flies buzzed over the plates of food and Jorbey hovered on the edge of the party, wondering how soon he could make his escape. His sharp ears had informed him that his own people were bathing and playing upstream and he intended to join them. He knew he would not be missed but he would have to wait until the Makiwa had eaten their lunch. As soon as the food had been eaten he was summoned to pick up the plates, scrape off the partly eaten food into a paper bag for his own use and to take the crockery down to the river to wash off the debris and grease in the fast flowing water.

In regulated couples, the family rose to their feet and gradually drifted away towards the thick bush, to do what we knew not nor cared. When they sauntered back, they spread themselves out on the rugs and slept. Stella and Billy lay giggling in the grass and Tom and I earnestly dug our tunnel in the sand, thankful that for the present our tasks were finished. Uncle George in his best cream tussore suit and grey trilby hat, sat picking his teeth and longing for the signal that tea was ready and departure was imminent. He could not see the reason why he was obliged to sit in the fierce midday sun on a hairy blanket, assailed by mosquitoes, flies and beetles, in order to eat a meal he would have refused at home. Rested but sun-scorched, at last Aunty Betty and her family strolled up to the bar of the hotel, leaving Jorbey, Tom and me to load up the lorry, and soon my father joined us to drive back to Salisbury, saying playfully 'Thank Gawd termorrer's Monday.'

Many new friends came to the house. Amongst these were Berry and Amelia Fagan whom my aunt had met at a sale on the Market Square one Saturday morning. Aunty Betty had decided after some ten years, that she would buy a bed for Vinyu who had started to complain of a back ache. She knew that he had always slept on the floor of his hut, wrapped from head to toe in his blanket, but she could not afford to have him sick and unable to work. She now stood amongst the bidders waiting for the iron bedstead to come up for the auction and when her bid had been successful, she was alarmed to find herself in possession of two beds. She did not wish to spoil her servants and looked about to find a likely buyer for the second, unwanted bedstead.

Mr Fagan, too, was on the same quest and noting her alarm, he approached her and raising his panama hat he asked 'Do you want both beds? I'm looking for just one and would take one of these if you don't need both.' Flattered by his good manners, she readily agreed to his request and from that moment, they became friends and enjoyed a mild flirtation for many years. He was a tall, portly man with a shock of beautiful white hair setting off the tan of his skin. His jet black eyes twinkled as he introduced his wife, a sad-looking lady who drooped at his side. She wore a long pale chiffon dress, T-bar Charleston shoes, white crochet gloves and her black, glossy hair was plaited and coiled over each ear. Her skin was dark and her lips the colour of the inside of a red plum and she looked as though half asleep. When she smiled the effort seemed to exhaust her, and she slowly opened and closed her eyes as she stood under her flowered sunshade. She had been bitterly disappointed to find herself in a barely civilised colony and still longed for the sights and sounds of India and the hot humid climate of a more tropical latitude.

'And these are your little daughters?' Mr Fagan laughingly asked. My aunt drew us to her side saying, 'No, they're my brother's kids, just spending a few days with me.' They stood chatting and laughing and suddenly Mrs Fagan, who had said nothing till then, awoke from her trance and asked 'Would their father let them come and spend a day

140

with us? Our own girls are almost grown up and they would love to have them stay for lunch with us.' Arrangements were made and some days later my father desposited us at the Fagan's house in Rotten Row, where it stood in a row of other bijou houses overlooking the race course. The garden was overgrown with creepers and vines, flowering shrubs and bright cosmos six feet high which made my eyes water and my nose run.

'This is Netta our eldest and Tootoos our baby,' said Mr Fagan, proudly introducing his girls who were in their middle teens and who wore the latest fashions. Both girls were strikingly pretty, their olive skins and sparkling black eyes set off by their brilliantly blond hair, a combination I had never seen before. 'Pleased to meet you,' they both said in their curious sing-song voices and we were invited to their bedroom to view their new dresses. Netta went to stand by the window while Tootoos groped under her pillow and extracted a packet of cigarettes and matches. 'Keep Cave,' she asked as she lit up, but presently we heard the shuffling footsteps of their mother coming towards the bedroom. Cigarettes and matches were quickly snuffed out and hidden and presently Mrs Fagan entered the room carrying a tray of tea things.

'Tell me about yourselves,' she asked. 'Are you really sisters?' But I stood silent, leaving explanations to my sister who told her that we were indeed sisters and that we were boarders at the convent. 'Where's your mother then?' she asked wearily, patting her hair into place. 'Dead,' said Stella. 'She died a long time ago and my father's too poor to have us to live with him.' 'You poor little girls' remarked Mrs Fagan as she gathered up the tea cups. 'But you're both so different, you don't look like sisters, it's only your voices that are the same,' and she drifted out towards the kitchen.

'After tiffin,' asked Netta suddenly, 'can we go with Pa to see Clancy?' Mrs Fagan looked disapprovingly at her daughter and asked, 'Must you? You know I don't like you mixing with that class of person, they're so common and you know what the sun does to your hair.' 'We'll take our sunshades,' said Netta, 'and we won't talk to anyone without Pa's permission.'

After tiffin, which had disappointingly turned out to be an ordinary lunch of Irish stew and cabbage with rice pudding to follow, we walked with the two girls and their father down to the Langham Hotel to witness the phenomenon of Clancy, a visiting Irishman, trying to beat a world record for swinging the Indian clubs. Mrs Fagan had declined to accompany us and had drooped off to sit in her dark little sitting room with her fancy work, the many embroidered little mats which adorned

141

every surface in the sitting room and right through the house. She sighed deeply as she bade us goodbye and said she would not see us again, she had letters to write.

Clancy was a retired sergeant major from the British Army, said our host, 'not to be compared with the glorious Indian Army', he added, as we stood in the foyer of the run down little hotel on the fringes of the coloured quarter of the town. We were ushered into the main dining room which had been cleared of its tables and chairs and joined the crowds who had come to see Clancy. He wore immaculate white trousers held down by a strap under his white tennis shoes and his oiled muscles bulged under the snow-white vest as he swung and manoeuvred two heavy Indian clubs above his head, in front and to the side. Dexterously he executed turns behind his back, under one raised leg or tossed them high into the air, both at the same time.

Red faced men in loud checked suits, their hats pushed to the back of their heads, stood about with glasses of beer in their fists, shouting 'Get on with you Clancy me boy' as they took bets from each other, or called for the waiters who scurried about with laden trays. Passing shoppers, drawn by the hullaballoo, peered through the main doorway and each window was crowded by laughing black faces as they followed every move.

'The record is ten days,' explained Netta. 'Clancy has been swinging those clubs for nine days and if he can last another day, he will have broken the record.' 'When does he go to bed?' I asked, marvelling at this phenomenon. 'He doesn't,' said Netta. 'He just stands there day after day, swinging those clubs,' and she looked at him with admiration. 'But when does he eat?' I persisted, feeling sorry for the little Irishman. 'Watch,' said Netta. 'His friend will give him something to eat in a minute.'

Frenziedly Clancy swung the clubs. Over his head, behind his back and under his raised legs, the sweat glistening on his body and the gathering patch under his armpits, spreading downwards. Then I saw his aide approach him. Deftly a small egg was broken into the opened mouth, then another, followed by a spoonful of something dark and viscous and all the while the clubs whirled and swung about his head. After a few minutes, I could not resist the question which really bothered me. 'When does he go to the lav?' Netta laughed. 'Every hour he stops for five minutes so I suppose he goes then. But he mustn't stop for longer, otherwise he'll be in trouble.' I was greatly impressed and I longed to rush home and tell Tom of this wonder.

We only spent that one day with the Fagans. 'They were very good,'

Mr Fagan had assured my aunt, 'but it's the mem-sahib,' he explained, 'her ticker's not too good, she can't stand a lot of excitement.' 'Not like you Berry,' said Aunty Betty with a sly wink over our heads. His face turned red and pausing only to relight his cheroot, he remarked, 'Another time, another place, please my dear.' He grasped her hand, looking at her earnestly, and with pleading in his voice. I looked past them both, pretending I had not heard.

'We enjoyed having the girls,' he went on, 'and that younger one is quite a card.' I found this reference to me very gratifying, and I was glad I had pandered to his wife, hanging on her every weary utterance, fetching her glasses of water, taking messages to the girls in their bedroom, settling the cushions in the chair for her and blowing on the meagre fire to start it burning brightly for her as she shivered and huddled into her cardigan, in that sweltering, airless little sitting room on one of the hottest days of the year.

On Saturday nights, parties were held for my aunt's new found friends. They dressed up in fancy dress as clowns, pirates with a patch over one eye, soldiers or policemen, ghosts in long white sheets, hula-hula girls in crinkle paper skirts hurriedly assembled by the resourceful Claudine. The most popular choice was the Desert Sheik, copied from the touring company from England which played to packed houses every night of the week at the Palace Cinema in the city.

Many of the guests we had never seen before, people who had just arrived from that mythical 'home', newly set-up tradesmen, old customers, friends of Georgie's or Jack's and immigrants from England, seeking a better way of life. Some had curious names like Mr Salisbury Jones, a gaunt black-haired man who hoped to inveigle my aunt into a business partnership, or Mr Bulawayo Wilson from the town which had given him his nick-name. Mr Tex Austin, the police chief, brought his pale little wife; the Logans who lived next door to the Smiths, and the beautiful Mrs Smith herself, with her stern-faced husband, they all came.

Stella and Tootoos Fagan sat hopefully eyeing the men and I was put in charge of the gramophone, at last entrusted to change the needle when the old one began to scratch, and to turn the records over. In between, I sat in the kitchen giving Tom, Vinyu and Jorbey a running commentary on the goings-on and claiming my share of the left-overs Vinyu had kept for me. Jorbey had put on his best clothes for the occasion, but deigned to come right into the kitchen, standing diffidently on the back step, his head peering around the door frame, his eyes aglow with excitement and he clicked his teeth to the beat of the music.

I saw Mrs Smith in the dimly lit passage, quietly talking to a man who was not her husband. Mr Smith would never have agreed to dress himself up as a two-gun cowboy. 'Isn't it a lovely party,' she called to me as I came back to change the record, but I had noticed that she struggled to free her hands from her companion's and when she leaned down to speak to me she asked in a whisper, 'Don't tell.'

Bewildered by all the noise and the strange faces, Uncle George sat smoking in the shadows of the verandah, chatting quietly to his cronies and drinking bottle after bottle of beer, until his sons would be summoned 'to help Dad to bed'. My father, mindful of an early start on Sunday morning, sat in the shadows with his arm around Mrs Hulley, the District Nurse who was reputed to be a widow, and who was a newcomer to my aunt's circle of friends.

The dancing became more abandoned; shouts of 'Change that bleedin' record, let's have the other side, the one wot says Blue Heaven and You and I, for Gawd's sake,' rang though the smoke and babble of voices. Couples left the room for the darker parts of the house or garden, and here and there came loud raised voices, tearful denials and, sometimes, sharp slaps as recalcitrant wives were rounded up. The herdboys, now joined by Jorbey, stood in the shadows of the peach trees, slapping their thighs and imitating the antics of the Makiwa, or collapsed laughing into the rose beds.

'My weh!' exclaimed Vinyu as he viewed the sight the next morning when he came in to clear up, sweep, and cook breakfast. Once again Jorbey was conscripted to give a hand and as he packed the beer bottles into the crates for return to the store next day, he drained each one, smacking his lips with relish and anticipating a bigger mouthful with the next bottle. Those guests who hadn't been able to get home slept on the settees and chairs of the magnificent verandah, slumped against each other or huddled alone, still in their fancy dresses. Others staggered about, bleary-eyed and bedraggled, begging for a drink, an aspirin, a Prairie Oyster or even a cup of tea – anything to ease their misery. Mangled remains of half-eaten sandwiches, abandoned meat-pies and other food were scraped off the floor or dug out from the settees and chairs where they'd been squashed; kicked off shoes and strange pieces of clothing were gathered up and laid out on the dining room table to be claimed.

Cars, motor-cycles and bicycles stood out in the yard or leant against the wall, amongst them Mr Bulawayo Wilson's latest Model T Ford sedan cheek by jowl with Mr Salisbury Jones's spanking new trap, his pony still in harness, trying with great difficulty to nuzzle the pony he could see reflected in the shining headlamps of the motor car. Strong tea was brought around, groaning heads lifted to wonder where they were, and from the gate came the urgent summons of my father's hooter. 'Get a move on you kids,' he yelled, 'yer know I've got to fetch the bleedin' swill before eight o'clock.'

It all came to an end when a letter arrived by sea mail from England. The morning tea parties, the tennis matches on Saturday afternoons, and the frantic dances which followed, ceased. 'Oh Gawd Almighty,' exclaimed my father as he sat reading the letter to Aunty Betty. 'The old lady says she can't manage on 'er own and needs a holiday.' My aunt looked disconcerted and bit her lip. 'She's got a bleedin' cheek,' she said. 'I send her enough money each month, what's she want to come out 'ere for, I ask you?' They looked at each other for a moment and then Aunty Betty asked, 'And where'm I going to put them?' 'Dunno,' said my father. 'Put them two kids and Stella on the verandah and the old girl and Annie in Stella's room.' 'That'll have to do,' sighed Aunty Betty, 'unless you can take the two little 'uns?' My father's face fell. 'But I ain't got room Bet,' he said. 'And if I did, you'd still have Stella looking for a bed.' My aunt's hope of shifting us back to our father would become a permanent arrangement, he knew, and would conflict with his own plans concerning the District Nurse. Glumly my aunt agreed. 'They'll all have to sleep on the verandah until they go back to school, and I'll put the old girl and Annie in Stella's room. It's the best I can do.' She sighed heavily and rose to give Vinyu his instructions.

Months later, when we returned for the school holidays, the house seemed to have lost its jaunty air. Aunty Betty was at the brickworks helping Uncle George, the servants sat laughing around the compound fire or were playing tsoro under the mulberry trees. The house looked neglected and from the spare bedroom came the sound of my grandmother's querulous voice and Annie's muted replies. We had not seen them yet so we hung around the passage nearby waiting for someone to emerge.

Suddenly the door was flung open and a fat little old lady dressed in black came out of the room. She peered at us over her half-glasses and shouted, ' 'Op it you little buggers, what d'ye want anyway?' 'I'm Stella,' announced my sister, 'and this is my little sister and brother.' Tom and I were speechless. 'We just wanted to say hullo,' said Stella. 'Well, you said it, now bugger orf,' said the old lady, and then she paused: 'But get us a coupla beers from the pantry first.' She smiled ingratiatingly, showing her toothless gums. 'There's a crate full behind the pantry door,' she added, 'and while you're about it, you can put these empties back.' We had only just eaten our porridge and I knew it was very early, but Stella did as she was asked. 'Now bugger orf,' said my grandmother as she backed into her bedroom, clutching the bottles of beer to her large bosom. Tom and I made for his tree house in the bush and Stella walked over to see her friend Roma Smith.

We were dawdling away the rest of the day with Vinyu as he sat on the back door step, waiting to be called to serve the evening meal. The family were gathered together in the sitting room and we heard the hum of their voices, as they spoke about the day's events. Suddenly there was a piercing scream, followed by a high pitched trilling which sank into a strangled, gurgling crying, and there in the doorway stood Annie. Her lips were drawn back and she tore at her hair and her clothes, fell to the floor, banging her head against the doorpost and whimpered 'No, no please don't.' She lay rigid and still, her eyes wide open but un-seeing and a dribble from her mouth running into her dark hair.

We were transfixed with horror and ran back to stand beside Vinyu asking, 'What's the matter, what's she doing?' My father and cousins crowded around to lift her up. The screaming had ceased, her eyes were still open but she lay limp and still. Was she drunk? I wondered. Had she drunk all that beer which was taken into her bedroom? My silent questions were answered by Aunty Betty who turned to us saying, 'Get back into the kitchen you kids, she's only having a fit.' 'What's a fit?' I asked but she left us standing there with the servant.

He drew us to his side. 'Don't be frightened,' he said, 'she won't hurt you. She does that all the time and nobody knows when, it's some sickness in her head, something happened to her a long time ago and when she remembers it, she gets frightened and tries to run away. She won't hurt you, only herself.' I was terrified and crying, longing like Annie, to run away from the terror I could not understand. What had happened to her that she should wish to hurt herself? Why did she cry so piteously 'No, no don't please'? What did it all mean? But I did not really want those frightening questions answered.

I had often heard my aunt quarrelling and arguing with her mother. Annie had not been looked after properly, said Aunty Betty, she should have been kept at home, not brought all this way out to Rhodesia. What would people say, she asked, when they heard that Annie had fits? 'They'll say it's all your bleedin' fault,' retorted Grandma, suddenly riled. My aunt was furious. 'After all I've done for you,' she cried and she stood threateningly before her mother. Grandma's courage left her as suddenly as she had shown it and she turned away and started to whine: 'I didn't mean it Bet, honest I didn't. Everyone knows what you've done for us, honest I didn't mean it.' For minutes they glared at each other. 'If you'd kept off the beer, this would never have happened, but you only think of yourself, you're a selfish old woman. Gawd knows what I'm going to do with the two of you. Don't think I don't know what you two get up to the moment my back's turned. I know you put the kids up to pinching the beer from the storeroom.' My grandmother sat in her chair sulking, her hands folded, grim-faced, unrepentant.

But Grandma had her own solution. Early one morning, she got out of bed and dressed hurriedly in her long, old fashioned dress and bonnet and stumped off down towards the river, through the outspan, until she disappeared in the direction of the town. Passing motorists hooted at her as they drew level, but the offer of a lift died on their lips when they saw that angry, tight-lipped face, and those who persisted drove off quickly when she raised her umbrella and shouted 'Bugger orf for Christ's sake, leave me alone.'

Later in the day a perspiring, panting servant appeared at the house, bearing a note from one of the bars in the town. I was called to read it to my aunt. 'Come and fetch your mother. She has been here since early morning and won't leave. Says she has no money and owes me £3. Signed L. Parsons, Posada Bar, Manica Road.'

This became a regular occurrence. In a fury Aunty Betty would drive off into town with her two sons and soon they re-appeared almost carrying between them the sodden old lady, her dress pulled up disclosing her long white bloomers, wet and soiled, her black cotton stockings collapsing around her fat white ankles, her bonnet hanging by its ribbon around her neck. She struggled all the time, and muttered 'ger-orf, leave me alone you silly sods, I ain't done nothing, ger-orf.' When she sobered up, she cried as she followed Aunty Betty around the house asking, 'But what have I done Bet, what's the row about?' My aunt was grim-faced and unforgiving, replying 'You're a disgrace Ma, I'm ashamed of you and I don't know what people will say.'

Grandma's spending money was stopped, the pantry door was locked, but she got up earlier and earlier, often arriving in the town hot and perspiring, before any of the shops had opened. She was distinctive in her old-fashioned clothes and word passed quickly between the hotels, bars and beer-halls as she waited for them to open; servants washing down the pavements in front of the hotels and bars nudged each other and turned their eyes to the old lady patiently sitting on the edge of the paving, wondering who she belonged to, curious that any family should allow their revered mother to behave in this strange fashion. Perhaps she is mad, they said to each other, after all only they and their people sat on the ground like that, not the Makiwa who were their masters.

Word passed quickly through the bar-rooms that old Mrs Sadler was on the rampage yet again. 'Garn,' she would implore the publican who had misguidedly admitted her, 'me daughter's got pots of money and a big new motor car, she'll pay. Said I was to wait 'ere for her and she'd pick me up when she's finished with the bank manager. Told me to wait 'ere. Garn, give us a drink, I've told you she'll pay.' When the barkeeper refused, she became abusive, shouting at the world at large, attacking the barman with her handbag, and then collapsing, crying piteously, hoping to soften his stony heart. Aunty Betty would be sent for, the damage and hurt feelings soothed by pound notes, and the drunken old lady driven home.

But she never gave up trying. 'Give us a few quid Bet,' she would wheedle. 'I gotter have some new stockings and I ain't had a fag since Gawd knows when.' Stonily Aunty Betty eyed her mother. 'I bought you six pairs only last week,' she reminded her. 'There's plenty of fags on the table,' but Grandma would not give up. 'Be a dear Bet, and take us for a drive out to Hunyani,' she pleaded. 'Too far,' said Aunty Betty, 'it'll take hours, it's twelve miles there, you know.' 'Then what about the Ardbennie Hotel?' persisted the old lady. This so-called hotel lay just outside the city, past the rapidly growing Harare Location, past the cemetery and the coloured houses where lived the small Indian population. It was owned and run by a loquacious Irishman known as Pat, but better known for the open house he kept with scant regard to the licensing laws. Rumour had it that coloured girls who were employed by Pat as domestic servants were very willing to oblige his European customers at any time of the day or night, and the curtained and closed rooms at the back of the hotel were always occupied.

'Ardbennie Hotel?' exclaimed my aunt. 'That dirty little hole? It's in the middle of the bush, always full of drunks and coloureds. What do you want to go there for?' 'Just wanted a bit of a change,' pleaded the old lady, and tears welled up in her eyes and ran down her raddled old face. 'Don't go anywhere, don't see anyone, can't even get a glass of beer, just sit 'ere waiting for her,' and she nodded her head in the direction of her bedroom, 'to start that bleedin' screaming and banging about. I don't ask much out of life Bet, just a drive out of town.'

'If I did run you out to Ardbennie, what would you do there Ma? There's the skittle alley, but perhaps you'd like one of those quiet little rooms at the back for the day?' asked her daughter, and she started to laugh at the thought of her mother entertaining one of the workmen from the road gang camped in the bush behind the hotel. 'Don't talk dirty to me my girl,' angrily retorted Grandma. 'You're 'ard but I'm still your ma, Gawd help me,' and she started to cry. 'Anythink would be better than this sittin' about,' she argued. 'I could order meself a nice little pot of tea and a plateful of them sangwiches and spend a quiet afternoon on the verandah there, watching the people come and go.' 'It's quiet here,' retorted Aunty Betty, 'and you can watch Annie instead. I've heard it all before Ma, you might order your pot of tea, but there'd be bottles of beer to follow and before you know what happened, you'd be making a nuisance of yourself all over again. No, I'm not taking you anywhere, you can sit here with the rest of us.' Grandma hunched herself down in her chair, her tears becoming loud racking sobs. She glared at me as I stood watching her. 'Bugger off yer little bleeder,' she shouted as I took to my heels and fled to the servants compound.

Although we were terrified of Annie and kept well out of her way, we were not averse to making bets as to when she would publicly have another fit. The doctor came to see her every day, leaving behind medicine and pills, but always shaking his head and admitting that he was baffled. 'I don't know what else we can do,' he would say, as my aunt paid his call fee. 'I've never had a patient like this before and I really think she'd be better off in an asylum.' These words were like icy shafts, indicating a streak of madness, but the nearest mental asylum was in Johannesburg, many miles to the south, and to send Annie there was unthinkable. People would talk, said Aunty Betty to my father, and she couldn't have that.

No effort to entertain Annie and Grandma or take them out, could be made. The fits were unpredictable and could happen at any moment, and my grandmother was seldom sober. Aunty Betty had at last realised that her mother would stop making a spectacle of herself in the town only if she had enough to drink at home, so the beers were doled out every day, just enough to keep her happily drunk.

No longer did Annie run about the house screaming and battering herself against the walls, or lie rigid or comatose on the floor. She took her medicine and sat quietly on the verandah watching the fluttering birds in their cage, or lay half asleep on the sofa, or quietly walked about the garden smiling to herself. But at night the fits returned with a vengeance, one running into another, and they lasted for many hours. The nights were full of eerie sounds, of hushed voices, of hurried footsteps down the passage into the kitchen and of one of the garden boys summoned from his bed to take the master's cycle and ride as fast as he could for the doctor in the town.

The lights of the motorcar as it ground up the hill in the stillness of the night woke me, and I crept to the door of Annie's room, only to be met by Aunty Betty in her nightgown. 'Go back to bed,' she whispered, 'Annie's having a bad one, we've sent for the doctor,' but I had seen the white face, the staring eyes and the clenched teeth and I also saw that she was tied down in her bed. As the seizure passed and she regained consciousness, she moaned and whimpered 'No, no, don't, please don't,' and when her tormented sobbing at last died away, she slept.

Sometimes, as I sat high in the branches of the pamplemousse tree, I saw Annie walking about the garden in a different way. She retraced her steps, peered intently under shrubs, poked at the soil, went backwards and forwards through the flower beds and past the pomegranate hedge, inspecting each bush as she went. She shook her head, mumbled to herself, then started all over again. Around and around the garden she searched, stopping only to stare about and then with a terrifying cry she turned and ran into the house, her hands over her ears, screaming that phrase 'no, no, don't, no.' The doctor would be sent for, more medicines given and once again, those tormented cries came from her room in the stillness of the night.

'What's Annie always looking for in the garden, do you know?' I asked Billy. We had become better friends under the burden of the visitation of our English relations, and he was privy to all that happened in the house. 'Dunno,' he replied. 'I've seen her walking around the garden ever since she first arrived. Looking for something I s'pose', and he paused. 'I've seen her poking with a stick,' I told him, 'all over the flower beds and around the trees, and she does it over and over again.' 'S'pose she might be looking for the baby,' he said. I felt the blood drain from my heart. 'What baby? She's not even married, how could she have a baby?' 'Of course she isn't married', he answered, 'but the Dutchman she used to meet in the bush, he gave her a baby and so Ma sent for Mrs Grey. She came one night when you kids had gone back to school and did something to Annie. They pulled the baby out and buried it somewhere in the garden.' He kicked at some stones in the pathway and

150

added, 'I s'pose she thinks she'll find it, p'raps she thinks it's still alive.'

After four months of the visit, my aunt decided she had had enough. She was afraid for her reputation, knowing that her mother's drunken sorties in the town had become well known. Shopkeepers asked after the old lady, giving Aunty Betty a sly wink as they did so, bar-keepers called after her as she walked down the street 'Where's the old girl then?', and ribald comments greeted her when she gave her order at the bottle store. Even the waiters in Wright's Tea Room had nudged each other when she ordered her tea and had smiled pityingly when they brought the tea things, but she was not to know they smiled hoping for a tip, a practice recently introduced into the capital by new arrivals from Home.

With my father in her confidence, they wrote to the Union Castle Company in Capetown, asking for a double cabin to be reserved on the *Walmer Castle* sailing to Tilbury in England, in a month's time. One of the passengers was an invalid, wrote my father, and would require certain nursing attention and the other, an old lady, was in a delicate state of health. Any extra charges for the service would be gladly met before the ship sailed and to this end my aunt enclosed a large cheque to support her request.

As soon as the telegram arrived confirming that a two-berth cabin was reserved as requested, Aunty Betty made the announcement to Grandma, pointing out that the hot weather was coming to its end and that she and Annie would arrive back Home at the beginning of the English summer, and would miss the dust, the cold and the howling winds of our African winter. Doctor Hawarth had willingly given her a large dosage of medicine for Annie. Betty told her mother 'Give her a stiff dose at night as well as during the day and keep her in bed.' Grandma grumbled and muttered to herself, but her enthusiasm grew as she realised that she would be travelling first class, that cabin service was excellent and free and that the discomforts of her little house in Forest Gate would be allayed by the nearness of The King's Head, The White Hart, The Queen, The Jolly Sailor and many other public houses.

My father's new friend Mrs Hulley, the District Nurse, was bribed to take her holiday and to accompany the two travellers to Table Bay Docks by train, all expenses paid, and soon the day came when Grandma, still muttering to herself and more than a little unsteady on her feet, stood on the verandah waiting for the car to be brought around. She was not too distressed. My father had thoughtfully given her two big

151

bottles of the finest brandy 'for medicinal purposes'. Her hairbrushes, toilet articles and a clean nightgown for the train journey lay under her bed where she had thrown them to make room in her dressing case for the brandy.

Sweating and grumbling, Vinyu and Jorbey trailed out after Annie with trunks, bed-rolls, hatboxes, overcoats and baskets of food. Annie seemed totally unaware of the journey which lay ahead, and looked steadily about her as though anticipating an afternoon drive around the suburbs. Only for a moment her eyes flickered over the garden as she followed her mother out. When she reached the gate, she hesitated as though to go back indoors, but when she saw her sister sitting at the wheel of the car, she slowly walked up to her and stood still. With all the venom and hate she could muster, she leaned into the car and looking straight at her sister, she said the only words apart from her protesting cries that I heard her utter in all those long months, 'You killed him!'

'Get in,' said Aunty Betty grimly. 'You don't know what you're saying, you're bloody mad.' Car doors were slammed, the engine started and furiously Aunty Betty turned and drove off towards the river crossing and on towards the railway station in the town.

We danced and skipped about clapping our hands, relieved that the guests had gone at last, but I felt sorry for the poor tormented creature our aunt had become. We were not to know that for her the decision to re-visit Africa had been the utmost folly. It was finding herself once more in surroundings which had awakened sleeping horrors in her mind, which had reduced her to a state of near insanity, and on the voyage back to London that state gradually receded. She spent most of the three weeks drugged, barely aware of life on the ocean liner, keeping to her cabin while her mother patronised the First Class saloon until the Purser suggested cabin service offered more scope. On arrival home Annie reverted to the un-demanding, subservient person she had been before that ill-fated excursion; the familiar little terrace house in Forest Gate, her cousins down the street, the markets and shops near the square all helped to erase the torture she had endured.

On my return to school I learned that I was eligible for a bursary which, if won, would pay the school fees for a year, thus releasing my father from the ever recurring demands which came from the school office. He was summoned to the Convent and we were allowed to see him before he was interviewed by the Head of Studies. 'What's it all about? What've you been up to?' he asked anxiously, afraid that some news of his divorce had reached the Convent. But it was merely to discuss the possibility of a bursary, Sister Georgina, the deputy, told him and all that was required of him was a copy of my birth certificate.

'Gawd knows where I'll find it,' he remarked as he drove off to start the search. A week later he returned empty-handed, saying he had looked everywhere for it but without success. 'Strewth,' he muttered, 'yer bleedin' mother couldn't even do that proper, Gawd knows what I've done to deserve this. I'm for the high jump, you can bet she never registered you.' The registrar of births and deaths reported the matter to the police, I was fetched to confirm the fact that I did indeed exist, and my father was let off with a light reprimand. 'You'll have to tell the nuns some story or other,' my father said. 'I'm not getting into trouble for something I ain't done, you'll have to think of something, tell 'em you're like Topsy, you just growed.'

'My father says he doesn't think I've got a chance to sit the bursary,' I told Mother Frances, 'he says it's no use, I'm not clever enough.' 'I think I might be the judge of that,' she replied shortly, but when I began to cry at the disappointment, she ushered me to her study door and said in her soft accented voice, 'I'm very surprised your father has taken this line, but no matter. You must pray to Our Lord that He will look kindly on you.' What's the use of that, I asked myself; it was my own father I wanted to look kindly on me, not that remote, distant deity to whom I prayed so earnestly.

The nuns could not understand our situation. They knew of my aunt's business reputation and wealth, and she had always responded generously to their appeals for funds for the new Chapel, so they could not equate our present circumstances with her life style, nor could they understand the differences which existed between my sister and me. 'Do you really live with the Stotters?' asked the Boarders' Mother. 'Your clothes are in a very bad state but your sister's are not; you seem to come from two different families.' 'My aunty has a lot of us to look after,' I replied in defence of Aunty Betty to whom I knew I must be grateful. 'My father does his best for us both,' I told the nun, 'but he's quite poor.' She sniffed her disbelief at this story and continued to hold up my uniforms, threadbare and too short. 'I will write a note to your father at the end of term,' she said. 'He musn't let you come back with clothes like these.'

Summoning up all my courage, I appealed to Aunty Betty to put the matter of my school clothes right. 'Ask your dad,' was her only reply.

'I've got my own kids to see to.' I broached the question to my father. 'Where d'ye think I'm going to get the money?' he asked angrily, 'd'ye think—?' But before he could ask the familiar old question I intervened. 'No, I don't think it grows on trees, but why can't I have the same as Stella and the other girls? I'm the only one whose clothes aren't enough and Sister is always picking on me.' 'Don't you get cheeky with me, miss,' he shouted. 'All you think about is your bleedin' self, you want this, you want that, nothing's good enough for you, you make me sick.' And once again he addressed the Almighty, asking what he'd done to deserve this child who sat like an incubus on his shoulders.

There was nothing in the Cast-Offs Box to fit me, but a blouse or a gym frock borrowed here and there from another's cupboard was handed me by the Boarders' Mother, who said, 'We'll put them back when the girls pack for the holidays, you can wear your Sunday dress the last few days, but take these in the meantime.' Underwear was also quietly diverted from other girls' cupboards to mine. I dreaded a change of staff, doubting that any other sister would be so helpful and understanding of my plight. When I became a Girl Guide in the school troop I had to attend only alternate meetings because I was sharing a uniform with my sister. In return I made Stella's bed, helped with her homework and promised not to tell our aunt that Charlie Heath at St George's College had written asking her to be his girl. As a result of all this my inferiority complex threatened to overwhelm me and I no longer worked hard, feeling that it would make no difference to my life and that no one really cared. I got into trouble countless times, for idling, for being disrespectful, for being lazy and cheeky and for being bottom in class.

My father barely read my school reports and my cousin and his friends drew me into their circle, realising that I was, after all, no better than they were although my earlier reports had indicated otherwise. I volunteered for everything, ran messages for them, cleaned their bicycles, carried the cricket bat and pads, allowed myself to be the renegade Indian in the games of Cowboys and Indians, ran panting through the bush back home for things they had forgotten and gladly took the blame for anything they should not have done. This seemed far more worth while than all the effort I had put into school work in my desperate attempts to earn my father's goodwill.

Only Vinyu seemed to disapprove. He clicked his teeth as he surveyed the mess I'd left in the kitchen when I'd run off to play with my cousin, or re-hung the washing I had let fall to the ground in my haste to get

154

away. 'What's the matter with you?' he asked angrily. 'Because you are getting a bigger girl, you think you can do what you like, running through the bush with those boys and playing all the time?' He leaned forward and tweaked the front of my dress, and his eyes twinkled. 'You are getting a big girl now, nearly twelve,' and he sucked at his teeth and flicked at my legs with his dish cloth, eyeing me carefully. But I did not care what he thought, resolving only to escape any responsibilities or duties inflicted on me, and to join in with other children.

PART FOUR

There was never again to be the old dependence on Vinyu. Slowly I turned to new found friends amongst the homesteaders who lived along the banks of the river, all new immigrants from England and the Empire like my father and aunt. Among these was the Samuels family whose two sons went to the Jesuit College with Billy and Tom, who was old enough now to leave the Convent. They possessed the most exciting back yard I had seen. Rows of vines grew beyond the orchards full of orange, lemon and grapefruit trees, a long line of dog kennels full of strange brown and white dogs with puppies stood amongst the plum and peach trees, and stacks of hay in bales towered above us as we stood watching the puppies playing together. A row of servants quarters lay half-hidden by a line of paw-paw trees and I knew that they were furnished with tables, chairs and proper beds, just like those white people had in their homes. But for us the main attraction was the two other houses on the property, one for the parents and the other for the two sons of the family.

In the main house, which was really a number of beautifully built native huts, thatched and white-washed and standing near a pool of waterlilies and bullrushes, lived Mr and Mrs Samuels. They were surrounded by bookcases full of thick leather-bound books and stacks of magazines and papers. The walls were adorned with native carvings, animals skins and beautiful water colours of local scenes painted by Mr Samuels. He was the Chief Brewer at the new brewery in the town and was driven to his office each day in a large black Buick by his Shangaan driver who wore a dazzling white uniform and who answered to the name of Porteous.

Mrs Samuels, still quite young, had a mop of fine white fly-away hair. She was always carefully groomed but she refused to follow the latest fashions and wore ankle length close fitting dresses, usually black and white, and smoked little cigars in a long green holder. She employed a

159

cook and three houseboys and spent most of her day reading her books or writing letters to the newspapers. She was involved in politics, poetry and civic affairs and exhorted the Government to set up schools for African children and to devise schemes to educate their mothers in child-management. She even suggested to her husband that his native employees should form trade unions, but housekeeping and her own children were mysteries she did not wish to plumb.

In the smaller house lived Jim and Angus, her two sons. They had their own servant to tidy and pick up after them and they lived and did exactly as they pleased in their own domain, staying in bed as long as they wished, entertaining their friends as they pleased. They were expected to obey only two rules. One was to present themselves punctually for dinner at night and the other was always to address their father as 'Sir'. They lived in a state of great disorder, their beds untidy and unmade, their clothes hanging from the furniture or on the floor, and they fought each other constantly and persuaded friends and any other visitors to join in if they cared to. During the holidays they roamed the bush with the other sons of the settlement, but during term time they applied themselves to school work and refused to join in the games their friends had devised.

I had left the boys' house and was speaking to the house servant when I saw Mr Samuels dismounting from his car before it was driven into the garage. 'Come and see the new puppies,' he called, and then he asked who I was.

I told him and he nodded as in his mind he placed my family, and then he asked 'Why are you, a little girl, playing with these ruffians? They'll make you do all the work and take all the blame. Come and meet my wife.' Conscious of my too-short dress, my dirty legs and bare feet, I followed him to the main house and Mrs Samuels rose from the window seat and held out both hands to me saying, 'I see he's managed to get you away from the boys, come and sit by me and we'll have tea.'

'Do you like playing such rough games?' she asked. I explained that I knew no other children and then added that if I had known them, they probably would not want to play with me. She put her hand under my chin, raising my head to her eye level and asked 'Why ever not?' 'Oh, I don't know,' I replied, 'I've got no other friends except some girls at school but they live in Northern Rhodesia, and my auntie says I'm just a toe-rag and nobody wants to be my friend.' She burst out laughing, but passed the biscuits saying, 'What a strange thing to say to a little girl! It's very important for you to know that you're just as good as any one else.

160

I'd like to be your friend, do you think we could be?' I was overcome by shyness. Tears filled my eyes and she put her arm around me and drew me closer as I sniffed loudly and groped for the hem of my dress to wipe my eyes. She hugged me and handed me the handkerchief from her pocket, saying 'Has Mr Sam shown you the puppies? Shall we go and see them?'

'Come and see me again and leave those boys to fight amongst themselves,' she urged some time later, as I stood by the gate, ready to follow my cousin home. 'But don't leave it too long, come tomorrow,' she said, and with a feeling of delight and pleasure I followed Billy home, glad that I had a new-found, grown up friend all to myself, someone who I was not afraid of, who made me feel important and who did not swear and curse all the time.

A few days later I was once again sitting in that lovely little sitting room; colobus monkey skins lay over the backs of the chairs and settees, groups of tiny carved ivory animals stood on the polished table and a bowl of late sweetpeas adorned the windowsill, their perfume heady and sweet. I had carefully washed my legs and wore my clean tennis shoes, but had had to cut the toes out to get my feet in. My dress had not suffered from my exertions during my morning's tasks. From the distance I could hear the yells and shouts of the two boys and their friends as they wrestled and fought around the haystacks, and I hoped that I would not be missed.

'I've asked the little Gibbs' girls to tea this afternoon,' said Mrs Samuels when she came into the room. 'You'll like them, they're about your age,' and she sat down to pour out the tea. I did not want her to ask the Gibbs girls, already I hated them and was afraid my friendship would be jeopardised, and I was intensely jealous. There was a sound from the doorway and a native servant stood there with two little blond girls who came in and curtseyed to Mrs Samuels and lifted their faces for her kiss. 'This is Edith and her little sister Muriel,' said Mrs Samuels as she took their coats from the servant and told him to go to the kitchen to tell the cook to bring the hot water for the tea. They came in and stood looking at me, and the older girl took my hand and said, 'I know who you are, you're Mrs Stotter's little girl and you go to the Convent.' We smiled at each other, the ice broken, and after tea the draughts board was brought out and they showed me how to play.

When their servant returned later, I walked with them to the gate, still feeling pangs of jealousy, but they were unconscious of any ill-feeling and urged me to come and play with them tomorrow at their house. I

161

was apprehensive and remarked to Mrs Samuels that perhaps their mother wouldn't want me at her home, she might not want me as a friend to her girls, thinking I wasn't good enough for them. 'Why ever not?' she asked. 'If you like, I'll send my boy with a note to her this very evening, she's a very nice woman and the girls would be nice friends for you. But of course, you may prefer the company of your cousin and his friends?'

'No,' I replied. 'I spend all the time with Billy and his friends because there's no one else and my auntie doesn't want me around the house during the day.' 'But you have a sister, what does she do?' Mrs Samuels asked. 'She's a little lady, everyone says, and goes to Roma Smith's house every day.' 'You do sound sorry for yourself,' she observed drily. 'Self-pity is destructive, do you know what I mean? It eats into your very soul and the sorrier you feel for yourself, the more unlikely anyone else will care about you. It's such a pity, I had thought better of you.' Silently I began to weep, despising myself for my shortcomings, but I understood every word she had said. 'I'm sorry Mrs Samuels,' I said, rising to go home. 'I'm very sorry, please don't be cross with me,' and I made ready to go. She pulled me towards herself and hugged me saying: 'Think about what I've said and come again tomorrow, I'm sure you're not a completely lost cause,' and she laughed as we walked to the gate.

Early the next morning I sat on the top bar of the gate to the Gibbs's house, waiting for someone to appear. Their rambling wooden house stood on piles, and underneath the house lived a collection of chickens, ducks, dogs and cats, and sometimes snakes had slithered out to lie basking in the hot noon-day sun. Long-lost shoes and pieces of clothing were often found there and it was the first place anyone looked for anything that had been lost.

At last the two girls came out of their back door, their hair tidily plaited, their clean cotton dresses freshly ironed and their feet bare, like mine. 'Can I come and play?' I called and after some moments of desultory chatter, I was invited to join them on their verandah where their mother sat in her chair. Mrs Gibbs was a big, fat, pink lady who overflowed her chair where she was directing her servants at the milk separator or rolling out pastry and making little cakes. I liked her and when she spoke to me, she put her arm around me and drew me close and her face cracked into a broad smile. Her husband was a tall, very thin man, English I was told and his older brother was a lord in England. Mr Gibbs wore thick tweed knickerbockers which fastened under his knees over heavy woollen stockings which in turn disappeared into

162

black brogues, and a cap with flaps over his ears.

He carried a walking stick which he could turn with a flick of his hand into a seat on which he sat at the gateway, inspecting the cattle as the herd boys turned them out to graze on the scrubby bush. Mr Gibbs lived in a feudal style as he had been accustomed to in far away Scotland before he had come to the colony. His servant hierarchy was controlled by a boss-boy and the household staff by a major domo and he spoke only to these two men, giving them their orders for the day. He encouraged them to have their wives and families living in the compound, and he wholeheartedly countenanced his wife's efforts to run a small health clinic for the women and children, smiling benignly and patting the picannins' heads on his daily inspection of their quarters.

'Come and see the new calves,' said Edith when we had become bored with her dolls, and we crept into the darkened byre, empty now, but still redolent of the sweet smell of milky cows and their calves. Once I had seen a stuffed day-old calf hanging on the wall and Edith told me that in England farmers often stuffed the small dead animal with straw and put them to the cow whose milk was slow in coming.

We heard Mrs Gibbs calling from the verandah and we were called back and offered the newly baked jam tarts. We sat on the step savouring the taste of the hot jam, and as I licked the crumbs from my hands I glanced up to look at Mrs Gibbs. 'Are you sick?' I asked, noticing that her face and eyes were red and puffy, but she blew her nose and wiped her face with her handkerchief before replying, 'No, cookie, run along you girls and play in the garden.' 'What's the matter with your ma?' I asked Muriel. 'Why's her face so red?' 'Mind your own business,' retorted my new friend and the incident was soon forgotten.

I had not forgotten my promise to call on Mrs Samuels that same afternoon, so bidding the girls goodbye and feeling I had done something of which she would approve, I ran home to get ready for my afternoon visit. 'Do you read a lot?' Mrs Samuels asked me as I carried the basket around the garden with her. She was picking flowers and snipped them vigorously as she gathered them. 'Only the English papers my father gets,' I said, '*Titbits* and *Football Weekly*. They don't have any books at home but I read the school library books when I'm back at school.' I did not tell her that they were heavily slanted to Catholicism and were mainly about conversions to the faith, lapsed heretics returning to the fold and unrequited love between priest and parishioner.

'When we've had tea, you can choose two to take home with you to read,' she said, 'and when you bring them back, you can take two more, they'd be better than all those quasi-religious books you are reading.' I chose *Beau Geste* and a book by P.G. Wodehouse, and I hid them under my dress when it was time to go home. We stood at the gate about to say goodbye when Mrs Samuels asked 'Would you like to come and spend the weekend with us? I will write a little note to your aunt and ask her, or would you ask her yourself?' I agreed to do that and ran home through the dusky night hugging the books to my skinny chest and savouring the thought of the coming weekend.

'No,' said my aunt, when I put Mrs Samuels' invitation to her. 'Who does she think she is, inviting a toe-rag like you to stay? You ain't got the proper clothes, you can't even behave properly. No. What next, I ask you?' 'Why can't I go?' I asked, feeling cheated. 'Because I say so, that's why, so stop asking.' But the next morning I ran along the sandy road and arrived breathless at Mrs Samuels' back door and said I could only stop for a minute my aunty needed me, but just to say perhaps she would ask again later on in the year? She seemed satisfied with my lies and I told her that I had been to the Gibbs' house and had met the parents and had been asked to come again.

'That would be better than playing with the boys,' she said. 'Plenty of friends of your own kind, and books to read when you want to be alone.' I was about to turn and run home when she added, 'Let those boys get on without you, you shouldn't spend so much time with them, you should be thinking of other things, not running around the bush all day with a bunch of ruffians.'

'Do you have lots of friends, Mrs Samuels?' I asked, knowing that I should not be dawdling like this and that I should start for home. 'Only a few,' she said with a sigh. 'When you get to my age, you only need a few, but I never get bored, I have all this,' and she pointed to the shelves of her books. 'They're my best friends, whom I love dearly. But I live in an intellectual desert, there's nobody really interesting to talk to, but Mr Sam is buying me a wireless set and I will be able to listen to that. When it comes, you must join me and we will see what you can pick up on it. Daventry I know, but perhaps Paris and Rome or even the States, who knows?' She seemed to be unaware of my presence and was lost in her day dream.

The arrival of her cook with a note from a neighbour aroused her and she turned to me asking. 'But you and I will always be friends, won't we? Come and see me again soon and tell me what you've been doing.' 'I'll come again day after tomorrow,' I said getting up to go. 'Tomorrow Billy is taking us to see Arthur Rose's Father's Arm, and I'll see you then.' She burst out laughing and when I looked back from the road, she was still standing on the edge of the little pool, still laughing.

Arthur Rose was a newcomer to the settlement and lived with his parents in a small corrugated iron house across the river. He was reputed to possess a fiery temper and was not to be trifled with. It was said that his mother beat him with his father's razor strop for his misdeeds and was equally to be feared. Once a week she rode up to my aunt's house to play cards and take tea and gossip, but her hard face did not invite idle chit-chat or banter and she was always deferred to in an argument.

I was fascinated by Arthur Rose. He was quite a small boy, heavily built for his size, and he possessed the biggest nose I have ever seen. It rose out of his face, glorious in its Romanesque proportions and aquiline shape. He also suffered the most appalling, strangling stutter. He grew red in the face as he gagged and spluttered, commandeering the conversation, sweating and spitting as he fought to bring the words he wanted under command. We stood about, embarrassed at his display but too frightened to help because if we tittered and giggled, he hit us. He assumed leadership of the gang of boys and was very ready with his fists when challenged, but he kept them all in check, threatening them in a long, exhausting, stuttering tirade.

'You lot,' he stammered, 'can come up to my place later and if you do what I say, I'll let you see my father's arm.' 'What's the matter with it?' I asked. 'Nothing,' he spluttered, 'but all my friends at school have seen it, and now, you do what I say, and I'll let you see it.' We were much in awe of this brash little bully but were consumed with curiosity, so we happily jogged along the footpath to his house, wondering and speculating about the treat that lay ahead.

Like the other householders, his parents kept a few cattle and donkeys and there had recently arrived in the Rose's back yard a great number of bales of hay and straw for the livestock. We were ordered to arrange the bundles to make a bunk-house so that we could continue our games of Cowboys and Indians, obsessed as we all were by their exploits as given in the comic papers we passed around. We had even built an Indian teepee and stockade down by the river amongst the mimosa trees, and had made good use of a convenient stack of neatly trimmed gum poles we had found there.

We obeyed Arthur's every command, sweating and straining to lift the heavy bales into position, and I outdid myself offering to clean his

165

bicycle for him, fetching him drinks of water, and constantly scanning the road for his father's arrival.

The afternoon was almost over and I could feel the chill of the approaching evening through my thin dress; shadows were lengthening and we knew that soon we would have to forego our expected treat and hurry home before houseboys were sent to find us.

Mrs Rose stood at the back of her kitchen, holding a large kettle in her hand and called Arthur to fill it from the water tank. 'You kids'd better run along this minnit, his father will be home for his tea soon,' she said. 'Run along with you now.' 'But,' I called out, plucking up my courage, 'Arthur says we can see his father's arm before we go.' She looked me up and down and turned to go. 'Get-away this minnit, I tell you,' she called, banging the door behind her. Disappointed, we turned to go when I suddenly espied a figure in the distance, cycling down the path from the main road. It was Mr Rose, a large corpulent man dressed in white shirt and trousers, his blanco-ed topee on his head, his long white whiskers blowing in the wind, his stomach protruding over the handlebars. But something was wrong. And then I saw it.

He held the handlebars with only one hand, there was no other hand, just a short stump where his arm should have been, the sleeve pinned up with a big steel safety pin. Dexterously Mr Rose steered his cycle around the disintegrating stack of hay bales, jammed on the brake and came to a surprisingly gentle stop.

As fast as we could, we ran home, deeply disappointed after our long afternoon's hard work. 'What happened to Mr Rose's arm?' I asked as I panted along beside my cousin. 'What did he do? Was it sore?' 'Nah,' said Billy. 'One of his kaffirs gave him some cheek, so Mr Rose hit him. Hit him across the face he did and the kaffir had his mouth open. His teeth caught on Mr Rose's hand and blood poisoning set in. It went up and up along his arm and he had to go to hospital to have it cut off.' I flinched. 'He could have died,' said Billy. 'Kaffirs are so dirty and never wash, that's why they're poisonous.' Poor Mr Rose, I thought, but wasn't Arthur lucky to have something to boast about. It made up for that awful stuttering.

Many years later I met Arthur Rose again. He had joined the Civil Service as an office junior and had worked himself up into something important in the Federal Government and had been posted to the Consulate in Washington DC. He looked extremely prosperous and well pleased. His beautifully cut suit hid his large paunch, his handmade shoes and shirt and faultless hat removed him in time and place from the shack near the cross-roads, from the Red Indian encampment in the mimosa thicket, from the gaggle of sycophantic friends and from the fame of his father's arm. But no longer was he the same brash, boastful, swaggering lout I'd been so anxious to please; a long stay in a smart American speech clinic had erased that strangling, frustrating stutter and he spoke softly and clearly, each word as clear as only a perfectly enunciated word can be.

Some days after our visit to Arthur's house a car drew up to the front gate. Recognising Mr Samuels sitting in the back, I went in to the kitchen to hide, hoping we would not meet. When I peeped through the window, I saw Porteous open the rear door of the car and out stepped dapper little Mr Samuels. He carried his newspaper and wore eyeglasses pinched against the bridge of his nose. 'Mrs Stotter in?' he asked the houseboy who had answered his knock. I heard them going around to the verandah room and I climbed into the nearest peach tree and strained to hear what was being said.

'My wife would like your youngest niece to come and spend a few days with us,' he told Aunty Betty who was pouring out tea. 'We would like her to come, my wife often longs for another female's companionship, all her friends live the other side of the city and she does not see them very often.' My aunt studied Mr Samuels' face as he spoke. 'But she's only a little kid,' she replied, 'she'd only be a nuisance.' 'Let me be the judge of that,' he said. 'They get on well and we find the child very entertaining.' My aunt sniffed: 'Tells a lot of stories, if you ask me, not all of them true.' But Mr Samuels would not be put off. 'She's never told us any, but she has quite a vivid imagination. Surely you could spare her for a few days?' They spoke for a few more minutes and then Mr Samuels said his goodbyes, standing on the step. 'Ta ever so for calling,' said Aunty Betty, 'and for the invite, I'll sent her along tomorrow.' Mr Samuels flinched at the refinement of the conversation but smiled genially and climbed back into his car and was driven away.

No one, said my aunt, was going to say she neglected me. She went through my sister's wardrobe, searching for something that would fit me. If necessary, she continued, she would herself take me into town that very afternoon and buy me something. I was astounded and prayed that this threat would be carried out, already visualising my arrival at the Samuel's front door clad in flowing georgette and high-heeled shoes and perhaps wearing a pair of crocheted cotton gloves; the picture became

167

ever rosier as I contemplated it, but I was sharply brought to reality by the sound of Stella's complaining voice. She was reluctant to part with her best dress but Aunty Betty was adamant.

The next day at noon I walked the mile down the road, my hair newly washed, my fingernails and hands clean and with Stella's freshly blanco-ed tennis shoes on my feet. Jairos the house boy accompanied me, carrying the parcel with the borrowed clothes in it.

'Tomorrow we're going for a picnic,' said Mr Samuels at dinner that evening. 'Where shall we go?' The two sons of the house looked at each other in consternation. 'But sir, we've arranged to spend the day with Douglas and Ian Thackwell,' said Jim, 'we made the arrangement days ago.' 'If you've already committed yourself, then you must go, we three shall have a day out together,' said their father; and then he added: 'Any suggestions as to where we could go?' 'What about Mermaid's Pool?' asked Jim. 'Lots of the fellows at school have been there and you could tell us what it's like.' So it was settled and shortly after breakfast the next day Porteous took the wheel of the car and we bowled along the road towards the east. This road, I knew, led to the eastern border of the colony and after some miles, we turned off the main road into the bush following two deeply rutted tracks for some miles.

I sat between the parents, very excited and wondering what lay ahead. Suddenly we heard the faint roar of a waterfall and looking ahead through the trees, I saw where the water came tumbling and cascading down a steep granite slope, to fall into a big, deep pool. Towering msasa trees fringed it and the light from the sun, filtering through the upper branches, twinkled on the shimmering surface of the pool. Ferns bordered the banks of the stream which drained the pool as it filled from the waterfall, and cactus and euphorbias blazed in full flower. Picnic parties were paddling in the shallower water at the edges and people at the top of the cascade called to each other to join them on the slide down the granite slope through the swiftly flowing water.

Porteous and the servant set up the table and chairs and unpacked the lunch basket. Delicate little chicken pies, slices of pink ham, egg salad and crisp lettuce from their garden were served just as though we were at home, and when the meal had been cleared away and coffee served, the two men were given permission to spend the rest of the afternoon as they wished.

'There's a beer drink, Inkoos, at that village we passed,' said the driver. 'We will walk down there and greet our brothers but will not stay long.' 'See you are back here when the sun is there,' said Mr Samuels, pointing to the horizon, 'and don't drink too much, we have a long way to go home.' The servants were dismissed and the parents settled down with their books while I played happily in the stream, searching for pebbles to take home. It was an idyllic day.

I must have fallen asleep on the drive home for when I woke we were quite near to the house. Pointing to the sky ahead, I asked, 'Is that a veldt fire do you think? Or is it a dust cloud?' The sky was a clear blue save for a thick column of dark grey smoke which billowed up from the direction of the river below the house. Mr Samuels called for the car to stop, we leapt out and with the two servants we ran as fast as we could down to the river, leaving Mrs Samuels to make her own way to the house. The nearside river bank was alight, thick white smoke billowing through the trees as the branches caught fire, the dry mimosa trees exploding into bright puffs of smoke as the fire rippled through the long grass destroying everything in its path. Overhead circled storks and kites, waiting for the mice and small rodents fleeing the fire. With a crackle and a hiss the gum trees caught alight and within minutes Mr Samuels' precious new apple trees, recently imported from the Cape, were smouldering and charred.

'Beat it out,' cried Mr Samuels as he broke branches from unscathed trees. Calling to the passing natives who had stopped on the far bank to come to his aid, he soon had the fire under control. But utter devastation remained, everything was blackened and ruined and Mr Samuels surveyed it with a look of disgust, his eyebrows singed, his tussore suit blackened and dirty. He told the natives who had helped to make their way to the house and to wait for him there.

'Where could it have started,' he asked, and turning to look around, he saw Jim coming towards us from the Indian camp. 'What are you doing here,' he asked. 'Do you know anything about this?' Jim looked uncomfortable and avoided his father's eye. 'Answer me when I ask you something,' demanded Mr Samuels. 'What do you know about this fire, and where are Angus and your friends?'

'I don't know sir,' said Jim. 'They ran away when it started.' Mr Samuels looked at him with disbelief. 'When it started?' he roared. 'So you boys started it, did you?' His face grew redder and he was very angry. 'I want to see this camp of yours, come along, where is it?' Silently Jim led the way through the smouldering grass, down the river bank into what remained of the mimosa thicket. There stood the sorry ruin of our teepee, the poles collapsing against each other, no vestige of the hessian sacking we had imagined to be buffalo hide. The stockade was still smoking.

Mr Samuels clapped his hand to his forehead. 'I just don't believe it,' he said, 'those are the poles I sold for wireless aerials,' and furiously he turned upon his son. 'Who gave you permission to take those?' Jim hung his head and scuffed at the grass. 'Nobody sir,' he said meekly. 'Get up to the house,' roared his father, 'and wait for me. I want to know exactly what happened this afternoon, and it had better be the truth, or you'll wish you'd never been born.' He stamped through the ashen remains of the camp and angrily stalked off towards the house.

'You're in for it,' I commiserated with Jim. 'I'm going,' and I ran to catch up with my angry host and not another word was said between us. Sadly Jim trailed behind me but there was no sign of his recent companions and I left him to join his mother who was quietly sitting in her little sitting room drinking a cup of tea.

'Now my boy, let's hear all about it,' demanded his father. Jim hung his head as he stood before him. 'We stayed to play in the camp and Angus and Ian fetched some mealies and we decided to make a fire to roast them. The sacking of the teepee caught alight and before I knew what had happened, the fire spread along the grass and the trees were alight. The other three ran away and I was trying to beat out the fire when I heard you calling to the boys on the other side of the river, to come and help. That's all sir, I'm sorry.' Tears came into his eyes and he wiped them away with the back of his hand.

Mr Samuels breathed heavily. He left us for a moment to go out and thank the natives who had helped and to give them packets of cigarettes and a few shillings, then he was back. He appeared to calm down somewhat and stood for a long while considering his verdict. 'You're gated,' he said at last, 'for the next month. No more friends to visit, no sneaking away to play with them, and bread and water for the next week. Now get out of my sight but before you do, tell your brother I want to see him. Right away!' Jim slunk out of the room and disappeared towards his own house to find his little brother.

But Angus had disappeared and for the rest of that short stay, I saw neither of the boys. I helped sort out books, carried the basket for Mrs Samuels when she cut flowers for her sitting room and once spoke to the cook whose name was Ishmael when I was sent to ask for a vase. 'Is my brother Vinyu still with the Inkossikaas?' he asked. 'Yes,' I replied, 'but I did not know he was your brother. Do you have the same mother?' 'No,' he said, 'but we are brothers, we come from the same village.' 'I will tell him,' I said knowing of the extended family system which existed amongst the African people and knowing that everyone in the same village considered themselves to be bound by a tie of brotherhood to everyone else.

I was to wait for Porteous to take me home when he returned with his employer. I had asked if I could say goodbye to Jim in spite of the embargoes placed upon him, and ran down to the children's house where I found him lying on his bed reading a book. 'Do you know where Angus is?' I asked. 'Your mother is so worried, she says she hasn't seen him since Sunday and it's Tuesday already.' He grinned, and putting his finger to his lips, he glanced out of the window to see if either parent was about and then said, 'Come, I'll show you where he's been for the last two days,' and he led me through the orchard, past the grape vines, along the side of the haystack, into the dog kennels.

There, sitting amongst the puppies who were spread about their mother, was Angus. Dirty and dishevelled, but seemingly unconcerned at the trouble he had helped to cause, he lolled against the bitch and smiled at me. 'Have you been here all the time?' I asked. 'Your servant told your mother you hadn't slept in your bed and he didn't know where you were – what have you done about food?' He looked at me and his smile widened. 'I've been sleeping here with the pups,' he said, 'and Tess lets me have a suck whenever I want,' and he bent down to illustrate what he meant. 'Sis Angus!' I cried, using that word we all used to denote anything we found repulsive or distasteful, 'how could you, she's only a dog.' He fondled her ears and lay back against her body and said 'I know she's only a dog but she never gets cross with me and lets me do as I like, don't you?' Tess wagged her tail with pleasure and Angus applied himself to the teat again with some defiance. 'Don't tell ma, she won't like it but I'll come with you to ask her pardon. She'll be so pleased to see her little darling and all will be forgiven and then tonight, she can work on the old man for me.'

I was amazed at his audacity and secretly admired his resourcefulness, but I knew that many of the householders regarded him as very strange. He had been seen riding on Mr Smith's brown and white Afrikander bull, a large ferocious animal with red eyes led out of his byre each morning at the end of a pole attached to a ring in his nose, by the herd boy whose sole responsibility it was to care for him; on another occasion Angus had been seen to up-end all Mrs Thackwell's beehives, saying afterwards that he felt sorry for the little bees, all squashed together in

171

such a little house. When he had been despatched to capture a hostage for the Red Indians, he had impaled Roma Smith between her two smallest toes with his father's old army bayonet and he had only escaped punishment because he had been able to run faster than the irate Mr Smith. Nothing could disturb the homesteaders more than the sight of Angus happily playing in their backyards and they knew it was hopeless to reprimand him. He was defiant and always had reasons for his behaviour. He and Old Glory, the fearsome bull, were friends, he'd insisted. It was his avowed intention to remove that ring from the bull's nose and Angus was the only one who had not been afraid of the animal and who took many liberties with him.

Now he followed me to his mother's house and before I could say a word, he had thrown himself into her arms. 'I've been with Tess,' he cried, 'aren't you pleased to see me?' 'Indeed I am, you naughty boy,' said his mother, 'but you're both gated for the next month on your father's orders so go along and have a bath and change those dirty clothes, you smell like Tess,' and she wrinkled her nose. 'It wasn't my fault Mater,' he said. 'It never is,' his mother said, smiling, 'but you were there.' Sheepishly he left the room but her glance was fond as her eyes followed him down the path to his own quarters.

Farewells were said, promises to stay longer next time were made and soon I was sitting next to Porteous as he solemnly drove me home. I put my hand over my cheek where Mrs Samuels had kissed me, and resolved to find out what 'gated' meant. It seemed to be something which could easily be overcome.

Several days later I sat with Edith and Muriel on their back verandah, discussing the fire which they had seen from their house. Mrs Gibbs was in her usual chair, having a small tea party with some of her neighbours. They all wore their good cotton dresses and second best hats and pecked daintily at their cakes as they sipped their tea. 'Well,' began Mrs Thackwell, a lugubrious woman who was feared as a gossip, 'the kids of today don't give a darn for their moms and dads any longer, they do just what they like, it's no use talking to them,' and she reached for another cake. 'But don't you worry Trudi, she'll get over it, it's only a passing fancy,' and well satisfied with the stone she had thrown into the pool of her hostess' self-satisfaction, she wiped her hands delicately on her handkerchief. Looks of consternation flashed between the other guests and, leaning forward, Mrs Bugler from next door asked, 'What are you talking about?' 'Don't you know?' asked the aggrieved Mrs Thackwell.

172

'That girl Hester, she's had her eyebrows plucked, that's what she's done,' and she sank back into her chair, well pleased at her hostess's embarrassment. Mrs Gibbs dabbed at her face with her handkerchief and started to cry, and I remembered that her face looked the same the other day when I asked her what was the matter.

An excited ripple ran through the good ladies as they paused in their eating and drinking. 'Yes, that's what Hester's been and gorn and done, to her poor ma's everlasting shame,' Mrs Thackwell continued. Poor Mrs Gibbs sank even lower in her chair, but I could not imagine what all the fuss was about and dared not ask. But 'plucked', I wondered? Was there another meaning to the word? Billy plucked the doves he shot in the mealie lands and Vinyu plucked the fowls for Sunday lunch, but what could have happened to Hester? I resolved to find out and ran home as soon as I had found an excuse to do so to corner Vinyu in the kitchen. 'What did Mrs Thackwell mean, that she made Mrs Gibbs cry?' I asked, as I repeated the conversation. He looked at me and then admitted he did not know, but no doubt it was very serious if the Inkossikaas had cried. 'Ask Miss Hester yourself,' he suggested and slowly I retraced my steps, walking past the Gibbs' home to sit on the milestone where the roads forked, one leading to the town and the other to the brickworks.

It was getting dark and cold when at last I heard the sound of bicycle wheels on the road and saw the light of her bicycle as she rode into view. She hummed quietly to herself as she pedalled towards me, her pale linen dress floating behind her, the impasto of her make-up still perfect. 'Isn't it late for you to be out?' she asked. 'It doesn't matter,' I replied. 'I wanted to see your eyebrows, Mrs Thackwell said they'd been plucked and I didn't know what she meant.' Smiling, she brought her face down to my level and raising one perfectly pencilled eyebrow, she asked: 'Have they been talking about me again?' 'Your mother cried,' I told her, 'so I thought it must have been something awful that you'd done.' 'They're just a lot of old biddies,' she replied as she remounted her cycle and rode off into the gloom towards the welcoming lights of her home. The moon was bright in the east as I ran home, its silvery brightness throwing up the long shadows of the msasa trees and glinting on the grass, but my thoughts were occupied: how had Hester removed her eyebrows in favour of a pencilled line?

To me Marian and Hester were the very essence of sophistication with their fashionable clothes, office jobs in the city and their many friends. 'That girl's fast,' said Aunty Betty as she dished up the evening meal. 'Goes to too many bioscopes, if you ask me, and all those boy friends!'

173

She sounded disapproving as she carefully removed some mashed potato from Tom's plate and put it on someone else's. 'She'll come to a sticky end, you mark my words.'

The sisters continued to fascinate me and I nurtured my friendship with the two little girls in the hope that I would often be asked to stay late to play with them. The older girls rode to work on their bicycles each morning and on pay day at the end of the month, they barely paused between opening their pay envelopes and begging for an hour off 'to do a little shopping'. In great triumph they rode home in the dark, juggling boxes, slippery parcels, awkward packages – all the spoils of an afternoon's shopping. Lengths of dress materials, new shoes, silk stockings, hats, necklaces, scarves, white-paper parcels from the chemist's shop which I knew contained boxes of face powder, rouge and lipstick, expensive dark glossy green boxes of scent. Always there was something special for their mother. A box of handkerchiefs or a bottle of Eau de Cologne. Sometimes a packet of expensive tobacco for their father. I looked with admiration at the pieces of georgette, Moygashel linen, spotted voile and crepe de chine which their mother would sew into dresses for them, but it was the shoes that impressed me most.

High heels, cuban heels, Louis heels; multi-coloured Charleston shoes, white shoes to be cleaned at the end of each day's wearing by the houseboy, black patent leather shoes polished with Vaseline by the cook to whose hands only could they be entrusted; shoes of silver or gold to be worn with those floor-sweeping evening dresses sewn so carefully on their mother's machine.

One day Hester brought home something so outrageous she dared not take it from the box it was packed in. 'Promise Hester you won't tell Ma?' she asked. 'Promise?' Seriously I and her sisters nodded, and slowly she removed the paper, holding the parcel low down by her knees in case someone should look through her bedroom window. There was a rustling of tissue, and there they were. A pair of brown and white court shoes which she held up to her face saying 'Aren't they pretty? They're called co-respondent shoes, everyone in England wears them and the Prince of Wales was the first. Aren't they special?' Clearly she was overjoyed with her purchase, but I failed to see what made them any different from those others sitting in their rows in her wardrobe.

Hester's sights were set very high and she was much loved by her devoted family and all her friends for her beauty and her gentle nature. When I saw her again, many years later, she had married a very wealthy white farmer and drove around Salisbury in a smart, very modern little sports car, the first of its kind to be seen. 'Jump in girls,' she would urge. 'Hester will drive you around to the Rhodian for an icecream,' and we sat in the back, speechless with enjoyment as the wind whipped around our heads and our eyes watered. 'She's a show-off and I don't think she's pretty,' said my sister.

The big talking point was the bioscope. Silent black and white films were shown in the only cinema, the Palace and everyone at school spoke about what they had seen there. When I learned that the entrance fee was sixpence, I realised that there was no possibility of our going; we had no money nor the means of acquiring any and although Billy was given weekly pocket money, it was highly unlikely that he would spend any of it on us. 'Ask your mother if she will give us some money,' we pleaded. Realising that if he wanted to go, he would have to do so by himself, he eventually wheedled a half crown from his parents but not without cost to us. If we wished to accompany him, he said, Tom and I would have to clean and oil his bicycle for the next week; my extra task would be to write out his Latin translation, complete the 'lines' he'd been given at end of term as a punishment by his form master and to clear out his white mice cages. He knew that if he asked any of his friends to accompany him, he would have to pay for their cold drinks at the interval whereas in us he had two willing slaves who would do his every bidding without any cost to himself, and during the interval he could ignore us. We wanted to see the bioscope so badly we would have agreed to any terms. As the time for our departure to the city drew near he called us to his side and said, 'You and Tom had better leave now, it'll take you about an hour to walk to town. Stella can ride on my bicycle bar and we'll leave after we've had lunch.'

A hasty scrub around the knees with a cloth, dress changed and carrying our school shoes in our hands, Tom and I set off the four miles to town. We ran until we grew tired and then stopped by the railway bridge for a few minutes rest. We skirted the rubbish dump, the brickworks, the sprawling native compounds teeming with life, and the railway shunting yards and when we got to the edge of town, we stopped to rest and put on our shoes and arrived breathless at the cinema with only minutes to spare. Billy had arrived in good time and with mounting excitement, we entered the darkened Palace, still panting.

Aloud I read the dialogue to Tom as he sat next to me, but his eyes were fixed on the lady pianist sitting in the orchestra pit, doing her best

175

to match her music to the action on the screen. The jerky antics of Charlie Chaplin, Harold Lloyd, Laurel and Hardy and the Three Stooges held our attention, but it was the serial which gripped us. Tom Mix and Buck Jones were our idols. When we came out into the daylight, rubbing our eyes at the harsh light of a late afternoon, we felt desperate at the thought that we might never learn what happened next, since whether or not we saw the next instalment depended entirely on our cousin's whim.

Once more we did our utmost to please him. He kept us in uneasy suspense, saying he would be spending the day with his own friends, and as we sulked and cried, he drew out the torture. But when Saturday came and my aunt wished to pursue her own plans, the half crown was handed over and once more Tom and I took to the road. We left the house earlier and earlier, stopping at the brickworks to speak to the Indian while he watered his vegetables, at the abandoned house where Sammy and Aisha had lived. We peeped through the windows and tried the doors without success and spent many minutes swinging on the grenadilla vines which he had trained over an archway, and we ate the green, acrid fruit, pausing only to glance up at the sun to see if it was midday. 'When your shadow is the smallest,' Vinyu had told us, 'it will be twelve o'clock', and this had always been our guide.

Onwards we trudged and when we came to the railway crossing, we joined the crowds of Africans who came and went to the city, lost amongst them as they journeyed to their homes in the bush, or to their places of work. Sometimes we begged lifts from those who drove ox or donkey carts piled high with firewood. Vegetable sellers, loafers, gangs of young picannins, native women with piles of freshly laundered washing on their heads jostled with us as we threaded our way past them. When we reached the railway line, we paused to chat to the bread-seller where he sat at his stall; he poured dark sweetened tea into old jam tins for his clients at a tickey a cup, and handed out slabs of greying bread to his eager customers. Groups of men stood about laughing and joking as they crammed the food into their mouths, eyeing us curiously as we stood hand in hand next to the bread-seller. 'What do you want?' they asked but we were too shy to speak. 'They are my friends,' called back the bread-seller, 'they always stop to talk when they pass this way,' and he grinned, showing his strong white teeth. Turning to me he said, 'If you have a tickey, you can buy some of my bread.' In the vernacular I answered, 'I have no money but I will buy some next week,' and grasping Tom's hand, we took to our heels and ran. Past the tribesmen, the wagons and carts, the children and women and ducking under a long line of freight cars, we emerged at the bottom of the street

176

leading to the cinema. We stopped only to put our shoes on and then meekly joined Billy and Stella who had been peering anxiously up the street.

'You know the bread-seller by the railway line?' I asked Vinyu that night in the kitchen. 'What tribe is he? His tribal marks are very different from yours.' 'He is a Mashona like you,' he replied as he dug me in my ribs. 'I am of the Manyika people, we live on the Portuguese border but the bread-seller is the same as you.' I was glad I was Mashona only in name and only to the African people; I had been born in Salisbury, and Stella who was born in Bulawayo constantly reminded me of the fact that the Matabele were in all ways superior to their Mashona brothers. And I was also glad I had not had to endure the naming ceremony when a child's face or body was cut with sharp stones, leaving distinctive cicatrices which would identify him for the rest of his life.

'You shouldn't go that way to town,' advised Vinyu. 'There are many people there who are curious about the Makiwa. You are only a small girl but one day, someone might harm you.' This was the first intimation I had had that any black person could molest me. 'Don't be silly,' I cried, 'they're my friends, why should they hurt me?' 'Soon you will be a young madam,' he replied, 'with a handbag and a job in town and you will forget your friends, and then what?' I did not reply. The mere idea that an African would do me some injury seemed as preposterous as my owning a pound note.

We had been back at school for some weeks when we were called to the parlour where visitors awaited us. It must be someone from far away I thought, and as I pondered, I realised that the only people we knew from any distance away were our grandparents. As if she read my thoughts Stella suddenly stopped and said, 'If it's the Williamses I don't think we should see them. Aunty Betty would be very cross if she knew they had come to see us. And Daddy says they're the cause of all his troubles. No, let's go back to class,' and she turned to go. But I was curious and there was a longing to see my grandmother, the only person I had thought really belonged to us, so I persisted and we entered the dimness of the visitors' parlour where I saw my grandmother sitting in the straight-backed chair and my grandfather standing by the window looking at the garden.

I was suddenly shy and while I longed to run and hug her, I hung back, feeling that they had become strangers. Grandma had never conformed to fashion and wore the same long black silk dress, but her hair was grey at the sides and she looked pale. For some moments we stood and looked at them. 'Aren't you going to say hello to your grandmother?' asked the old man. I smiled and advanced a few paces. 'Have you nothing to say?' she asked in her carefully accented English, but we continued to stand and stare at them, ill at ease and frightened.

Gone were all the memories of their love and the happiness we had shared, and quite clearly I could hear Aunty Betty's scornful voice: 'Your mother didn't love you, or she'd never have run away and left you,' and I remembered all the innuendos about Charlotte's family – Grandma's foreignness, their poverty and their audacity in thinking they were in some way superior to my father's family. Carefully I sidled up to my grandmother and leaned forward to kiss her, but it was only a peck before I drew away. 'They've forgotten us', she said to her husband. As though the situation was completely normal, he smiled and asked, 'How are you getting on at school?' For some moments we chatted but the conversation was strained and halting. I longed for them to go, but knew that I would regret it when they did.

'We're going to the Cape,' said Grandad jovially, 'Your grandma has been ill and needs a holiday, but we couldn't pass through Salisbury without seeing you.' Take me with you, I wanted to cry out, take me away from here, from my aunty's house, from the cousins and all their friends, don't go without me; but I stood there, tongue-tied and afraid, and said no more. Stella had never left her place by the door, nor had she said very much, and at last, realising that the years of our growing up had created a gap which could not be bridged, Grandma arose from her chair and followed Grandad out to the gate. Hesitantly I followed, regretting my rudeness to them but still remembering the desolation of our last sight of our mother.

'Cheek,' said Stella as we slowly went back to our classes. 'Just you wait till I tell Aunty Betty, she'll be very cross.' We had never paused to think what it must have cost our grandparents to make the visit, to be confronted by two unfeeling, ungrateful, unloving little girls whom no doubt, they had longed to see. Desperately I regretted my attitude and wished I had been kinder and nicer to my grandmother; I had not even asked about her illness, nor about my uncles, and for many days afterwards the feeling of deep regret remained with me. But fear, too, was not far away. What would my father's family say when Stella told them of the visit?

* * *

Stella had begged my father to let her leave school at the end of the year and the only obstacle was her music exam. 'Trinity College of Music is what I'm going to do,' she would say, proud of her piano-playing, but when she went home and the cousins begged her to 'give us a toon, what about *Bye Bye Blackbird* or *Souvenirs*,' she looked at them scornfully and reminded them that she was a Classical Pianist and did not go in for that sort of thing.

She longed for the day when she could discard her school uniform, have her hair waved and use face powder. Her next priority was an office job and before the term had ended, my father had enrolled her to start in Miss Clarkson's Shorthand and Typewriting College in the town. A few more months of the school year remained, however, and for her the time dragged interminably. I applied myself once more to class work, terrified that if my reports were bad, I too would be removed from the Convent and sent to the secretarial college. It did not occur to me that my age prohibited any such action.

'You must be sorry your sister's leaving at the end of the year,' her friends would say to me. Yes I was, I told them, knowing that I would be alone without a big sister to turn to; but I did not add that I looked forward to inheriting her school clothes and thus putting myself on a par with the other boarders. 'Your sister's sweet,' they would tell me, 'we'll miss her. You don't look alike at all, she's so pretty and you're so dark and skinny.' The barb did not miss its mark.

When we went back to Aunty Betty's for the long holidays, she once more sent Vinyu to search for Sammy, this time to the coloured quarter of the town where she understood he had bought a small house. But he could not be found and in spite of Christmas and all the parties which lay ahead, my aunt took out her sewing machine and set to work to make Stella's new wardrobe. Little cotton dresses with lace collars, pinafore dresses with matching blouses and a dark linen dress for future interviews all hung in the kitchen for Vinyu to press. Expeditions to town were organised to search for the right hats and shoes, and to my chagrin her Sunday dress was altered for her to wear to the college. My father bought her a bicycle and looked proudly at her as she took a turn around the yard. 'She's a beaut ain't she,' he asked. She was indeed a pretty girl, appealing and winsome, with a passive nature unless denied her heart's desire. She always looked innocent and shared Billy's knack of shifting blame, so Tom and I bore the brunt of her misdeeds. 'It's them bleedin' toe-rags,' my aunt would cry when any crime was discovered, hotly denying that Stella or Billy could be responsible.

179

I felt that my sister was now beyond my reach and returned to school with a near-bulging school trunk, intent on doing well. I was determined not to get into trouble, to remember to keep my vest on in the bathroom, not to switch lights on when I had removed all my clothes, to curtsey to every nun I encountered even those who worked in the laundry or the garden, and to adopt a pious air at all times.

Essays I had written were published in the school magazine, my Latin and French translations were eagerly sought after and I volunteered for table duty at meal times, but I lived a double life. As surely as a fly is attracted to honey, I was drawn to lark about with the naughtiest girls in the school, but always with a ready excuse when cornered: 'But Sister, I was trying to tell those girls not to do that,' I would convincinly tell the nuns when summoned to their study. Later, when my betrayed friends lay in wait for me and threatened to abandon me for my double-dealing, I offered to do their homework, promising my accomplices to let them know which day girls were easy touches for their playtime sandwiches, pocket money or forbidden books.

For the first time since its inception, the Convent now engaged a games mistress. Mrs Rule showed us how to climb ropes in the new gymnasium, how to swing on the row of rings, hang from the trapeze without falling off and play hockey, tennis, netball and rounders. On Saturday mornings she mustered us into a long crocodile and took us to the Town Baths where we watched her effortlessly doing the crawl, the breaststroke or backstroke, and when my turn came I floundered about with the rest, trying to remember what I had learned on our holiday to the coast so long ago.

Games became very important to me and I was determined to excel, and took part in them all thanks to the Boarders' Mother who unearthed an abandoned tennis dress as well as a racquet, and a hockey stick unobtrusively marked 'CB. Convent Boarder.' My father felt obliged to call once a month to see me, but he showed little interest in what I did. 'Come and see us playing hockey,' I would urge. 'We're playing next Thursday.' 'Nah, I can't come that day. Gotter get me pigs ready for the Friday market,' and he tapped impatiently on his steering wheel as we sat in his lorry under the shade of a nearby jacaranda tree, eager to leave but unwilling to make the first move. 'Well, I'd better be getting along,' he would say eventually, both of us relieved that a decision had been made.

When I returned for the holidays, I found the house in turmoil. Plans were being made to drive to the Zimbabwe Ruins, a distance of some two hundred miles, for a fortnight's stay. The journey would take four days said my aunt, and we would have to take tents, bedding and enough food for the trip, and would replenish our stores at Fort Victoria, the town nearest to the ruins, which were almost unexplored at that time.

'You take your three kids, Jorbey, the tents, the petrol and the food,' said Aunty Betty to my father, 'and I'll take George, Jack and Billy and we'll follow you.' Uncle George grumbled and groused, offering to remain at home, but his wife ignored his pleas that he had no interest in traipsing through the bush to look at a lot of old stones and in any case he hated picnicking and getting his clothes dirty.

A long time was spent packing and unpacking the lorry and car. Stores and boxes were re-arranged, tents moved about but still there was hardly enough room on the lorry for us three children. 'Stella will have to come with us,' said Aunty Betty. 'She can sit between Jack and Billy,' and Stella, who now considered herself grown-up, happily agreed. 'How far is it?' I asked my father. 'I don't bleedin' know,' he shouted, irritated because he could not untangle the mound of rope he was trying to tie down the petrol boxes with, but at last all was ready and we went to bed knowing that an early start was hoped for and speculating about the ruins.

A quick shake, lights on in the house and from the yard came shouts for Jorbey to hurry and to not forget his blankets. Everything was loaded, last minute instructions were given to Vinyu who appeared in our midst with a tray of cups of tea, Uncle George was routed out from the sitting room where he sat twiddling the knobs of the battery radio, trying to find Daventry and the reassuring sound of an English voice. 'Come on George,' cried Aunty Betty. 'It's nearly three, time we was going, buck up now.' 'Three o'clock in the morning,' sang my father in remembrance of the London music hall where he had first heard that song many years before. The doors were locked behind us and the car and lorry were started.

Tom and I snuggled down amongst the sacks and stores and pulled a blanket over us. Where had I been before, I wondered, when I had lain looking up into the starlit sky on a dark night such as this? My thoughts were brought back to the present by the appearance of Jorbey; over his shorts and shirt he wore a long army greatcoat which swept the ground, and on his head was an old discarded hat of my aunt's, shiny black straw, a bunch of flaking red cherries nestling coyly under the brim, and around his neck a long piece of discoloured curtain netting. He smiled as he stowed his blanket roll amongst the petrol tins and gathered up the skirts of the coat and climbed into the front seat. 'Keep warm,' he said. 'This is the coldest time of the night.'

At last we set off, the bright headlights scanning over the yard as we pulled out. It was mid-winter and the best time to contemplate a long car journey. It would not rain for another three months and the rivers which lay ahead were either very low or completely dried up. There would be no bridges to negotiate, only the soft river beds which intersected the road. Through the sleeping town we went, through the shopping areas, past the Indian traders, past the second rate hotels, the rooming houses of the very poor whites and into the coloured area where half-castes and others of uncertain origins lived. Ahead loomed the long whitewashed buildings of the Masonic Hotel where prostitutes lurked and where illicit gold dealings were reputed to take place. I had friends at school whose fathers eked out a living in the Mazoe hills where they worked two stamp mills searching for that lucky find which would make them rich. But in the meantime, they lived in poverty in the bush and came to town once a month for stores and to sell what little gold they had found, in dubious dealings in the bars of the Masonic while the prostitutes eyed them and sized them up.

The headlights of the lorry swept over the cemetery which lay near to the roadside, lighting up the crosses, the marble guardian angels, the carved urns and the newly turned graves and I shivered in fear – but more so when the cemetery came to an abrupt end and there lay the graves of the unbelievers who had not wished to lie amongst their more righteous fellows. Another fence and there stood Salisbury's newest acquisition, the Hindu crematorium, its chimney pointing like a finger to Paradise, smokeless and solitary amongst the casuarina and flame trees.

Ahead lay the vastness of the native Location, where hundreds of native workers lived in dormitories and hostels. They were employed by the City of Salisbury and did all the menial jobs which kept a city running smoothly. Power station labourers, road workers, rubbish collectors, sweepers and the men who emptied the lavatory buckets of the white householders. They came from as far away as Nyasaland and Northern Rhodesia, but their wives and families remained in their mud hut villages, growing their own crops and knowing that they would only see their menfolk once a year when they travelled back to their homes for a month's leave.

Soon we had left the city behind us and were on the open road

182

towards Enkeldoorn which lay a hundred miles to the south. Mile upon mile of savannah stretched before us, rolling grassy plains dotted here and there with clumps of trees, but it was too dark to see clearly and we slept.

Suddenly I awoke to find the lorry had stopped, and behind us I saw the dim lights of Aunty Betty's car as it drew nearer. 'See those trees ahead?' asked my father. 'The Umfuli must be near, always find a river when there's a long line of trees like that,' and he gently eased the lorry forward over the rutted road while the lights of the oncoming car grew brighter. There it was, but there was no sign of water, just a bed of thick white sand. Carefully my father shifted the gears as we bumped and lurched through the eroded approach and as he changed gear to gather speed for the steep incline of the further bank, the motor died.

'Strewth,' cried my father, 'just my bleedin' luck! You kids, hop off and help Jorbey give us a shove, but for Gawd's sake man, take off that bleedin' coat, it's too bloody long.' Regretfully Jorbey removed the offending garment and we stood shivering beside him, still half asleep. But push as we might, we could not shift the lorry and presently my aunt got out of the car and shouted 'try the crank handle.' My father handed it to Jorbey and after two or three ineffectual tries, the engine burst into life, and Jorbey removed the cherry-laden hat and stowed it with his overcoat.

'I'll take a run up the bank and you kids can hop on then,' said my father and we watched with open mouths as he accelerated and then breasted the hill. We ran after him, Jorbey seized Tom and heaved him on top of the tents and I scrambled up as best I could, leaving Jorbey panting behind. He ran around to his seat but as he tried to leap on my father accelerated slightly, to tease him I think, and he disappeared from my view. I heard the lorry as it crunched over something solid in the roadway and then the terrible cries from underneath the lorry. 'Mama, mama,' he screamed as the lorry came to a stop and my father leapt out of his seat. I heard him shout to Aunty Betty who had drawn up behind us. 'It's the bloody boy, he fell under the truck, give us a hand to get him out.' But Jorbey screamed and cried and my father knelt down, calling for a lamp or a light and then he stood up and said, 'He's broken his bloody leg.'

As we stood there, the whimpering stopped and I knelt down to look at Jorbey. He held his leg in both hands, his face was grey streaked with tear marks, his hair was dusty and his clothes were torn. 'Is it sore?' I asked. He started to cry again and I heard my father say 'Cut down some thick branches and let's get him out,' and while Jorbey screamed and sobbed, they pulled him out from under the lorry. Jack and Billy took an axe and cut down two saplings and my father, heedless of Jorbey's tortured cries, bound the broken leg between the two splints, using the net curtaining to tie it securely between the two poles.

When I looked again, Jorbey's head lolled to one side and his eyes were shut. 'Thank Gawd', said my father, 'he's fainted, so let's get him up before he comes around,' and they heaved and pushed until Jorbey was back in his seat, his head fallen back against the petrol tins, his mouth open and his leg straight before him resting on the bonnet of the lorry and wedged firmly against the headlight.

The engine was still running, car doors were slammed and the cavalcade moved on. My father struggled to keep the lorry on the road as it rattled and shook over the corrugations and then I saw Jorbey had opened his eyes and was looking about him. 'Water please, Inkoos,' he asked, but my father shook his head, saying, 'Can't stop, we gotter get you to hospital pretty soon,' and he squinted up his eyes as he peered ahead. 'I'm cold, Inkoos, can I have my coat,' Jorbey asked. 'What's he say?' asked my father, but I reached forward and pulled out the coat and draped it as best as I could from my position over the shivering boy. 'He's cold,' I told my father, but he looked grimly ahead, only turning to ask 'Is your aunty coming?' 'Yes', I said and then I asked, 'Can't you stop for just a minute so he can have a drink of water?' 'Shut up,' was the reply, 'I know what I'm bleedin' doing.'

The sun had risen and hung like a golden ball in the sky when we drew up at the garage in Enkeldoorn. Jorbey lay asleep or unconscious in his seat and we shivered as we peered around, but my father was asking the way to the hospital and a few minutes later, we drew up at the low red brick building. Aunty Betty was right behind and within minutes the door opened and two native orderlies sauntered out pushing a stretcher on to which they lifted Jorbey. His coat was draped over him when he opened his eyes and called out 'Can I have my hat please, Inkoos?' I jumped down from my perch and ran with it to him. 'Don't worry, you'll be all right,' I said, but he shook his head. 'I'm frightened, what will they do to me?' he asked. There was nothing I could say, I knew how afraid natives were of hospital, believing as they did that they would not come out alive and afraid of the white doctors and nurses, of what they would do to them, knowing that they possessed strong medicine which could make a man sleep as they wished. 'Don't be frightened,' I said again, and then I heard my father shout, 'We ain't got

184

all day, you know, get a move on.'

'I'm not staying here,' announced Uncle George. 'Nothing but bleedin' Dutchman everywhere, let's get back on the road and stop somewhere for a cuppa tea,' and we drew into the shade of a clump of blue gums on the side of the road out of the small town. Apart from the solitary youth at the petrol pump, we had seen no other sign of life, but prejudice was strong in Uncle George and he did not wish to have any dealing with the hated Boer.

Sticks and wood were soon gathered and tea brewed. Starchy-eyed and grumbling, Jack and Billy strolled off into the undergrowth with Tom following, and when everyone's needs had been met, we resumed our places and pressed on. We had left the savannah behind us and now drove through thick bush, the narrow, sandy road snaking ahead. Now and then we saw families of natives ahead of us carrying large bundles on their heads and leading their small children by the hand. At the sound of the approaching cars, they turned to look and then ran as fast as they could into the trees, away from the frightening noise of the motors.

Sometimes we passed native villages, the thatch of their huts silvery in the bright sunlight, the brown mud walls adorned with garishly painted symbols and always the thorn-bush kraal nearby, where they coralled their goats and cattle at night. The women hoed between their rows of mealies and pumpkins or gathered in groups to collect water from a distant river and their men sat under the tall trees, smoking and talking as they whiled away the day. Groups of adventurous picannins, braver than their parents, ran eagerly at the sound of the motor cars, to stand at the side of the road, arms outstretched and calling 'Penny inkoos?' as we swept past them.

Early in the afternoon, a halt was called; everyone was tired after the night's events and when we saw a line of trees ahead, we drew off the road and into the shade of the mimosa and wild acacia which grew thickly along the banks of a long, shallow pool which trickled away into a small stream. The men stood about wondering where to pitch the tents, bemoaning the absence of Jorbey, but at last the camp site was laid out, bottles of beer sunk into the cool shallows and a fire made to boil a kettle. It was cold as we stood around the fire eating our meal of bread and cold meat. No food could be cooked and the discomforts of travelling and camping without a servant to search for firewood, scrape off dirty plates and fetch water from the river, were all too apparent. As soon as we could Tom and I crawled into our blanket on our leafy bed and huddled together to get warm; the men stood around the dying

185

embers of the thorn bush fire, drinking beer and yarning before they turned in.

There had been little mention of Jorbey, no speculation as to his broken leg, and it was as though the accident had never happened. It all seemed like a fading dream but I could still hear his agonised screams and the pitiful crying for his mother as he lay in the dust under the lorry. Now my father and aunt were complaining at his ineptitude and carelessness in getting under the lorry, and all the blame was put on him. Poor Jorbey I thought, as I wondered what they had done to him in the hospital, and thought of the terror he must feel as he lay in such alien surroundings.

It was the next afternoon at sundown when we at last drew into Fort Victoria, on the edges of the low veldt. Men in faded khaki trousers and shirts lounged about on the verandahs of the few small shops, others drove donkey and ox carts along the sandy street and women in long cotton dresses and cloth kappies stood gossiping in groups, only pausing to eye our entourage with suspicion. Groups of half-clothed natives gathered to squat on their haunches to look at us; Tom and I, perched on the top of the stores on the lorry, listened to their excited chatter as we waited for the lemonades we had been promised when the family had filed into the dark little hotel for some much-needed refreshment.

A native waiter in a pair of tattered shorts and an old tweed waistcoat came out of the back of the hotel carrying a tray with our drinks, and as we drank them we tried to hear what the tribesmen were saying but the language was strange and we could not understand it. 'What is your name?' asked Tom addressing the foremost native who wore a breech clout and a very old tweed jacket, remarkably similar to the waiter's waistcoat. His face creased into a grin, showing the stumps of his blackened teeth and he spat expertly between his front teeth as he answered 'I am called Rice, Inkosi.' He gave Tom a mock salute. 'When did you learn to speak Shona?' asked Tom. 'You speak some other tongue we cannot understand.' The man shifted on his haunches, and conscious of the appraisal of his friends about him, he rose and said, 'I worked on a farm near Enkeldoorn for an Englishman but he died of the fever so I came back to my own people', and once more he squatted down amongst his friends. For some minutes we sat and looked at them and then he asked, 'Do you travel far, Inkosi?' 'No,' said Tom. 'We are going to Zimbabwe ruins, we are many people and the others are in the hotel.' All eyes turned to confirm this fact as my aunt and her party emerged, refreshed and in better temper.

186

'Clear off you lot,' cried my father as he regained his seat. 'Always talking to bloody niggers, first chance you kids get,' and he paused to light a cigarette, flicking the spent match at the retreating party of natives. 'Friends of yours I suppose,' he added. And then a sudden thought struck him. 'Don't suppose he wants a job for the next two weeks?' he asked. 'Run after them, and ask that big chap you were talking to, if he can come with us. Could show us the way too,' and he dismounted and went off to speak to Aunty Betty, while Tom and I scrambled down from our perch and ran after the tribesmen.

'Rice,' we called at the retreating backs, 'Rice, come back, we need someone to show us the way and to work for us for two weeks.' He disengaged himself from his friends who wandered off towards the bush, and accompanied us back to the cars. 'Can you show us the road to Zimbabwe?' we were told to ask, 'And how much pay do you want? You have to fetch water for us, make the fires, look after the camp and clear up, and we've got mealie meal for you.' Rice rubbed his chin for several seconds and then replied. 'If the Inkoos pays me ten shillings I will come with you. But my blanket is with my brother. Wait while I fetch it,' and he disappeared to the native quarters which huddled in the back yard of the hotel.

He was engaged for the fortnight and although my aunt complained about his breech clout and the rank smell which hung about him like an aura, he added to the enjoyment of the short holiday. He took us with him into the bush to gather wood and showed us the baobabs which stood like up-ended trees, their branches strangely root-like, bare and spindly, with foetid pools of water in the forks of the branches which he told us elephants came to drink; he was much in awe of the ruins and trod quietly and spoke in hushed tones as he led us around the high wall which encircled the main temple. He led us through the bush up to the Acropolis which stood high on the towering heights of a vast granite kopje, from where we could see as far as the horizon, but he gave us no explanation as to the origin of this mighty edifice or of its ancient history. The ruins had always been there, he said, since many years before his father's father's time. He showed us the bare slopes of the granite boulders and pointed to where the blocks of stone had been cut, and he led us along low tunnels which connected the decayed village to the main temple.

Tom and I spent most of each day with Rice. There was no river nearby and we were puzzled about the buckets of water he produced each morning; he took us down a steep slope into the thicker bush and

187

pointed to a group of thick, lush ferns growing at the base of a large stone; he bent down and scraped away the damp earth and instantly the water bubbled up from a spring, clear and sparkling. 'Drink,' he said as we leaned down to scoop the cold water into our hands. He showed us where to find marulas, that acrid fruit which grew in such abundance and which lay rotting and fly-covered under the shady trees, and he told us of the herds of elephants, lured by the pungent odour of the fruit, who came thundering through the bush at midday to feast on the fermenting mass. They got drunk, he said, and staggered around the bush, colliding with trees and each other before falling into heaps to sleep off their drunkenness. 'That is the time the men of my tribe creep through the bush with our spears and kill one for our people. We have little meat and one elephant feeds many people. We hang the meat we cannot eat right away in the branches of the trees until it is dried, and we take it to our kraals where we know we have food for many months,' and he grinned at the thought of such munificence.

The family sat about the encampment under the trees, reading or having read to them the saved-up English newspapers and periodicals, and drinking from the diminishing crates of beer. Sandwiches were hastily made up from the fast-drying bread and shrivelling slices of cold meat bought from the butcher shop in Fort Victoria, and at nights platefuls of stew were passed around. Trips to the distant town, which took most of the day, were organised to replenish the stocks of beer and food, and some days scrawny chickens were purchased from passing tribesmen and stewed in the big pot over the wood fire. During the afternoons everyone slept on their improvised beds and in the early evening Aunty Betty and her family gently strolled over to look up at the Acropolis, tripping over the rough terrain in their high-heeled shoes and best boots but declining to go any nearer. 'Just a lot of old stones from Gawd knows where,' remarked my father. 'The Phoenicians built these,' I volunteered. 'In our books at school we read all about it. The Queen of Sheba lived somewhere here and it was called the Land of Ophir; people came from far away to buy the gold they had found here, and slaves too. Do you see those palm trees over there?' and I pointed to the distance where two such trees rose above the others, incongruous among the baobab, iron-wood and mopani. 'When you get to the top of the Acropolis, you can see clumps of those palms right to the horizon and Rice says that's where the Arab slave traders led their bands of slaves. They ate dates as they went along and dropped the stones and the trees sprang up along their route. They're foreign to this country and came from Arabia.' They looked at me open-mouthed and I was suddenly surprised at my own loquacity.

'Garn,' said my father, 'you're making it up.' Suppressed giggles from Stella and Billy added to my embarrassment but I had not finished. 'That place that's called the temple was really a market place and the round huts outside the wall were slave pits. Buyers waited in the temple area and the slaves were driven through the tunnels into the open market so that the Arabs could look them over. They also brought gold here to sell to the traders, and that's why it was called the Land of Ophir and this is where the Queen of Sheba ruled.'

'Gaw,' exclaimed Uncle George 'don't she know a lot?' 'Most of it I read in my school book but Rice also told me that people were bought and sold here long ago, so it must be true. His own people also knew about it from a long time ago.' Stunned silence greeted this outburst but it was not enough to tempt the party to explore the ruins any further.

'Why are you called Rice,' I asked the tribesman as he squatted on the ground, chopping wood for the fire. 'It's a silly name for a man,' I said, but he merely grinned and said he had first tasted rice when he worked for the English Inkoos at Enkeldoorn, and had liked it so much, he had decided to keep the name for himself. His real name was Nkulundi, he said, but the Englishman had not been able to pronounce it properly so Rice had suited them both.

The days crept by and soon it was time to return to Salisbury. Last minute forays were made to look once more at the ancient pile which lay about us and at the top of the steep kopje but my father dismissed the theory I had put forward. 'No bleedin' niggers could have built that lot,' he said contemptuously, 'they ain't got the brains and I ain't never seen any nigger work hard.' He could not be persuaded that our history books were true, nor could he offer any solution of his own to this phenomenon. The lorry was loaded, the left-over provisions given to Rice with his fee of ten shillings and last minute visits paid to the latrine he had dug, and then we were off. Tom and I waved to him as he stood there in the early morning and he raised his arm in farewell as we swept out of sight.

My aunt could not face the thought of another night's camping, so when we reached Fort Victoria, three rooms were booked at the only hotel: two for the men and one for Aunty Betty, Stella and me to share. 'A good wash, a decent bed and some better grub than them sandwiches and stews we been eating, and sleeping on the ground like kaffirs,' announced my aunt. 'No more camping for me.'

After dinner the family gravitated to the verandah for their beers; Uncle George puffed contentedly at his cigarette, happy at last to be going home where everything was orderly and clean and comfortable. He leaned forward and blinked at me. ' 'Ere, d'ye really think it was them niggers who built them ruins?' he asked. 'The school books say it was the Phœnicians who did, but they may have been the same as the natives,' I replied. 'D'ye mean them Fernishins were black like kaffirs?' he asked. 'I don't know, they might have been,' I answered.

'You're a proper know-all,' burst out Billy, 'you think you know everything, don't you?' 'I know a lot more than you do about it,' I replied, realising that I was heading for trouble, but unable to stop myself. 'Just because you read all those books you get from Mrs Samuels, you think you're cleverer than anyone else,' he said, 'but you're just a stupid girl and you don't know nothink.' He arose from his seat and came towards me. 'I'm not stupid and I don't always come last in class,' I retorted; somebody laughed and I heard Uncle George's chuckle from where he sat. 'Ma,' cried Billy, 'listen to her,' and he raised his fist.

'You just say you're sorry this minute,' cried the enraged Aunty Betty, but I rose from my seat on the floor and left the verandah, banging the door behind me as hard as I could. 'Come back here,' she ordered 'come back and say you're sorry at once,' but I ignored her and went into the bedroom. I undressed and crept into the foot end of the bed which I was to share with Stella, and lay there listening to the thumping of my heart and wondering why I had acted so defiantly.

I thought of the many menial tasks Tom and I had had to perform. At every stop, we had gathered wood from the bush, made fires, boiled kettles, blown on the damp wood until our eyes streamed. We fetched water and cleaned plates and loaded and unloaded the lorry. When there had been a puncture we were first off our perches to find the tools and crept under the cars to scrape away the earth so that the jack could find a steady hold; we fetched basins and filled them from the water bags so that the inflated tube could be immersed and then we mended the punctures, blowing on the sticky solution to dry it before the patch could be applied. When the tube had at last been inserted into the tyre, we were told to tighten the bolts and to apply ourselves to the handpump so that we could limp into the nearest garage where the services of a compressed air pump could be found. No spares were carried and any breakdown was dealt with by Jack but no other member of the family was willing to dirty their hands while Tom and I scurried about looking for pieces of abandoned wire, a nail or anything which could be used to effect a repair.

As these thoughts tumbled through my mind, and just as I was getting my breath back, the door was flung open. 'Just what d'ye think you're doing?' cried Aunty Betty. 'Go and say you're sorry to Billy this very minute, yer bleedin' toe-rag, or else you'll cop it.' 'There's nothing for me to say sorry for,' I replied defiantly. 'I didn't say anything that wasn't true.' She leant forward and pulled the blanket away shouting, 'If you don't say sorry this minute, you can go and sleep in the lorry, I'm not putting up with a cheeky kid like you.'

Without a word, I got out of bed, picked up my dress and knickers and stalked out to the lorry standing under the jacaranda trees. I climbed up and burrowed under the tents and stores; but for a long time I lay listening to the thumping of my heart, beginning to wish I had not spoken as I had.

'To the Sacred Memory of those Settlers Killed in the Matabeleland Rebellion 1896' read the inscription at the intersection of two dusty roads, and few people were about. My aunt and her family were having their breakfast in the hotel dining room, but I had escaped when I realised no one had said a word about my behaviour of the night before; I was to be ignored.

I looked up to the tower where the bell hung, silenced since that day so many years ago when the Matabele hordes had swept down from the hills to slaughter the settlers in the fort while their men filled the water barrels down at the river and the herders tended to the livestock on the Outspan. I read the names of the men, black and white, and of their women and children, and I shivered as I slowly retraced my steps to the hotel verandah.

'If you're quite ready we can start,' shouted my father sarcastically, and I ran to clamber up next to Tom. 'They're cross with you,' he said. 'You should have heard what they were saying at breakfast time.' 'I don't care,' I replied recklessly. 'One of these days I'm going to run away.' 'When you do,' said Tom, 'I'm coming with you. But where will you go?' Where indeed, I thought to myself, there is nowhere else I could go; and to change the subject I asked, 'Do you think we'll stop at Enkeldoorn and ask if Jorbey can come back with us?' He looked at me in astonishment. 'They've already forgotten about him.'

We sped through Enkeldoorn but there were still a hundred miles to travel before we got back to Salisbury. Tom and I made the fire as before when we stopped under the familiar blue gums, filled the kettle from a small pool in the river bed and made the tea while everyone else sat about in the shade or strolled down to the river.

'Come down to the river with me,' said my father, 'I've gotter speak to you.' Still defiant about my treatment of the night before, I followed him, and when we reached the sandy river bed, he sat on a dead tree trunk and asked 'What am I going to do with you? We're all fed up with you, the way you speak to your aunt. You're getting too big for yer bleedin' boots, you are, and it's got to stop. Aunty Betty's given you a good home, but it won't be for much longer if you go on like this, she won't put up with it, you're getting too damned cheeky,' and he aimed a glob of spit at a lizard scurrying by.

I thought of all the menial tasks Tom and I did at home and which had been our lot on this holiday trip, fetching and carrying for them as though we were the household servants, while my sister and cousins ordered us about. Perhaps if we'd been black like Vinyu, Jorbey and the other servants we would not have minded, but we were not black. We were white, yet we were treated so differently. I thought, too, of our situation in the family home; we took our meals in the kitchen and had to wait there until invited into the sitting room, if anyone remembered to. We were not allowed to touch the bowls of fruit and sweets on the verandah tables; our meals were different and sometimes not enough, and cakes and puddings were only for those who ate in the dining room. Perhaps that was the price Tom and I had to pay for a roof over our heads, but why was there any distinction? But what I resented most was the problem of my clothes. I wore cast-offs whether they fitted or not and only when Stella left school and passed her uniforms on to me, did I have enough.

I turned all these grievances over in my mind but did not speak about them. It was useless. Suddenly I realised I had not answered my father. 'Billy is allowed to say anything he likes, whether it's true or not,' I said. 'Nobody defends me but what I said was true. He always comes last in class, and can barely read and copies from other boys.' My father rose from his seat, and began to walk away.

'You're going to have to change your ways my girl,' he said. 'Yer aunt won't put up with yer nonsense much longer. Now run along and get us a cuppa tea and two sugars.'

* * *

192

'We've been to Zimbabwe Ruins,' I told Mrs Gibbs later when I went to see the girls before my return to school. 'That's nice, cookie,' she replied off-handedly and I could see she wasn't really listening to me. 'Did you go to your farm?' I asked. 'No dear, not this time. Run along and find the girls, they're somewhere in the orchard,' and she turned away to her sitting-room. But the girls were quiet and subdued too, and did not seem interested in all I had to tell them.

'Is something the matter?' I asked, wondering if they'd heard about my quarrel with my aunt. Edith looked at her little sister and asked, 'Shall I tell?' It was Muriel who burst out: 'Reenie Smith shot her dad the other night.' 'Dead?' I asked. 'Is he dead?' 'No,' replied Edith. 'Reenie shot him through his neck, he was trying to kill her mommy, and had her head between the bars of their bedhead. Reenie heard her mom crying and she ran back to her room, fetched her pistol and shot her father to make him stop. He fell off the bed onto the floor, and there was blood everywhere.' This last piece of information seemed particularly gratifying but I was struck with horror at the thought of Reenie trying to kill her father.

'What happened then?' I asked, 'did the police come? Is Mrs Smith all right?' But the girls knew no more; their father had quickly silenced his wife when she had brought the story to the dinner table, and he had forbidden any further discussion of the topic in his home. 'You run home and ask your cook, he'll know, his brother is Mrs Smith's cook,' said Edith and without pausing to say goodbye to their mother, I ran home.

'Why did Miss Reenie try to kill her father?' I asked Vinyu when I found him sitting on the back doorstep, cutting up vegetables for dinner. 'Why was he trying to kill his wife?' I asked. 'Who told you?' he asked and I told him I had been to see the Gibbs girls. 'Was the Inkoos Smith drunk? Is he dead?' I persisted. Vinyu spat through his teeth. 'I do not know but it is a bad business. He came home on Sunday just like he always does and when he saw the Inkossikaas sitting in the garden with that Mr Reynolds, he started to shout and swear. You know the man I mean, he is always at their house and I do not think he has a wife of his own. Mr Reynolds was angry too and when he left, Mrs Smith went into the house and she spoke harsh words to her husband. Miss Reenie was in her bedroom when her father began to beat his wife so she called to the two little ones to fetch the milk from the cowshed and then she ran into the bedroom to stop her father. He had the Inkossikaas' head through the bars of the bedhead and was choking her. Miss Reenie ran

193

back to her room, took the pistol and shot her father. The bullet went through his neck, but he was not killed. But he was badly wounded.' Vinyu shook his head in disapproval and spat on the ground.

'My brother says he saw that gun many times when he put clothes away, but I am sure he never thought that the young madam would try to kill her father.' He shook his head in disbelief. 'Did she mean to kill him?' I asked. 'What's going to happen to her now? Do you think she will have to go to jail?' 'I think she is already there, she had gone from the house.' He was quiet for a few moments and then went on. 'My brother ran to the policeman's house, Inkoos Austin, and told him what had taken place. The policeman got in his car and with the boys' help, they got Mr Smith into the car and he was taken to hospital in town. When they came back, Inkoos Austin asked Mrs Smith and Reenie to tell what had happened, but they could not. They were crying so much they could not speak properly, so Inkoos Austin took the other children, Roma and the little brother Binkie to his own home for his wife to look after. My weh, there is bad trouble.' He paused to scratch his head. 'The next day the policeman came back with another policeman and they took Reenie away with them. They told her mother that she would be charged with murder,' and he picked up the dish of vegetables and went into the kitchen.

My blood froze at the thought of my beautiful idol in a convict's dress emblazoned with big black arrows, handcuffs on those delicate wrists where Mortimer had so often balanced unsteadily, her lustrous red hair cut short and those sparkling green eyes reddened from crying for what she had done. 'What about the Inkossikaas?' I asked. 'She is there, in the house but she will not speak to those who knock on her door,' said Vinyu. 'My brother told me that the Inkoos Smith was not badly hurt and that he will come home soon,' and he raised his eyes to heaven as he speculated what might happen then.

The whole settlement was agog with the dreadful occurrence and many notes were sent with equally curious houseboys from one house to another for the latest bulletin. But Reenie was not to return to her home again; in due time she was acquitted of the charge and late one afternoon she arrived with a girl friend from town, to collect her clothes and to speak to her mother. Had she taken Mortimer H. Smith with her, I wondered? She was going to live in one of the many boarding houses in the avenues, and I hoped there would be a convenient bush near her window so that she could look out and speak to Mortimer H., as he groped his way through the foliage, his eyes swivelling as his long tongue darted out to catch a fly.

Roma and Binkie were returned to their parents and soon Mrs Smith appeared in the garden, snipping at the dead roses or tying up creepers and giving orders to her staff. Mr Smith, his neck heavily bandaged, sat on the verandah watching his wife, before stirring himself to take a walk down to the river. I watched him as he went, in his white suit and topee, swinging his walking stick as he swiped at the black-jack weeds in his path. But no one spoke to him. Had he not tried to kill his wife and caused his elder daughter the anguish of an arrest for attempted murder? How often had she witnessed attacks on her mother and for what reason did she possess a deadly pistol so readily available? No one thought to question Mr Reynolds' part in the affair or to wonder why he was such a frequent visitor. It was common knowledge that Mr Smith worked shift hours, returning home late at night, and Mr Reynolds's trap was often seen parked at the side of the cowshed even when Mr Smith had been at work.

With the other homesteaders, Aunty Betty called upon the luckless Mrs Smith, ostensibly to commiserate with her but hoping to hear even more details of that awful night. 'No Bet, it's nobody's business but Albert's and mine,' she would say. 'I don't want to talk about it, it's been a rotten time for us and the sooner we all forget about it the better.' She ignored all the questions, smiling sweetly and diverting the conversation, and if her husband still returned drunk on Sunday afternoons, nobody ever knew. To all intents and purposes the matter was best forgotten, but around the beautiful Mrs Smith there always remained an aura of mystery and temptation and the thought that another man had found her desirable.

When I knocked on my aunt's bedroom door to say I was leaving to return to school, she called me in and asked me to sit down, she wanted to speak to me. 'How are you getting back?' she asked. 'I'm walking and one of the garden boys is taking my trunk,' I told her. 'Same as I always do,' I added wondering why I had been summoned. 'You won't be coming for the next holidays,' she said 'Mrs Samuels has asked if you can go to them. Can't think why she wants a toe-rag like you.' I stood there and said nothing, I had heard that expression so often it no longer bothered me and I wanted to leave as soon as I could. 'It's something to do with another girl she's having, some other kid from the Girls High. So try to behave and don't let us down and don't get too big for your boots.

She reached for her purse and took out a half-crown which she handed to me, saying, 'Here's a little something for you to spend, don't want her to think you're going empty-handed.'

I had left the agonies and embarrassments of puberty behind me, explained and dealt with by the Infirmary Sister, a kind, gentle nun who seemed surprised that I had not known of the change which was taking place. 'You have an older sister, haven't you?' she asked. 'Did she not tell you?' 'No,' I replied, 'nobody told me anything.' 'Poor child,' was her only comment.

It was the sight of Porteous at the Convent gate which greeted me when I ran around to the visitor's parlour where Mrs Samuels sat in the quiet of the little room, speaking to the duty Sister. She rose when I came in, and having bobbed a curtsey, I followed her out to the car. As Porteous shut the door, I saw sitting in the corner seat a girl in High School uniform, pretty with her long brown hair held back by an Alice-band, her blue eyes sparkling. She leaned forward and said 'Hullo, I'm Betty.'

'I hope you two are going to be friends,' said Mrs Samuels. 'You'll be good company for each other during the holidays.' Betty's face creased into smiles and as I looked at her I realised she was everything I was not: vivacious, well-dressed and very sure of herself. We were to share a bedroom and I envied her her pretty clothes, her nightgown case, her silk dressing gown emblazoned with a snarling red dragon breathing fire and her bag with her hairbrushes and combs, all marked with her initials in silver.

'Did you only bring those few things with you?' she asked as I hastily stuffed my clothes into a drawer. 'If you haven't got enough, you can try some of mine, we're the same size and you can borrow anything you like.' I lay on her bed as she brought out her dresses one by one and I admired the matching necklaces and clip-on ear-rings, the hats with their little net veils and bows and her high-heeled shoes. 'How old are you?' I asked. 'Fourteen and a half,' she replied. 'I know you think my clothes are far too old for me; Mrs Sam does, but my daddy lets me buy anything I like and he says nothing's too good for me.' She said it without a trace of superiority but I suddenly felt out of place and wished I had not come.

'Mrs Sam told me that your mother is dead, is that true?' she asked. 'Yes,' I replied without hesitation. 'You poor thing, I thought I was unlucky; my mother ran away with her boy-friend, at first I used to miss her but my dad made up for her going, and now I don't mind any more.

Sometimes I spend a holiday with her and my step-father and they take me out with them when they go dancing; I like Phil, he says I mustn't call him dad, my own father is that, so I call him Phil. He's nice.' And she crinkled up her face as she fell back on her bed laughing. 'You should see me when I'm dressed up at nights, I wear a long dress and all my jewellery. Old men come and ask me to dance and my mother lets me. It's fun, but I don't tell my dad, he wouldn't like it, he says I will have nothing to look forward to if I do everything now when I'm young.'

How I envied Betty's complete lack of inhibition and her honesty, and I wished I could have been as honest as she was. What would she say if I told her that my mother, too, had run away with a boy-friend, but that we had all pretended she was dead because my father had minded what people would say? What would she say if I told her that I had been brought up by native servants and had been treated as one? Perhaps I would tell her when I knew her better.

'Your dress is so pretty,' said Mrs Samuels to Betty at dinner that evening, 'but if you don't mind my saying so, dear, it's rather grown-up for a girl of your age, don't you agree?' Betty glanced down at her dark orange crepe gown which reached her ankles, cinched in by a broad turquoise belt which matched perfectly her heavy bead necklace and her high-heeled shoes. 'Shall I change quickly?' she asked but I did not miss the look which passed between them as Mrs Samuels slid her eyes over me, sitting there in my best school Sunday dress and black lace-up shoes. 'Better still,' she said, 'you have so many pretty dresses, why don't you lend our friend one of them. I think your shoes would fit her too, run along and see what you can do.'

We rushed out as the cook returned the dishes to keep warm in the kitchen and half an hour later, we both entered the dining room to the loud greetings of the two sons and many admiring looks from our host and hostess. I wore Betty's white linen dress and shoes and had knotted a red chiffon scarf around my neck, but I clutched at the chairs and sideboard as I tried to master the high-heels. From then on, we wore our plain cotton dresses by day and spent many hours debating our ensemble for the evening as we lay on a rug under the trees, playing the Samuels' gramophone records; we became friends and knew that we would see each other at the weekly tennis or hockey matches at our schools, and we both looked forward to the next holiday we would spend together.

When I returned to Aunty Betty's at the end of the year, I found Tom had been in bed for many weeks with a broken ankle. 'What happened?'

197

I asked as I looked at him, pale and drawn, dark circles under his eyes. 'Did you have an accident?' Yes, he told me, he had fallen over some rocks when he'd gone to find a tennis ball on one of the Saturday afternoon matches which took place regularly throughout the dry weather. He had felt the pain in his leg getting worse and had then fainted as he ran to pick up a ball for the players. Throughout that night, the next day and night he had stayed in bed, quietly crying from the pain in his fast swelling leg, and when my father called early on the Monday morning to give Tom a note for school, he had found his little son in agony. Without pausing to dress him or to ask why nothing had been done, he picked Tom up and drove him to the hospital where his leg was set in a plaster of Paris cast. He had stayed there for a week and was fetched home and put to bed where he had been lying ever since.

Vinyu brought him his meals and washed him, and once a day our aunt put her head around the door to ask if he was all right, but at nights he could not sleep and lay in bed crying, wishing he had not spent so much of the day asleep, but he had nothing to read and no one to speak to. The servants had their work to do and he saw no one. One night Jack had heard Tom crying and had gone in to see if he could comfort him, asking 'Is your leg hurting?' 'No,' said Tom, 'I've been awake for ages and can't go to sleep.'

'I'll wake my mom and see if she's got something she can give you.' said Jack and presently Tom heard their voices and their tip-toeing down the passage into the kichen. Aunty Betty came into his room carrying three bottles of beer and glasses and as quietly as they could, they sat there sharing the beer out between the three of them, making sure Tom drank most of the beer. He fell asleep and woke up the next morning alarmed he said 'with a terrible headache and a funny taste in my mouth – but I liked the beer.'

From that day until many weeks later, he was given two or three bottles of beer at night, and when the doctor came to remove the cast, he was surprised to see his patient looking so pale and shaky. 'Can't understand it at all,' said Doctor Harworth. 'He seems to have had a fever, but he has no temperature and his eyes are clear and there's no spleen.' He rubbed his hands together and as he went to the doorway, he said, 'It's the nearest thing I've seen to a good old hangover. Very strange,' but Tom looked at him innocently and asked 'Can I get up soon?' Vinyu brought one of the garden boys' little sons to play with Tom when he had carried him out to sit in the shade of the pamplemousse tree, and when he felt strong enough Tom leant on the picannin and gradually he regained the use of his leg.

Now that I was back, we began to make plans to run away, and when I head of his nights of drunken sleep, I was more determined than ever that we should do so before the big rains set in. 'Where shall we go?' we asked each other. Should we walk along the railway line to Rusape and to Grandma and Grandpa Williaams? Would they have forgiven me for my rudeness to them those ages ago when they called to see us at school? Or perhaps we should walk to our old home and look for Jim in the bush. But I could barely recollect where Jim's kraal was or what he looked like, and I had forgotten his patronymic and would not know how to ask for him.

Plans were turned over and over again. The walk of over a hundred mile to Rusape was abandoned. There might be lions or wild dogs along our route and the journey would take too long on foot and what would we eat? 'I haven't got much money, only ninepence,' Tom confessed. 'I got it the last time I fagged tennis balls. What about you?' 'I've got the half crown I took to Mrs Samuel's and didn't spend.' We thought of nothing else and eventually decided to hoard as much food as we could without anyone noticing and to walk to the railway station and get aboard the south mail train. We would hide in the lavatory, we decided, and try to avoid the conductor if possible, but we did not pause to think what would happen after that. The fact that we would be returned to Aunty Betty or placed in a Children's Home did not deter us, nor did we think of the punishment we would have to suffer.

The hoarding of food was as difficult as deciding on our destination. We were always hungry and it was impossible to save anything from our meals, except bread; that dried and went mouldy. We fed it surreptitiously to Billy's white mice, seeing our chances of escape vanishing before our eyes. Then I had a brain-wave. 'Let's ask Mother Prioress if we can go to the orphanage at Emerald Hill,' I suggested. 'But it's only for Catholics,' said Tom scornfully. 'No, we'll have to get on a train.'

When one of the garden boys called us to go with them to make an ishwa trap, this seemed to be the solution to all our worries about the food we could take with us. Ishwa were delicious, took up little space and could be hidden in our school bags, we decided; we ran off into the bush, following the men with their hoes and the sheets of corrugated iron they had filched from the back of the garage.

Each anthill we passed was carefully inspected. Josiah tapped the chimney which rose high above the hill with his knuckles, and then placed his ear against the wall, to listen. At last he found one to his liking

199

and the boys set to with their spades. From the anthill, they dug a narrow channel at right angles out to about ten feet, and at the bottom of the ditch they buried an old paraffin tin from which they had removed the lid. The ditch was covered with the sheets of corrugated iron, and earth and leaves were piled on top. The one other exit, the chimney, was blocked with a handful of mud.

'We will come back tomorrow at sun-down,' they said, knowing that when they did so, the tin buried in the channel would be full of wingless termites. They hatched in their millions in the depths of the hill and when the time came, they would fly out towards the light of the day, but this time their only exit was covered. As the termites flew about, they saw the small opening which had been left at the end of the ditch just above the tin. In their haste to seek the sunlight, they struggled towards the light, but as they jostled to get out of the narrow opening, most of them fell back, losing their wings as they did so. Josiah and his mates would pull out the tin and take their prize to the compound where the ants would be spread over sheets of iron and roasted over the fires. 'Ishwa' was the cry we heard, and Tom and I took hands and ran to join the labourers around their fire and to share the prize. 'Can we have some to take home?' we asked and we filled the paper bag we had brought, saying, 'We'll share them with the others,' but we had no intention of doing so. They were our stores for our getaway and we did not pause to remember that most Europeans despised the native food and would make us throw the ishwa away. 'Don't tell anyone about this,' we urged each other as we hid the bag in the rafters of the garage, and our spirits lifted at the thought of our coming adventure, thought about for so long but not planned carefully enough so that it was doomed to failure.

'Hurry, your father wants to see you', said Vinyu as we scrubbed the mud from our legs in the small bathroom. 'He's waiting on the verandah.' My father rose from his chair and dismissed me, saying, 'Clear orf, it's Tom I've come to see,' and he put his arm around Tom's shoulders and led him into the garden.

For a long time, they walked about, up and down between the flower beds and shrubs, and then with a wave and cheerio, my father left. 'What did he say to you,' I asked Tom. 'Does he know about us running away?' 'No,' said Tom, 'I'm not going back to school next year, Dad's made arrangements for me to go to Capetown and join the General Botha.' 'What's that?' I asked anxiously. 'It's the training ship for the Merchant Marine,' he said gleefully and then he burst out laughing. 'I'm going to be a sailor.' 'Do you want to?' I asked, seeing all my plans dissolve before me. 'Anything to get away from here,' he said. 'Aren't I lucky?' Lucky indeed, I thought ruefully, but why had my father made this sudden decision without consulting Tom?

Did he want to separate us because I was a bad influence over my brother? Or had he at last realised how badly Tom was treated in this house, where he was constantly bullied and reminded that he was of no account. Perhaps my father noticed more than I had given him credit for. But, I pondered, perhaps he and Aunty Betty had made plans for both of us, and Tom's were the first to be announced. What was going to happen to me?

My father took Tom into town and bought him the necessary clothes and trunk, and a few days later a second-class ticket to Capetown, two thousand miles away. He tied a label with his name and destination in the button hole of his new tweed jacket and gave him ten shillings and a book of meal and bedding tickets for the four day train journey; we stood, uncomfortable and self-conscious, on the station platform, envying Tom this great adventure, and when the second bell rang he kissed us all goodbye. 'I'll see you at Easter,' he called and we stood and waved at the retreating train until it had rounded the bend near the railway bridge and disappeared towards the industrial site where new factories had been built. Will I still be here at Easter I wondered?

When I was back at school Stella came to see me on her bicycle and said as she was leaving; 'Don't mind about Tom, he wrote and said he likes the training ship and has made friends with the other boys. He's coming back at Easter.' But my own future was very uncertain, and although I was in the senior class at school, nothing more had been said about what would happen at the end of the year.

I would be fifteen then, and I nursed a half-hearted desire to go to University, having listened avidly when the girls in my class disclosed their plans to do so. But as the year drew to a close, I was called to the Head of Studies Office. 'Has your father said what he wants you to do?' asked Mother Frances. 'No,' I replied, 'but I will ask him when he comes to fetch me and he can tell you then,' I suggested. 'Well,' she said after a pause, 'you have a year in hand and should ideally stay in your class for that year until you are sixteen. Would your father not like to send you to University?' she asked. 'I don't really know,' I answered. 'It would be too expensive for him, I don't think he could afford it.' I knew it would be a miracle for him even to discuss it.

201

'What next!' said my father when he called for one of his infrequent visits. 'You go to University?' and he threw back his head and burst out laughing. 'Now I've heard everything; I suppose you think me name's Rockefeller or King George,' and he wiped away the tears of laughter from his cheeks. 'No, my girl,' he continued, 'you can learn shorthand and typing like your sister done and get a job and learn what it costs to keep yourself, then you'll see what I've had to put up with all these bleedin' years.'

'But I don't want to learn shorthand and typing, I want to learn Latin and Greek and all those other languages and get a degree,' I begged. He leaned forward to switch on the ignition, indicating he wished to leave and that the matter was settled. 'Oh you do, do you? While I slog me guts out keeping you at school and university for the next I don't know how many years? Talk about selfish!' He pressed the self-starter and put the lorry into gear. 'Forget all them ideas,' he admonished me. 'Yer want to knuckle down and do a bit of work, same like we have to, not spend three years larking about at a university.' He drove off in a cloud of dust, leaving me standing there wondering what I was going to do.

Everything then seemed to happen at once. Mother Frances wrote to my father asking him to call to discuss my future and Mrs Rule called me aside at the end of a hockey practice. 'I want to put you up for the Mashonaland Trials,' she said. 'They will be held here in Salisbury next month and I'd very much like to put a schoolgirl's name forward; you are my best prospect, so please ask your father for the pound entrance fee.' This last request plunged me into despair, but I asked him. 'D'ye think I'm made of money?' he asked. I stood silent. 'I've just told Mother Frances I can't afford to send you to University but she has agreed to let you stay for another year. You can learn shorthand-typing in the Commercial class and stay as a boarder. But as for the hockey trials, forget it.'

'It's only a pound for the entrance fee,' I persisted. 'But it won't stop there will it?' he asked. 'There'll be a new gym slip, and a decent blazer, and Gawd knows what else, and money to spend too I suppose,' and he rubbed his chin as he contemplated his latest problem. 'Nah, I just can't afford it, better drop out,' he suggested.

I was bitterly disappointed but Mrs Rule was not easily deterred and said, 'Leave it to me, you'll play if it's the last thing I say' and she made her way into the school office. Several minutes later she emerged smiling and gave me the thumbs-up sign as she cycled out of the gate onto the main road. 'See you on Thursday,' she called as she pedalled away.

'Who give you the money for this caper?' asked my father when he

202

confronted me in the parlour the following month. He shook the sports page of the weekly paper at me and demanded 'Did yer borrer it?' 'No,' I told him, 'Mrs Rule arranged it all with the school, they paid because it's the first time a schoolgirl has been chosen and they were so pleased. It was a grant from a special fund usually only given to the Catholic girls.' 'Well don't go away with the idea that I'm paying any of it back. Strewth! Six bleedin' pounds for a stick, a skirt and a blazer; blimey, wish they'd reduce their fees instead of wasting it on bleedin' hockey matches.'

The decision to embark on a secretarial course did not meet with Mother Frances's approval. 'I'm disappointed in you,' she told me. 'I thought there may have been a spark of ambition somewhere in you, but I see I'm wrong.' I was ashamed that she should feel this way and wondered if she knew of the heavy backlog of fees which stood against my name. But Mother Frances did not concern herself with such earthly matters, her main concern was the academic excellence of the school and her own pathway to Heaven. 'My father says he can't afford to keep me at school and university and it's out of the question,' I repeated. 'I cannot tell you how sorry I am that he has such a poor opinion of your scholastic progress,' she said sighing heavily and escorting me to the door. 'I pray you won't regret this missed chance. You are not material for office work, and another four years would enable you to mature, if you went to university. Your sister was a different matter, she had no interests here and was quite grown up for her age.' She looked me up and down as she said it, but I answered, 'It's no use, my father's mind is made up.' We parted with a chilly kiss on the cheek and a bobbed curtsey.

With the abandonment of a scholastic career, I threw myself into the mysteries of shorthand and book-keeping and the frustrations of touch-typing as we sat together over our pseudo-office tables in the old school chapel, away from the academic block. Girls from the town joined us, their parents wisely deciding that the fees would be cheaper than those of that elegant establishment where Stella had spent a year; and where there would be strict discipline. The day girls came in their pretty dresses and high-heeled shoes, disdaining those of us still in school uniform, but when Sister Amata left us to say her daily office, we sat about gossiping and listening to their chatter about their boy friends, the new O.K. Bazaar which had opened in town, the coming 'talkies', their dress patterns and what they would wear to the bioscope on Saturday night.

Once again bargains were made; explanations of pot-hooks, line-positions, and the intricacies of the Trial Balance and the Profit and Loss account, in exchange for the contents of their lunch tins and tattered copies of *La Vie Parisienne* smuggled in to the country from Moçambique, and for full blooded descriptions of the Saturday night movie. But I still clung to my old school books and read and re-read my set books of last year.

I made friends with Olive, a newcomer to our school and some years older than the rest of us. She was strikingly pretty, her skin the colour of ivory, her hair like a spun gold helmet and with the blackest eyes I had ever seen. 'Is your hair really that colour?' I asked and she told me she dyed it with a mixture of peroxide and ammonia and that her mother helped her. She persuaded me to play truant and to accompany her to the Wednesday matinee at the Palace Cinema, offering to pay. When I met her at the cinema, we ran into the lavatory where I removed my shirt and gymfrock, put on one of Olive's old dresses and stuffed my school hat into her bag; and feeling less like criminals we sank into our seats to enjoy the film.

We were sharing an icecream at the interval when I heard a voice behind me, ask, 'Aren't you Bill Sadler's daughter?' I turned, horrified to be found out so soon, and looked into Sister Hulley's face. 'Are you allowed out of school on weekdays?' she asked, her eyes taking in my borrowed dress. 'Yes,' I replied, 'it's my birthday.' She smiled falsely and remarked, 'I thought your birthday was in October?' Olive leaned forward to scrutinise my tormentor and then said in a voice which could be heard several rows away, 'Why don't you mind your own business?' 'I'm not talking to you,' said Mrs Hulley as she sat back in her seat. 'Cheeky old cow,' hissed Olive.

'Who is she, do you know her,' asked my friend. 'Yes, she's my dad's girl friend,' I told her. Olive cast her eye over Mrs Hulley and then said, 'He must be hard-up,' in a loud voice, loud enough for the district nurse to hear. At the end, when the patrons rose for the National Anthem, Olive and I scurried out and within a few minutes I was out of the dress and back in uniform and trying to return my hat to its former shape. As fast as I could I ran back up the avenues, taking the route through the back lanes and into the Recreation Ground, where I would later swear I had been all afternoon.

Mr Samuels called to see me. 'We're moving to our new house in Highlands,' he told me, 'and Joanne hopes that you will be able to spend not the next holidays, but the one after, with us when we'll be properly settled. I've told Betty so you'll have her for company too. But what is this I hear, that you are learning shorthand and typing? We thought you might have gone on to university.' When I explained why I was unable to do that, he studied me for a few minutes and said 'Pity. Well, we mustn't lose touch with each other,' he said as Porteous opened the door of his car for him. 'Joanne sends her love,' and he was gone.

Betty and I met by accident at the Sunday morning church service and she seemed pleased that I would not be at school much longer. 'I'm leaving too at the end of the term and I'm going to stay with my mom and Phil in Durban,' she told me. 'My dad's getting so strict and doesn't like some of my boy friends,' and she picked at her red nail varnish, peeling it off in little strips. 'Well, I'm sorry I'm leaving,' I told her. 'I don't want to, but my father says he can't afford to keep me any longer, there's a depression coming.' 'You are a sap,' she told me. 'You should stand up to him. Catch me putting up with a father like yours.'

There really was a depression, and the country was in the throes of a terrible drought. Businesses failed, newly established factories closed their gates and signed off the work force and farmers went bankrupt. Their labourers joined those many others trailing back to their kraals in the bush of far off Nyasaland, Portuguese East and Northern Rhodesia. Cattle and livestock died in their thousands as every available source of water dried up, and their skeletons lay bleached and picked clean by natives or wild animals; crops failed and those which survived were burnt to the ground by veldt fires which lit the country from end to end.

White men, mostly tradesmen, lost their jobs and Georgie was one of them. He sold his little house in the suburbs, his motor bike and his furniture and made arrangements to move his family into his mother's home, but before he could do so, Claudine ran away with a travelling salesman from Johannesburg, taking Jackie and her new little daughter with her.

Solitary and lonely, he moped around his mother's house, wishing no doubt for the companionship of the long-gone Dingo, but every morning he trudged off to the city to look for work, returning in the evening more and more despondent.

Alarmed at the number of white men who had joined the native loafers on street corners or who lay about on the grass of the municipal parks, the Government inaugurated work schemes, and one of these, the Pick 'n Shovel Brigade, Georgie joined. The men were to build the country roads linking the smaller towns with each other and with the capital. They would be paid five shillings a day and were required to remain on the site of their immediate work. They slept under tarpaulins rigged up between trees, took it in turns to cook, and were grateful to work seven days a week.

All day long they dug and levelled the sandy, pot-holed tracks, and then laid two concrete parallel strips about two feet wide down the centre of the road, just wide apart enough to take the wheels of a car or lorry. What would happen, people asked, when two cars approached each other or when one tried to overtake another? It was carefully explained, with sketches in the daily newspaper, that each motorist would surrender the right hand strip to the other, and provided the corrugations of the surface didn't sent them bouncing into each other or into the bush, all would be well. Even so, there were confrontations between angry drivers who pulled off both strips and took to the bush, negotiating tussocks of grass, ant-bear holes and trees with great skill, in order to avoid fisticuffs with their rivals. Motor cyclists often hesitated until the last minute before giving way to four-wheeled vehicles, oaths were exchanged and threatening fists shaken, and donkey carts and ox-wagons withdrew to the safety of the bush, surrendering any right to the new road.

For some years my father had been employed in the Municipal offices and then one day he was called in and told that he would have to go. Staff was being cut back but there remained one vacancy, explained his superiors; perhaps he would consider that? They were mindful of his family commitments and knew that he had three dependent children but they wondered if it would be right to offer the job to a white man. It would have suited a Coloured man, they said, but naturally preference would be given to a white man and they knew he was desperate.

All the city roads were being re-laid and would be macadamised, and a man to operate the tar-spraying machine was required. He accepted the job. Accompanied by a gang of native labourers he followed the construction crew as they tamped down the newly laid surface of each road and avenue. Covered from head to foot in an old pair of overalls, his hat firmly jammed on his head, he wielded the tar-spray, sending out a fine layer of boiling tar onto the surface of the roadway, and then stood aside as his gang spread the gravel over the hot surface. The blackened boiler hissed and gurgled, the smoke from the stack could be seen for miles, and Bermuda tar clung to my father's skin, impregnated his clothes, inflamed his eyes and blackened his hands and fingernails.

My nickname was promptly changed from Saddlebackie to Tar Baby, and at last I began to feel relieved that I would soon leave school, possibly at the end of the year. I knew that Tom's fees were my father's main preoccupation and would have to be paid promptly when due, unlike the bills and letters of demand which I was given to pass on to him. He barely glanced at them as he rapidly consigned them to the furnace of the tar boiler saying, as he did so, 'Them bleedin' nuns can wait.'

My aunt's business too, was affected by the depression. Orders for building bricks dwindled away, but she was safely buttressed against any hardship by a considerable bank balance and was negotiating with Mr Salisbury Jones to acquire a block of land at Shabani where thick seams of asbestos had been discovered. With its low electrical and thermal conductivity, it would be in great demand for insulating material and fire-proof fabrics and Aunty Betty realised that electricity was to enhance and change all our lives.

Letters from 'home' continued to arrive. They contained news about the depression, the state of the Government and the strength of the beer, and in one of them the announcement that Uncle George's youngest sister, also called Anne, was about to leave England for a long stay in Rhodesia. 'Can't remember what she looked like,' said Aunty Betty, 'she was only a little tyke when I last seen her.' Uncle George gazed at the distant sky-line and then remarked, 'She didn't grow much after that bloomin' accident did she? Fell and broke 'er back when she was just a little nipper, and I don't know what she wants to come out 'ere for.' 'Where we gonna put 'er?' asked his wife anxiously. 'I'll have to tell Bill his kids can't come for the holidays, we ain't got the room.'

I was to remain at the Convent and was put to work in the Sewing Room, darning, patching and marking clothes; Tom was not coming home either, there was no money to spare for his fare and he would work on the training ship to earn his keep. I wondered if this new Anne would feel the need to make frequent trips to the city, as my English grandmother had done; I had seen the boarded-up windows of many of the bars and the closed and drawn blinds of some of the smaller hotels on my surrepetitious forays into the town, and knew that if Anne felt the need for any social contact, she would be sorely disappointed.

There was only Mr Vetsukis at the Criterion Café, but he too had reduced the number of tables in his restaurant and in any case, lone white women never ventured out by themselves; no longer did Mr Vetsukis greet his customers at the door, he had donned the cook's surrendered apron and wielded the basting spoon and grill tongs in the hot, dirty little kitchen while his large fat wife greeted the clients at the front, showing her new set of enamel teeth as she smiled amiably at the world. Mr Vetsukis had reduced his prices considerably, and had cunningly installed a machine of such novelty in the front shop that there was always a queue of anxious gamblers waiting to put their shilling in. With mouths agape, they stood watching the little silvery crane man-oeuvre and hover so temptingly over the unattainable wrist watch or cigarette case, before descending to grope up a few meagre green sweets which it dropped into the slot at the bottom.

The Hunyani Hotel signed off most of its staff, took down the Japanese lanterns which swung over the dance floor under the jacaranda trees and announced that it would open only at weekends. Most of the dismissed waiters and bedroom boys took their blankets and walked the eight miles down to the Ardbennie Hotel which lay off the Salisbury road and where business was booming. It was only four miles from the city and its easy-going reputation had spread far and wide. The genial host, Pat Finneran, sported a red carnation in his button hole and wore blancoed spats with his natty pin-stripe suit, and he elected himself as Friend of the Catholic Poor and turned up at the Emerald Hill Orphanage with boxes of fruit and sweets for the children. His next stop would be the Convent, where he dropped off cases of wine for those European palates, and then to Campion House where the Jesuit brothers lived near the Roman Catholic Cathedral, to visit with the Inspector-General before handing out boxes of choice cigars and rounds of imported cheeses.

But the event which would earn him his crown in heaven was the annual outing on St Patrick's Day for the senior girls of the Convent school. Pat hired mule wagons from the one and only cartage contrac-tors in the city and we climbed on to dangle our legs over the edge as the drivers whipped up their teams and drove us out to the cemetery for the pilgrimage to Mother Patrick's grave. This redoubtable nun had travelled up from the South with Cecil Rhodes's column in 1890 and had nursed his followers through fevers and sunstroke, only to succumb herself and die at the early age of twenty-six. We bowed our heads low and crossed ourselves as we recited Hail Marys and prayed for the soul of this gentle Irish nun who had died in a foreign land, but already our minds were on the event to follow.

We climbed back onto the wagons and sang and waved to people in the streets as we were driven to Pocket's Tea Rooms in the centre of the town. 'Order anything you like me darlins',' said Pat as he beamed at us and – when the nun wasn't looking – squeezed us gently. We scanned the menus, asking each other what we should order and eyeing the cake-laden trollies as the waiters pushed them nearer. Sated at last, we returned to the Convent, but still had to endure the long-winded tribute Pat was to offer from the stage of the Hall. Was it really true about those back bedrooms at his hotel, I wondered, remembering Aunty Betty's ribald aside to her mother a long time ago. 'Shall we give three cheers for Mr Finneran?' asked my immediate companion. 'He's a darling, isn't he?' But my mind was still at his hotel, watching one of the road gang embracing a Coloured girl, and as I dismissed the picture I told myself that Pat Finneran could not be so wicked as to allow that to happen; he was our benefactor and was a kind, generous old man. My sole knowledge of lust and sex was confined to kissing and hugging and I was completely ignorant of any other facts of life.

Suddenly, without warning, my father appeared in the Visitor's parlour and I was summoned from the Sewing Room. This time it was not to discuss unpaid accounts, but to arrange for my instant removal. 'Before the new term starts,' said Mother Frances. 'There have been complaints from the Boarders' Mother that your daughter has been fighting in the dormitory, that she helps herself to other girls' clothes and that she has been bullying the day girls for their lunches. In fact Mrs Burns has written that her daughter took everything which had been prepared for an afternoon's bridge party, to give your child in exchange for help with her homework, but this, which I have just received is the most serious accusation.' She fumbled amongst the papers on her desk and drew out a hand-written letter which she passed over to my father, and then she turned to me and told me to return to my work in the Sewing Room.

The letter which I had caught a glimpse of was from Mrs Hulley the District Nurse. She had been surprised, she had written, to see me in the company of a much older girl at the town cinema. She knew I was a boarder but it was my rudeness to her which had prompted her to write to the school. Ever mindful of her Convent's reputation, Mother Frances summoned my father and asked him to remove me at once. Silently he had listened to the catalogue of my misdeeds, outwardly stricken but enraged as her gentle voice continued. 'Your daughter seems not to care what she does and I believe you are mistaken in not sending her on to University. She is immature and the lack of a loving home has not made things easy.' 'Who says she doesn't have a happy home?' he'd asked, his eyes swimming with tears of outrage. Drily the nun had replied, 'She has been here for eleven years, we are not blind Mr Sadler'. He sat, twisting his hat in his hands and then said: 'Things haven't been too easy for me either Mother, but I beg you to give her another chance, I have no one else to turn to and it's only six months to the end of the year.'

'Just what d'ye think you're doing?' he hissed at me when I returned to the parlour. 'I've just had the worst ten minutes of me life, hearing all about your carryings-on, pinching other kids' clothes, fighting, stealing food and now this,' and he shook Mrs Hulley's letter under my nose. 'What bleedin' next, I ask you, sloping off to the bio with the day scholars, you've got a bloody nerve. And look what you've done to me. She didn't 'arf give me a doing over, wants me to take you away right now, but I ain't got anywhere for yer to live and your aunty's got no room.' Furiously he banged the letter down on the desk and went to stand by the window. 'Ain't yer got anything to say for yerself?' he asked. 'No,' I replied, 'it's all true what Mother Frances says, I did all those things and I'm sorry.' 'Yer'll have to be more than sorry', said my father. 'You'll have to apologise and promise not to do anything like that again,' and he came to stand nearer to me. 'And lay it on thick, like you was really sorry, so's she'll let you stay on and finish the year; I can't help you.' For many minutes we both stood there, silent, but my mind was full of the injustices I felt had been my lot. Should I remind my father yet again of how differently he had treated me? But I knew my words would fall on stony ground and I realised at last that the truest words he had ever spoken to me were 'I can't help you.'

'You may say goodbye to your father now and leave the room,' Mother Frances said as she swept in to the parlour. But my father refused my kiss, backing away to do so, and I ran back to the Sewing Room. I was allowed to stay at the Convent, but would have to do additional penances to pay for my sins; I served at table for the rest of my stay, cleaned out the lavatories with the native servants and helped in the Boys Hostel. There was neither time nor opportunity to make plans with Olive or any other friends, I was escorted from class by a dour-looking nun who could hardly speak English and put to my various tasks. No one spoke to me, I was in disgrace and I longed for the mid-year holidays when I could escape to Vinyu's compound, unburden myself and hope for his sympathy.

But these hopes vanished from my mind when I arrived at the servants' compound and found Jorbey sitting against the wall of his old hut, now occupied by the new gardener Amos. With some difficulty he rose from the ground and smiled at me saying, 'How you have grown? Soon I will have to call you Inkossikaas,' but I could see he stood uneasily and held on to the wall of the hut. 'How is your broken leg? When did you leave hospital? It is a long time since we left you in Enkeldoorn, almost a year.' Then I saw that the leg which had been broken was shorter than the other and that he used a walking stick to help him stand upright. 'I have come to ask the Inkossikaas for my job back, I am strong again,' he said and he turned and limped up to the house. I followed him.

'When did you get here?' asked Aunty Betty from the verandah where she was pouring tea. I had been let off early from school and had come only to collect my dresses before going to Mrs Samuels for the winter holidays I explained, and then I was called forward to meet the newest member of the family.

'This here's Anne, she just arrived from 'ome and is Uncle George's little sister,' said Aunty Betty as she led me to the settee where sat the smallest old person I had ever seen. She was quite plain, her hair already greying but her eyes behind her pince-nez were large and bright and she beamed at me as I shook her little hand. She smelled of face powder and her tailored silk dress was crisp and fresh, but I noticed she sat forward in her chair, tucking her neat little feet in their high heels, out of the way. 'Which one are you?' she asked and before I could tell her, Aunty Betty said 'She's the one still at school. The one Bill has had all the trouble with. Nearly got expelled, didn't you?' she asked. I was embarrassed to have all my sins paraded before this complete stranger. 'What did you do?' she asked. 'Bunked out of school and went to the bio with a day scholar,' I told her. 'Surely that wasn't enough to have you expelled?' she asked. 'There was plenty more', said Aunty Betty and with relish she went on to list all my sins. But Anne seemed dismayed that such petty crimes should warrant expulsion and then she stood up to say, 'They must be very strict.'

I was shocked to see that I looked down on to the top of her head from my five feet and a few inches and that indeed, she was very small. When she turned aside, I saw the deformity. One of her shoulders stuck out grotesquely, giving her the appearance of a hunchback. I was to notice later, that all her dresses were tailored to hide this disfigurement and when she went out, she always wore pretty hats garnished with ribbons or streamers to hide that twisted back. But she did not ask for sympathy and refused to admit that she was different in appearance from other women. Now she smiled at me again and said, before leaving

211

the room, 'You jolly well stand up for yourself,' and with a smile which crinkled up her face, she was gone.

'Jorbey is here,' announced Vinyu from the doorway. 'What does he want?' asked Aunty Betty. 'He has come to tell madam that he is ready to do his work,' replied Vinyu. 'He was discharged from hospital six months ago but has only now reached Salisbury.' My aunt thought for a moment and then said: 'Tell him there is no job here for him, he was away for so long we have taken Amos to do the garden. I don't need Jorbey, he can go.' For a few minutes the two men spoke and Vinyu presented himself again at the door. 'Madam, Jorbey says can he have his month's pay and his notice pay which you owe him?' My aunt looked dumbfounded. 'He's getting nothing from me, and if he don't clear orf, I'll send for the police.' Vinyu returned to his friend and then Jorbey came to the open door and sat down on the step. 'He says he will wait for the ma-johnny,' said Vinyu. If she had hoped to intimidate Jorbey, my aunt had misjudged him, he knew his rights under the law recently promulgated for the protection of all indigenous workers and he also knew that the police would uphold his request.

Reluctantly and grudgingly my aunt fetched her purse and paid out Jorbey two months' wages and signed his situpa so that he could find work elsewhere. 'I've no use for any bleedin' cripples here,' she said as she laboriously wrote her name on his situpa. 'I'm not having you hang around the compound, so clear off, voetsak,' she said using that offensive word so recently imported from the South and intended to dismiss a dog.

Vinyu walked with me to the boundary fence and stood waiting there, to separate the strands of barbed wire so that I could step through them instead of making my exit through the garden gate. 'So,' he said, 'you too are going?' I told him that there was no room for me here and that Mrs Samuels had invited me long before she had moved house. 'And Tom?' he asked. Tom would return only for Christmas, I said, my father could not afford the train fare more than once a year. Vinyu shook his head and then said 'I too, will leave before the rains come; I have been here for many years but it is time for me to return to my kraal to look after my family; you are all old enough to look after yourselves now.' There was an air of finality in his voice. I took his hand, something so unconventional, so apt to be misinterpreted by any onlooker, that I was immediately embarrassed; white people never shook hands with natives and avoided physical contact at all times, but this seemed different from the occasions when I had trustingly held his hand when I was younger.

He smiled, showing his yellowed teeth and crinkling up his eyes, then turned and walked back to his kitchen.

I was not to know that I would never see or hear of him again. For almost twelve years he had been our shield and protector and had served his employers faithfully, always deferring to their decisions whether right or wrong. He had been cursed and sworn at, depended upon and trusted, depending on the mood, and had never forgotten that he was a mere servant. He was missed only briefly in my aunt's home as they became accustomed to the regime of a new servant, but he remained alive in my memory and I have long remembered that sly grin, the mischievous delight over some family scandal and the concern he had shown when we had first arrived in that house.

No more did my father visit the District Nurse. He had been shocked by the letter she had written to the Convent, not because of its effect on me, but because of what it signified about their relationship. She had hoped desperately for marriage and it had become a frequent topic of conversation between them, but he had become more and more exasperated as she persisted. 'We could move into that little house of yours,' she had said. 'You told me the Inspector was moving out soon and I could make a nice little home for your girls.' So that was it, he mused, my expulsion would force his hand and before he knew it, he would find himself tied up to the District Nurse, putting up with broken nights when she would be summoned to visit her patients – and worse, she might give up her work feeling that her new family needed her more. He had no wish to marry Mrs Hulley although he enjoyed her company, the Sunday lunches together and the nights he spent in her small flat, but she was too old for him. If he was to marry again, it would be to someone much younger, like that old Mrs Kemp's daughter who worked in the printing works of the local newspaper. He made excuses for not meeting Mrs Hulley for Sunday lunch at the Criterion Café, for not being able to stay the night, and as her servant presented himself with her notes asking for his explanations, he either ignored the man until he left or consigned the letter to the fire in the tar-boiler.

In my aunt's home, matters took a different turn. Exasperated by the new cook who complained that there was too much work for one man, and by his ineptitude and atrocious cooking, Aunt Anne took over the kitchen. Cousin Jack built her three little steps to stand on so that she could reach over the Dover stove, and despite what people would say, she became the cook. She produced a neat little apron from the depths of her work-bag, bound a large handkerchief over her hair and ordered the luckless cook about in her rather shrill authoritative voice, threatening to demote him to the scullery if he continued to complain. The garden boys were forbidden to leave their pots soaking in the little bathroom and she locked everything up, carrying a large bunch of keys in her little dress pocket.

Her tyranny did not stop with the staff. Those members of the family who lolled about on the verandah settees were ordered immediately to the table when the meal was served, regardless of the state of their evening drinks or cigarettes, and she stood over them when they pushed certain items to the sides of their plates, asking why they hadn't eaten everything, what was the matter with her cooking? In spite of her smallness, she had a will of iron and would brook no nonsense or excuse, and she was determined to elevate the standards which had pertained for so long. No more fried food she ordained, no more rich suety puddings or cream cakes, and certainly no more of that dark, strong tea which was drunk at meals and throughout the day.

She lay in wait for the butcher's boy and inspected and rejected the meat he brought for the daily meals, giving him instead a long angry letter she had written, asking the butcher to close the account if he could not improve the quality of his meat. The baker's boy was sent packing because he had handed the erstwhile cook the bread unwrapped 'with his dirty hands,' she told the family when they complained at the lack of bread on the table, and she shouted angrily at the garden picannin when he returned from the Indian's garden with a basket of vegetables. 'Take them all back,' she would order the luckless child, who knew the Indian would not accept them and that he would be forced to throw the cabbages, beans and carrots into the river and hide for the rest of the day when his crime was discovered.

When she was not stamping around the kitchen abusing the staff, she sat quietly in the garden with her work bag or joined anyone who was sitting in the verandah room. From the depths of her embroidered work-bag she drew a large untidy bundle of thick lace and a ball of fine cotton thread which had a curious hook stabbed through it. As they sat and gossiped and laughed over the days' events, Anne crochetted, not once looking at any instructions as from her busy hands there unfolded lengths of lace emblazoned with roses, lilies, butterflies and swans, every stitch perfect as her fingers moved to some unheard rhythm.

214

'What's that for?' Stella had asked. 'It's for my bottom drawer,' said Anne. 'Instead of sitting there doing nothing, don't you think it's time you started on yours?' Stella was mystified, but Anne enlightened her, explaining that for the past twenty-five years she had been making things for her future home and now possessed every possible thing she would need for a home of her own. The only missing ingredient was, she said, a husband, 'But he'll come along one day,' she said smugly. 'Somewhere in the world is a man for me.' Stella didn't know whether to laugh or be shocked at the pronouncements which tripped so frivolously from this bossy little woman's tongue, but she was fired with enthusiasm for a few short days. She could not master the crochet hook and instead made two very elegant black satin tea cosies on which she painted bright birds and flowers. 'I should start on something else,' advised Anne as she inspected them.

'Are you engaged to someone then?' asked Stella, 'Is there someone you know at home, who wants to marry you?' Anne thought for a moment. 'I was engaged once long ago,' she said, 'but we would have had to live with his parents and I didn't want that. That was before I came out here, and I don't think about him any more,' and she rigorously applied herself to her lace.

Before long, however, her strict regime was her downfall and everyone in the house complained. Uncle George was deputed to speak to his sister. 'It ain't that they don't like your cooking,' he said apologetically, 'it just ain't what we're used to; Jack don't like all them stews and neither Bet nor me like all that green stuff you put on the table and Billy keeps asking where them puddings are that the cook used to make.' He listed all the changes she had made and when she took her handkerchief out to dab at her eyes, he regretted that he had taken on the task of bringing all the grievances to light. 'There, there,' he said as he patted her on her unblemished shoulder, 'you don't have to work here, you have a good holiday and enjoy yourself.'

'But I can't spend all my days doing nothing,' she cried. Nor did she, and every morning when the two cousins drove in Jack's car to their work, she accompanied them. She perambulated the length of both streets in the main shopping area of the town, looking at the shop windows, looking through the merchandise and trying on hats in the smart hat-shop. It was all so awful, she told herself, so uncivilised and dirty. Niggers on every pavement, their clothes ragged or held together with large safety pins, their feet bare and they would blow their noses in to the gutters. The white people so pleased with themselves, with their big houses and servants, so unaware of the dirt and squalor around them and so ignorant of what went on in the world. She would return to England, she decided.

But at that moment, she realised she had broken the strap on her shoe and that she had taken a wrong turning and was in one of the small side streets where Jewish traders sold bicycles and spares, Indian shopkeepers traded vegetables and fruit and where there were one or two small Greek cafés and tearooms. Standing in the doorway of the nearest café was a swarthy, pot-bellied Greek, smiling at her. 'Is there a shoemaker near by?' she asked. 'Ochi, I mean no Madame,' and he hurried to her side to help her into the dark café, saying 'Let me see if I can help.'

It was the beginning of the romance of Anne's life, which would lead her to that married state which she had so earnestly desired. Stathes Popadopoulos had been in the colony for twenty years, just scraping a living in his café where his clientele was mainly indigenous. Waiters, garage cleaners, office sweepers and messenger boys, coloured men from the Milling Company and coloured girls from the steam laundry dropped in to buy the penny buns and bottles of orange or lemonade for their midday meal; Indian youths stopped by for forbidden sausage rolls and the Muslim girls on their way to school called in to buy the garish sweets exhibited in a long row of jars against the wall. To Anne the little café was a challenge and although Stathes was an ardent gambler, he kept his two activities apart and never discussed money with her.

'Yes,' he admitted, he had been married in Greece, many many years ago, but Eva had refused to accompany him to a new life in the colony. 'You see my dear,' he told her over cups of sweetened Turkish coffee, 'she was only fourteen when we were married. It is the custom in my country to do so at an early age, but her mother would not allow her to come to me until she was sixteen years old. By then, I had left the country and although I sent money home for many years, I have only recently heard that Eva has died.' He shrugged his shoulders philosophically and added: 'But my parents-in-law were good people, and they have bought me a small piece of land in my village, and soon I shall sell this place and retire.'

Anne said nothing to her relations about her new friend, but she continued to visit him and soon she was spending one or two days during the week with him. 'Where do you get to in town?' asked Aunty Betty. 'You must have seen everything in every shop by now.' 'There's nothing like a good brisk walk,' replied Anne. 'I like to walk in the park,

216

the gardens are beautiful at this time of the year and the rosebeds are a joy. There's a band too, on Wednesday afternoons, and there's a nice tea-room there.' She had read this last piece of information in the daily newspaper, but she despised herself for the moral coward she was. 'Tell them the truth kyria, that you are spending the day with a man; you are no longer a young miss. You are a mature woman and answerable to no one', and Stathes playfully tickled her under her chin.

'A bleedin' dago!' screamed Aunty Betty. 'You've gorn mad, what d'ye think you're up to?' She was horrified that this little wisp of a woman should have ideas of marriage, apart from the fact that it was a dirty Greek she had in mind. 'Does he know what you really look like?' she asked. 'That you're a hunchback?' She looked contemptuously at Anne who sat there stony-faced. 'How dare you?' cried Anne. 'Stathes has asked me to marry him, he knows what I look like and he doesn't care. We're old enough to please ourselves and if you go on like this, I shall not bother to introduce him to you.' She got up to walk out of the room. 'He's no great catch either,' said my aunt. 'A greasy Greek with a little kaffir store, you're welcome to him I'm sure, but don't bring him here, we don't want to have nothing to do with him. Or you for that matter,' and she stalked past Anne, giving her a withering look as she did so. 'You'll make a funny looking couple, him a dago and you a hunchback.'

Tears of fury gathered in Anne's eyes, but she said no more. She packed her trunk, her few books and her work-bag and left them in the care of Amos to be collected later by a friend of Stathes; there was no offer to take her into town. Her only regret was that she had not seen Uncle George to say goodbye to, but she knew his opinion would be a pale reflection of his wife's.

They were married in the Registry office with two of Stathes' cronies to witness the event, and Anne became a dutiful Greek wife, standing behind the counter taking the pennies and tickeys, cooking their midday meal and caring for her treasured husband. She never questioned him about his evenings with his friends at the Criterion Café, although she had a shrewd idea that he went there to gamble, nor did she complain about their cramped living quarters at the back of the store. She did wish though that he would sometimes give her some money. There were charge accounts in every shop in the town and she could buy whatever she wanted, but no money in her hand, her husband had decreed. 'It is the custom,' he would say shrugging his shoulders expressively. 'Anything you want my darling, you can have, but money, no.' And then

217

jokingly he had added 'You might run away if you had a bagful of money.' She had not persisted but when the shop was closed and the evening meal cleared away, she brought out the beautiful new clothes Stathes had given her; dresses and coats made for her by an Indian tailor near the station, a fur jacket he had sent to Europe for, and the handmade shoes imported from America, for her tiny highly arched feet. She looked at them fondly, stroking the lustrous fur and admiring the fine stitching, but she had been forbidden to wear them, they were for the two months holiday in Greece he had promised her. 'I wish you to wear your ordinary clothes in the store,' he had commanded and she had stood dutifully behind the counter serving out buns and sandwiches, fruit and bottles of cold drinks in her plain cotton dresses.

'People say I am a poor man,' said Stathes. 'I like them to think so. I do not care. I am Greek and proud of it. You too, kyria, are Greek now and we will be happy together. Those relations of yours, they are barbarians,' and he bent down to kiss her lightly on the back of her neck. His friend Hari came to mind the café and store and Stathes took his little wife first class on the Italian Mail boat which sailed from Durban, for a leisurely cruise up the coast of Africa, into the Mediterranean and home to Greece. They were an incongruous pair, but they cared not a jot for the curious looks and whispers they attracted and Anne never forgot the day she had taken a wrong turning in the street and had broken the strap of her shoe. Who would have thought a year ago, she mused, that I would find myself on an ocean liner sailing to Europe with such a nice man as my Stathes, so kind and considerate to me, as Betty said, a hunchback?

These events had taken place while I spent the holidays with Mrs Samuels in her new home. On my return to school, I had had to see the dentist and was duly escorted to the town by Sister Amata, my class teacher. As we hurried back to the Convent, I saw Anne standing at the door of their café, speaking to a delivery boy and I wondered if I dared to talk to her. As we drew near, I whispered to the nun, 'I know that lady, Sister, may I please speak with her?' and Sister Amata nodded and walked on a few paces.

'Do you remember me?' I asked. 'I'm Bill Sadler's daughter, I was at the house just after you arrived from England, months ago.' Her face lit up and she took my hand. 'Of course I do, you're the child who was nearly expelled,' and she burst out laughing. 'Thank heavens someone in that family has some gumption, but you know of course, that I'm the black sheep now,' and she continued to laugh. 'When will you leave

218

school?' she enquired, 'Soon?' 'I don't really know,' I answered, 'perhaps at the end of the year.' 'Well when you do, and when you can, come and see me. You'll like my husband, he's a nice man,' and she squeezed my hand as I left her. I was glad she had broken away from her family who were still making fun of her as they recounted her short stay and subsequent marriage. Most of them had seen her at a distance as she swept the pavement outside the café or helped her husband carry boxes of fruit into the dark interior, and some of the more daring had even strolled past on the opposite side of the street. 'There she was,' they would reiterate, 'still in her slippers, that dirty old apron almost down to her ankles and that greasy dago picking his teeth and ordering her about.' It gave them great satisfaction to think she had got what she deserved, and Anne did nothing to gainsay them.

Stella had taken my father's place and came to see me once a month on a Sunday afternoon. 'Daddy is busy with his pigs,' she told me as though to assure me he had not forgotten me, but I enjoyed her company more than his although I did not say so. 'We're all going to see Willie Diss next Sunday,' she told me. 'He's trying to break the record and drive to Salisbury from Bulawayo in under ten hours, in a new Ford car. Do you think they might let you out for the day? I could ask Mother Frances if you're too scared to.'

Mother Frances gave her consent provided I was back by six o'clock, and on Sunday we joined the crowd which had gathered to witness this epic. People sat about in groups discussing the event, the distance, the trials of a three hundred mile speed dash, the bravery of the driver, the humidity, and the efficiency of the officials, timekeepers, and wayside petrol pumps. The bishop had railed at the event at the Sunday morning church service and I wondered if my soul was destined for hell-fire because I was there and not passing the day in reverential devotion.

Discussions arose about the state of the road – strips all the way, remarked those in the know – and watches were eagerly scanned. Wetted fingers were held aloft to gauge the strength of the wind and the horizon where the bush thinned out was searched for signs of veldt fires or dust storms. All was perfect, announced the sages, Willie Diss would arrive at about five o'clock they said, and slowly the crowds split up and sauntered back to their vehicles or picnic spots.

Slowly the day drifted by, the heat oppressive and the dust thick on every surface; games of football were started by the young children, fights and quarrels broke out between the young adults who were bored because nothing was happening, and irritable babies whimpered and cried. Small boys were called out of trees or away from suspicious holes where they inserted sticks in the hopes of disturbing some unwary animal or snake and the grown-ups congregated at the edges of the road as they hopefully scanned the horizon northwards, the direction the car would come from in its record breaking attempt.

A small cloud of dust in the distance brought everyone scurrying to the roadside, shading their eyes against the strong sun, but as it drew nearer there was a cry of dismay; it was a bullock cart loaded with cut wood from the bush. Another false alarm had the same effect and as each cloud of dust proved to be either a herd of scrawny cattle being driven into the city, or a group of native men returning from a beer drink in a distant kraal, mocking cries and jeers began to be heard.

Suddenly there was a cry 'This is him!' and everyone surged to stand once again at the roadside as the distant speck came nearer. Little boys who had started more interesting games were cuffed around the ear by angry parents saying, 'Come when I bloody call you,' and they whined and shuffled as they were pushed to the front to get a good view. Once again there was disappointment. The Mayor, in his chain of office and best Sunday suit, had hoped for a preview of the great event and had waited most of the day at the edge of the Umfuli river, under the trees. 'He won't be here for another half hour,' called this harbinger, only to be rewarded by catcalls of 'Gerr-a-way,' 'Buy a Horse,' or 'What else did you get for Christmas?' as they eyed his official vehicle, the brasswork and lamps gleaming in the afternoon sunlight, the body coated in a fine layer of dust. I began to worry that I would be late getting back to school.

Once again a cloud appeared on the horizon as the crowds began to drift disconsolately away, urging their servants and picannins to start packing up and to find the children. 'It's Willie Diss,' was the cry that went up and there was another stampede to the side of the road, all revels abandoned as the crowd craned their necks and shielded their eyes from the glare of the setting sun.

The car hove into view, caked in dust but stripped of every unnecessary refinement, mudguards removed, the hood folded and tied down securely and the mascot still bearing the mangled remains of a small branch collected when the intrepid driver had skirted too near the bush. Seated in the driving seat was the grim-faced idol of the young unmarrieds of the town, clad in leather cavalry jacket, riding breeches and flying helmet. His lips were dried and cracked and his face a grey mask of dust; eagerly he seized the water bag someone thrust at him as the cognoscenti chewed their pencils and checked the figures they had scribbled on the backs of cigarette boxes. 'Thirty-five miles an hour average,' observed cousin Jack, and then the cry went up: 'Three cheers for Willie, he's broken the record.' Self-consciously he bowed to left and right as he surveyed his supporters and waved cheerily to those still emerging from the bush, buttoning themselves up and asking querously 'Why didn't you call me?'

I slipped into my place in the refectory before anyone could dispute the time of my arrival back at school and eagerly recounted the events of the day. 'Three hundred miles in nine hours,' we called to each other, 'What a record.' 'What a man,' observed one of the prefects, a girl well-known for her free and easy ways with the St George's boys and reputed to have been seen in curious circumstances in the park with the head boy of that institution. 'You are lucky,' one of my classmates observed. 'Imagine actually being there to see that man break the record. I suppose in twenty years time, they'll be going at fifty miles an hour.' But this speed was beyond our comprehension and we marvelled and speculated about the wonders of our modern times.

PART FIVE

'Mother Frances wants to see you,' said my teacher and with a sinking heart I made my way to that familiar study. 'Sit down,' she said as she regained her seat and drew a slip of paper towards her. 'You know Mrs Harper who teaches the senior girls, don't you? Her husband is the manager of the United Tobacco Company in town, and he has called to ask if we have a girl in the Commercial Class who could fill the position as a junior in their office. We think you are suitable and I have suggested that you go with Sister Amata this afternoon, for an interview. Sister Mary Rose will drive you in our car so go and put on your Sunday dress after lunch and meet Sister Amata here. Remember that you are a Convent girl and we have great expectations of you; answer Mr Harper politely and remember all we have told you. When you return, please come and see me, I am anxious to know the result of your interview. You may go now,' and surprisingly, she accompanied me to the door and put her arm around me and kissed me lightly on the cheek. 'Don't be nervous,' she said. 'Tell them that you are almost qualified but don't accept the position if you feel you could not do it. You have my blessing and I will pray for you.'

The United Tobacco Company's Rhodesian factory had been established in the city for three years and lay at the southern end of the town, past the Langham Hotel, through the native quarter opposite the Castle Brewery. It was served by its own railway spur where trucks were shunted to wait for the cigarettes which were made and packed in the factory. Trucks of cured and dried tobacco off-loaded here into the steam rooms where it was sorted, treated and steamed before delivery to the factory, and the position vacant was for an honest, reliable girl who would keep the records of every pound of tobacco which went into the factory, every cigarette which emerged from the massive, thundering machines and every excise stamp which sealed the boxes.

But was I that girl? I wondered. Was the Convent determined to be rid of me at last? And what of my shorthand and typewriting speeds so arduously gained? It was the salary which tempted me to accept. Eight pounds a month, almost twice what my sister earned at the electrical firm, and the hours would be shorter 'to allow the girls to do their shopping; we are a long way from the centre of Town,' said Mr Harper. 'Yes,' I said eagerly, 'I'd like to take the job, but I am still at school and I won't see my father until the end of the week.' Arrangements would have to be made for me to leave the Convent and find somewhere to live, and my heart sank as I considered the obstacles.

'You know what this is going to mean?' asked Stella when I confronted her in her office, while the two nuns sat in the car outside, waiting for me. 'I'll have to leave Aunty Betty's. We'll probably have to go and live in one of those boarding houses, Daddy won't let you go alone. Why did you have to go and spoil things for me? It's not fair,' but she agreed to see my father and tell him the news. 'When are you supposed to start at this job of yours?' she asked as we walked to the doorway. 'I told the manager that I would speak to you and then to Mother Frances and that I could probably start at the end of this month, there are only ten days to go.' 'Well I wish you'd thought about me first,' she replied petulantly, 'I don't want to leave Aunty Betty's.'

At the end of the month I left the Convent, where I had spent eleven of my fifteen years and where I had been, for the most part, happy; and now, when I thought of what lay ahead of me, I was frightened and dreaded venturing into the business world where I would have to be responsible, trustworthy and efficient and where a completely different life awaited me.

Stella's predictions came true; we were to live in a boarding house while my father searched for cheaper quarters for us. He had regained his little house but was in no hurry to move into it and was casting about for a new tenant to whom he could rent it. The money would come in useful.

'How will I get to work?' I asked. 'Gawd blimey, there you go again, you're so bleedin' clever, ain't you got any ideas of yer own?' he complained. 'It will take me an hour to walk all that way,' I told him, 'and I'll have to go through that native area where there are so many loafers sitting about on the pavements.' 'That shouldn't bother you,' he retorted. 'You were always hanging around that Vinyu.' How I wished I

226

had never left school. The obstacles facing me seemed insurmountable and I recalled how I had cried when I had said goodbye to the nuns I had known for so long and how secure and safe I had always felt. Now I would have to fend for myself and would get no help from my father.

'Can't I have a bicycle like Stella's?' I asked. He thought for a few minutes and then said, 'I'll get you one on aitch-pee, but you'll have to pay me back out of your salary. Ten bob a month, five pounds for the boarding house, ten bob for yer washing, leaves two quid over. You can give me that to pay back for all the years I been keeping you at the Convent.' The injustice of it floored me completely. 'If Stella earns four pounds ten shillings, how will she pay five pounds and ten shillings and have a bicycle?' I asked. 'None of your business,' he retorted. 'What I say goes, so I want to see two pounds in my hand when you've paid your expenses.' 'What's aitch-pee?' I asked, hoping this mysterious thing could be avoided; I would have no spending money for clothes and only possessed two dresses to wear to my new job. The intricacies and pitfalls of Hire Purchase were explained in detail but inwardly I seethed and then I said: 'It's all right, I don't want a bicycle, I'll walk.' My father had no answer to that, so I kept the ten shillings for myself.

Every morning while the boys laid the tables for breakfast, I downed a cup of tea, seized my packet of lunchtime sandwiches and set off the four miles to work, arriving very often as the last factory girl ran in. My office sat in the middle of the factory floor and the air was filled with the thundering of the cigarette machines, the thud of the packing and stamping machines and the yelling of voices. Steam hissed and trollies full of tobacco leaf rumbled from the Cooking Plant, and the chatter of the packing girls made conversation almost impossible, although in time my ear became accustomed to the level of noise and I could hear a confidential whisper amidst the roar of heavy machinery.

The factory girls sat in long rows at tables with their packing materials around them, frenziedly filling the boxes with cigarettes, first inserting a tissue liner, then a sheet of silver foil before expertly tipping in the loose cigarettes, and taking care not to crease the foil. They worked on piece rates, earning twice as much as I did, as I sat in my office cross-checking figures and totalling up columns, issuing excise stamps and coupons to be exchanged for cigarette cases, wrist watches, pen and pencil sets and pairs of silk stockings. When the lunchtime hooter blew there was a wild stampede to the factory canteen where cups of tea could be bought by the factory girls, and they sat about on the lawns in groups or pairs, exchanging the latest gossip, sampling each others' lunch or reading tattered copies of *True Confessions*.

They were mostly white girls from the poorer parts of the town, Afrikaans girls from Ardbennie or Hatfield with names like van der Merwe, Potgieter, Fredrickson or de Villiers: daughters of railway men or engine drivers from the Railway Married Quarters, sad faced older women reputed to be widowed but suspected of being divorced or deserted, and several very flashily dressed older girls who arrived and departed daily in long, sleek black motorcars driven by equally flashily dressed men who hooted and whistled as they waited at the top of the road. The most highly paid girls who did specialised packing of Turkish cigarettes were coloured, and segregated to a corner of the factory where the whites would not be forced to speak to them, but they smiled diffidently at me when they tapped on my window to ask for stamps or coupons.

Although I worked within the factory I had been told that I was not to fraternise with the factory girls, assuming that I would want to. But I had nothing in common with any of them and I ate my solitary lunch when they had left the factory and I had been locked in to my little office, secure with the coupons and excise stamps.

When the four o'clock hooter blew there was a wild rush to jump on to bicycles and get to the shopping centre before the stores closed. I started off on my homeward walk, dreading the moment when I came to the native quarter, but not because of the jostling hordes of native men on the pavements or the cripples and beggars who reached out with their claws asking for money or food, or the raucous music which blared out from the Indian shops. At the street corner stood the Express Oil Company, owned and operated by the brothers Pichanik, and the two young men, well dressed and groomed, stood at the doorway of the factory, eyeing and calling out to any white female who passed their evil-smelling factory which belched out clouds of black smoke and polluted the air with the heavy oily smell of peanuts which they ground to extract the oil.

As I rounded the corner to pass them, they nudged each other and stood in my path, arms outstretched to stop me. 'Give us a kiss darling,' or 'What're you doing tonight?' they would ask, and as I crept past, frightened, confused and embarrassed, they would burst out laughing, holding on to each other, as they returned to the dark depths of their evil smelling factory. Young natives sitting on the edge of the pavements giggled and tittered as they glanced at me, but the old grizzled men in town from their kraals for a few days looked about disparagingly, clicking their teeth in disgust at the behaviour of men they thought should have known better.

There was no other way to the United Tobacco Company's office unless I made a long detour which I had no time for, and if I hoped that ignoring the two men would make them give up their teasing and leave me alone, I was mistaken. They put chairs out on the pavement where they sat waiting for me, or strolled towards me as I dodged and ducked between the crowds of natives, and when I continued to ignore them, they bowed low, or linked arms in their efforts to stop me. After a week of this, I walked in the roadway looking stonily ahead as I wove between donkey carts, mule wagons, cyclists and native pedestrians.

When I got home there were stockings to be washed, a dress to be pressed for tomorrow and the day's events to recount to Stella, but I did not tell her of my tribulations at the Express Oil Company. We sat about in the garden of the boarding house waiting for dinner and talking to friends. 'Do you go to lots of parties?' they would ask Stella, firmly ignoring me, who they knew had just left school, and when she said no, invitations to dances and picnics were extended, and accepted.

More and more I began to feel the lack of a bicycle. If I possessed one I could join the long column of factory girls as they cycled to work and thus avoid my tormentors, and I would not have to leave so early or arrive back so late; but I knew that my father would compain bitterly if I changed the arrangement. All these thoughts passed through my head as I walked home one afternoon, feeling the first cold wind of winter and wondering how I could buy a woollen jersey, when I realised a car was drawing up in front of me. As I drew level I saw it was Porteous. He stood deferentially by the side of the car, held his cap in his hands and called as I approached. 'Missy, I am Porteous, why are you here?' 'I have a job now at the cigarette factory,' I told him, 'and I have no bicycle yet, so I have to walk.' He ran around to the car door and opened it, saying, 'Get in missy, I am going to Highlands to fetch the Inkossikaas. They will be angry if they knew I let you walk through this part of the town, come, I will take you home.'

The next afternoon, I was called into the main office. Mr Harper was waiting for me in the foyer and led me into his office. 'I've had a telephone call from Mr Samuels at the Brewery across the road. You know him, don't you?' I nodded. 'He asked me to tell you to wait at the top of our road when you knock off, he'll give you a lift home.' 'Thank you Mr Harper,' I said as I rose to go. 'Just a minute,' he called me back. 'Am I right in thinking that you walk to work and back every day?

Where do you live?' 'My sister and I stay at Mrs Greenwood's boarding house in the avenues,' I told him. 'I'm saving up for a bicycle.' 'There's no need to wait until then,' he answered. 'We can give you a loan and you can pay it back over six months or a year.' For a moment I contemplated the freedom a bicycle would give me, but I knew my father would shout and complain if I made an arrangement without his permission. 'Thank you, but no,' I said. 'We're moving to somewhere nearer soon, it doesn't matter.' He raised his eyebrows and I excused myself and returned to my own office in the factory.

Mrs Samuels was sitting in the back of the car when I joined her. Factory girls streamed past, shouting and joking as they hurried by on their bicycles, and others were hastily shepherded into their father's dilapidated old cars or lorries, but they looked suspiciously at Porteous as he stood respectfully at the door. 'I can't believe you're working in a factory,' said Mrs Samuels. 'How long have you been here?' She was shocked to find me in this environment, but I assured her that I was Office Staff entrusted to monitor the output of the factory, to keep complicated records and to guard and account for the excise stamps. 'Yes,' she agreed, 'it sounds a responsible job, but it worries us both that Porteous picked you up walking along the road in the native quarter; all those loafers and coloured men hanging about, it's dangerous for a young girl like you. Haven't you a bicycle?'

As we drove sedately home, I explained the circumstances I was in, although I said nothing about my hateful tormentors nor my father's insistence that I surrender my pay to him. I told her that he was looking for cheaper quarters for us, something near both our places of work. 'Yes, I can just imagine,' she said drily. 'It is all wrong, two young girls like you living in this end of the town. Places like the Castle Hotel, the Langham and the Masonic attract the dregs of society, drunks and vagrants, it's really not good enough.' She sighed.

'Well, until then,' she went on, 'Porteous will call for you every morning and bring you home. No, it's on the way for Mr Sam too and I would worry about you. But I wish I could do more.' 'Please Mrs Sam,' I asked anxiously, 'don't worry about us, I'm sure my father will do his best for us both. He says it's time I stood on my own feet and he would be angry if he thought I'd asked you for a lift.' I was grateful for her concern and for the extra time I would have at the boarding house and when I stood at the gate watching Porteous reversing the car out, I saw that Mrs Samuels was wiping her eyes with her handkerchief. I felt guilty about her concern, for her disapproval of my father and because she, who was no relation of mine, should be distressed on my account.

For a long time Porteous called for me in the morning, with Mr Samuels sitting in the back of his car, reading his morning paper, and deposited me at the factory gate. Battalions of girls swept past me on their bicycles, calling out 'Swank!' but the more sympathetic added their voices, 'leave the poor kid alone,' but clearly they could not understand why I arrived and left in a motor car when my clothes and shyness indicated a very different life style. At last one was delegated to question me. 'No,' I admitted, 'they're not my parents, just people who I've known for a long time.'

It would be many years before I was to see either of my kind friends again, although they sent Porteous to help us move our few belongings to our new abode. When he had unloaded the last paper parcel and stood, cap in hand, waiting to say goodbye, I offered him a shilling and asked, 'If your Inkossikaas asks you where we've moved to, please say you've forgotten the address or something like that, I don't think she would like it if she knew.' He gave me a quizzical look and said, 'If she asks, I must tell her, but if she does not, I will say nothing.' He shook my hand, saluted smartly and drove away and Stella and I turned to inspect our new home.

'I've got just the place for you two,' my father had said. 'It's a nice little flat in Cameron Street and it's near both your places of work.' He looked pleased with himself. 'And its only two quid a month with linen, but you'll have to see to your food yourselves,' he added. 'Cameron Street?' asked Stella angrily. 'We can't go and live there. It's full of common people and there are even Coloureds living at the top end, why can't we stay where we are?' But he would not change his mind, saying that he had already paid the first month's rent and then remarked off-handedly 'Mrs Sherwin'll keep an eye on you, it's her place.'

The name struck a chord in Stella's mind. 'Is she Thora Sherwin's mother?' she asked. My father nodded. Thora had won the first beauty competition held in the colony and had been selected to be 'Miss Rhodesia' and was now in Johannesburg where she was to compete for the title of 'Miss South Africa'. Forseeing a rewarding friendship with this lovely Miss Sherwin, Stella changed her mind about Cameron Street.

It ran parallel to the main road through the city, and had once been the domain of the first white settlers. They had built large rambling houses, often on piles, with verandahs running all the way round, and

231

had laid out brick-pathed flower beds, orchards of orange and lemon trees and groves of paw-paw and guava trees to shield the main house from the kias where their servants lived. As the settlers had moved to the outer suburbs, the area had become run-down; the houses became boarding houses, and refuges for shop girls, lone women or men, abandoned families and drunks.

Our 'flat' consisted of one bedroom, furnished with two beds, two chairs and a wardrobe: washing facilities existed 'around the back', which meant a trip right around the house into the dingey bathroom where cockroaches scuttled under the bath and spiders hung from the ceiling and where a large notice announced 'No Washing of Clothes Allowed'. During the rainy season we were to discover that we got wetter during the rush from bedroom to bathroom than we ever were in the bath, where the water trickled into the rust-spotted bath from a lime encrusted tap. In front of our bedroom, facing directly onto the street, was a small verandah, just big enough for two chairs and a potted fern; and on one side was the kitchen – a lean-to, hastily built on to meet the demand by desperate families who could not afford to eat at the Criterion Café or the third-rate tea-rooms which were springing up in the town. It was made of corrugated iron and was furnished with a small table and two shelves. My father had thoughtfully provided a one-burner paraffin stove and by its feeble flame we were to make ourselves cups of tea or boil eggs.

For this menage, my father paid the rent of two pounds from our pay packets, handing Stella two pounds and ten shillings, and me, one pound and ten shillings; and when I insisted that my needs were equal to hers if not more so, he rounded on me crying 'There you go again, only thinking of yourself! What about me? I been living on the smell of an oil-rag for most of me life and anyway, Stella's the eldest.' I was baffled at this explanation but too cowardly to argue beyond muttering 'It's not fair.' 'What about meals?' asked Stella. 'That's a nice little stove, it cost me nearly a quid,' he replied. 'You've got four bleedin' pound between you both, that ought to be enough for food,' and he picked up his weatherbeaten old hat, jammed it on his head and left.

Clothes were our main pre-occupation. We haunted the sales and half price days, where we bought dresses for five shillings each, shoes at the same price and flawed stockings which laddered at the first wearing. We ate bread and jam, meat pies and dough-nuts and rapidly lost patience with the paraffin stove which we sold for the price my father had paid for it. We did not return the money to him and said we had lent it when he did, at last, ask.

Stella decided to sell her bicycle, saying that the distance to her office was only a mile and it was more interesting to walk than to ride amidst the traffic, dodging past mule wagons, motor cars, cyclists and pedestrians. There was also the possibility that she would have to pass other offices where several of her admirers worked, although we both giggled and walked faster when the two Katsoulis brothers came out of their bakery to stand and wait to accost us. Their pale blue eyes glinted as they watched us and they mouthed kisses when we drew level, asking in broken English 'Come out with me tonight,' or 'M-m-mh I like to kiss you?' Our pace quickened as we scurried past but their laughter told us they would have been equally embarrassed if we had stopped and engaged them in conversation. 'Cheek,' cried Stella. 'As if I'd let a dirty Greek touch me.' 'Why do you always say they're dirty?' I asked. 'Aunt Anne's Stathes is a very nice man.' Immediately she was on the defensive. 'I suppose you'd go out with one of them, if they asked you,' she retorted, but I had no desire to be asked out by a Greek or any man. I was afraid of all men.

Thora, the failed Beauty Queen, returned in triumph to her native city and we were invited to see her prizes, all dresses and underwear packed into smart leather luggage. We lay on her bed fingering the stuff of her new clothes, and she asked 'Come to the party with me on Saturday night, both of you of course, there's a shortage of girls.' We were thrilled but immediately our minds turned to that all-important matter of evening dresses. All functions after dark necessitated a long, sleeveless garment, preferably with a low neck and – even more daring – a low back and no such garment lurked in our wardrobe. 'We've got nothing to wear' we told our new friend, but she was not to be put off and invited us to look through her pre-competition dresses and to choose anything we liked.

We spent the Saturday afternoon before the party rolling our hair into lead curlers, and then lay on our beds with mud packs over our rapidly petrifying juvenile faces; and my sister crouching over a small mirror, deftly plucked her eyebrows. Eagerly we dressed, convinced that we would certainly be the belles of the party, and Stella twirled around in her ice-blue satin asking 'How do I look?' But I had overlooked one very important adjunct to my toilette and when I had donned the bright mauve satin dress I found it reached just below my knees and would not hide my brown and white brogues, the only shoes I possessed apart from my old school shoes. In a frenzy of despair I threw myself on the bed to cry that I could not come to the party, and at last Thora was summoned for her advice.

'I didn't know you were so much taller than me,' she said, 'but don't you have any other shoes?' I sniffed and shook my head. 'Well, I'll see if Ma's got something that will fit you,' and she left to re-appear some minutes later with her mother's best black satin, all bows and straps and completely backless and also with a pair of black and gold brocade shoes, slightly down at heel and almost three sizes too big. 'We'll stuff some cotton wool down the backs,' said the resourceful Thora, 'and you'll have to leave everything off underneath,' and she sniffed, 'unless you've got a low-backed brassiere?' I had no such garment and did not want to go to the party almost naked, with large boat-like shoes slipping off my feet, but my sister began to cry, saying 'You'll have to come, you look all right, honest you do. You can't stay here alone, so stop that noise, get dressed and let's go.' With my hair combed out and in a dress which was many sizes too big and which bunched around my middle and hung in voluminous folds down to my feet, I hobbled up the road to the party.

It was obvious from the beginning that none of the boys or men, in their best suits and Brylcreemed hair, was likely to ask me to dance and I volunteered to wind the gramophone and change the needle. 'Honestly, I'd love to,' I lied as I grappled for the straps which threatened to slip from my shoulders and to expose me, bra-less and naked; and I noticed some of the flashier young men tittering as they dared each other to ask me for a dance. But I had never been taught to dance; such matters were considered far too frivolous for a Convent girl and any mention of parties or dances drew disapproving looks from the nuns, so I was content – although still very embarrassed – to change the needle, wind up the gramophone and turn the record. Lights were put out and couples huddled together on the living room dance floor, fox-trotting, waltzing or two-stepping to whatever rhythmn their senses dictated, and from the bedrooms and the verandah came suppressed giggles and laughter and sometimes, slaps. 'I Want To Be Happy', 'Horsey Keep Your Tail Up', 'Always' and 'Yes We Have No Bananas' were the rage and those who knew the words crooned them softly as they lost themselves in the make-believe world of glamour, riches and handsome people.

With eyes half-closed and in the embrace of a spotty-faced young swain, Stella glided past me, opening her eyes fully to look at me and ask

'Why don't you dance with one of those fellows over there?' I shook my head and frowned, saying I hadn't been asked. 'No wonder,' she said. 'You look a real peach in that dress.' I picked up the folds of the offending garment, and holding the shoes in my hand I left the party and ran down the street, keeping well to the centre under the lights until I reached the flat. For a long time I lay in bed snivelling and feeling a complete fool, but when I heard Stella's footsteps on the verandah, I pretended I was asleep and ignored her whispered 'Are you all right?'

There were invitations to picnics at Mermaids Pool, drives out to Hunyani on Sundays and parties at other people's homes which came our way via Thora, but I found excuses not to go, saying I was brushing up my shorthand and typewriting; I wanted an office job like my sister's and I envied her for her popularity with her friends, her clothes and her easy, sophisticated manner, and felt that I was in a rut in the factory office. The real reason I refused invitations was that I did not possess a bathing suit or the most elementary clothes for outings such as those and was determined not to make a fool of myself again.

It was an accident which precipitated our change of residence. We were about to go for a walk up to the town to look at the shop windows and I had just washed my hands and was running for a jersey. As I put my hand to the bathroom door it slipped and went through the glass panel, almost severing my left thumb and small finger. Blood gushed out and splattered on my dress and when I looked at my hand and seized the wrist to stop the flow of blood, I saw the severed tendons and the skin, hanging loose. Screaming with fright more than pain, I wrapped my hand in a towel and dashed into the main house to ask Mrs Sherwin for help. No one was at home and when my sister reached me, we realised it was the matter for a doctor. But it was late at night and we knew no one else in the house and so, half running and half walking, we went to the Main Hospital at the northern end of the town where we rang the night bell.

'It's a mess,' said the nurse. 'I'll bind it up now but you'll have to come in early in the morning to have it stitched,' and she made a note in her book and handed me several small tablets which I was to take during the night when the pain got bad. 'Where do you live?' and when we told her, she tapped her pencil on her teeth and asked how we had reached the hospital. 'We walked,' I told her and she frowned, saying, 'I wish I could admit you, but I can't. I'm sorry but you'll have to come back early

235

tomorrow, as early as you can.' I hardly slept that night but sat up rocking backwards and forwards, waiting for the pill to take effect, and then dozed for a few hours. At last, just as it became daylight, I got up, dressed and started on that two-mile walk back to the hospital where I went straight into the theatre to wait for the first doctor on day duty.

At midday, when I had come round from the anaesthetic, I was given a cup of tea and shakily and slowly I walked home, to fall onto my bed and sleep until Stella came back from her office. 'I phoned Aunty Betty from the office,' she told me, 'but she said she was busy and couldn't come, but she'll let the old man know so perhaps he'll be along to see you. What did they charge you and how many stitches did you have?' she asked. 'I told them to make the bill out to T.W. Sadler and you shouldn't call him the old man,' I retorted, 'he won't like it,' and I gave her a description of the hospital theatre, exaggerating the number of scalpels and tools I had seen. I told her that my thumb and finger had been stitched and that altogether I had a total of fifty-four stitches in my hand. 'But what about the factory?' I cried, 'I can't go to work for at least two more days and I'll get the sack.'

My father came that night, grumbling at the inconvenience of a night trip to town when his lorry battery was flat, and at my incompetence in opening doors. 'You'll lose yer bleedin' job if you go on like this,' he muttered, almost as though I had done it on purpose. There was no sympathy for the pain and fright I had endured, nor any comfort or solicitude, but he left saying he would call at the factory and explain my absence. 'But you'll have to pull your socks up and get back to work as soon as possible,' he said, 'as soon as that stops bleeding; thank Gawd it ain't your right hand,' and he left.

Two days later, with a hand like a boxer's glove, I reported back to my office and found to my delight that one of the office girls had taken over the schedules, coupons and stamps and that I was to operate the new Moisture Testing laboratory which was located in the vast storeroom away from the factory. I started work later and left when the last samples had been weighed, the loss of moisture noted, the furnace switched off and the cupels cleaned ready for tomorrow's tests. I enjoyed the quiet and solitude and the absolute lack of noise, and I read everything I could find, borrow or buy; the factory girls' *True Confessions* abandoned on the lawns, copies of *Mabs* and *Women's Weekly* abandoned by the Sherwin family, and all Edgar Wallace's stories lent by Mr Warner who lived in the flat next to us came my way and were eagerly read. I ventured into the world of P.C. Wren and John Buchan, not realising that I was about six years behind in my choice and that

236

other sixteen-year-olds had long since done with those authors. I haunted the book shops in town and had books put aside which I paid for out of my meagre allowance. 'You're wasting your money,' said Stella, who boasted that she had never read a complete book in her life.

'What's all this?' angrily demanded my father, shaking the hospital account under my nose. 'Couldn't you get the chemist up the road to see to your hand? He's open until ten o'clock,' he said. My sister snatched the account from him saying, 'You're lucky she didn't stay in hospital. The nurse on duty wanted to keep her but we knew you'd moan about the cost.' Meekly he looked at her and then shrugged his shoulders. 'S'pose yer right, but I've also had it in the neck from your Aunty. She met Mrs Samuels the other day and they had a proper old barney. Don't know what its got to do with that bleedin' woman. Said you shouldn't be living here on yerrown, so I've got a bit of furniture I bought at the market square and the house is quite decent. I've already seen Ma Sherwin and told her you'll be leaving at the end of the month. You girls will have a nice little home and I've put down a deposit on a coupla bikes. Much better all round. Just me and me two girls,' and he grinned slyly at us before taking his hat and going to the door. 'Ta-ta then,' he said merrily and he chugged off down the road in a cloud of exhaust smoke.

Stella was furious, and sat whitefaced and biting her lip. 'Live out in the bush!' she cried. 'Nobody asks me what I want. Just pushed about, and when I'm beginning to make friends and meet other people, we've got to move to live with *him*.' She spat out the last words with venom. 'And ride to work with the niggers through the bush,' and she threw herself angrily onto her bed. 'Nobody's going to come all the way out of town to take me out and he'll never allow me to go out when I want to. It's not fair,' she cried; but we packed our few belongings and were fetched to take up residence with our father in his newly refurbished house.

We were hardly better off. There was no bathroom in this house and water was hauled up in a bucket from a deep well only a few yards from our bedroom window. Stella and I slept in a double bed and kept our clothes in an assortment of cardboard boxes or behind a corner curtain. Reuben had been sacked for a minor infringement and one of the garden boys had brought his brother, Time, to work as cook and houseboy. 'That's a silly name,' I said when I heard it. 'Whoever gave him that?' 'As long as he can iron me shirts and do us a bit of stoo now and again, it don't matter,' said my father. But Time had only been with us for a few days when my father began to complain. 'That bleedin' nigger ain't ever 'ere,' he said. 'When I come home I want a nice cuppa tea, but the whole bloomin' house is locked up.'

We did not have long to wait for enlightenment. Our servant had not appeared to cook our evening meal and Stella and I were struggling to light the Dover stove when we suddenly heard the sound of many feet running up the path from the compound. We looked out of the window and saw all the five garden boys huddling against each other, and banging on the back door. 'What the bleedin' 'ell's going on,' yelled my father as he opened the door. Grey faces and rolling eyes met him, and the most senior man spoke up. 'It's your cook, Inkoos,' he cried. 'He's a tagati, he's making medicine in his room and we are afraid he's going to put the evil eye on us. We will die, Inkoos, and Philemon who brought him here, is now lying on his bed, sick.' 'What the devil are they saying,' asked my father, sensing that something very serious was afoot.

I remembered Vinyu's explanation of curses and the evil eye and explained that the men had accused Time of being a witchdoctor and that at this very moment, he was busily engaged in putting together powerful potions or casting spells and that the men were terrified. Angrily my father stalked down to the compound where he banged on Time's door, shouting at him to come out this minute. Stella and I clutched at each other as we stood with the garden boys, expecting to see the hideous mask and trappings of a witchdoctor emerge, but instead the servant came out clad only in a pair of shorts and a white vest. For minutes there were accusations and denials, mutterings and shaking of heads and long pauses when everyone stood staring at the ground. 'What are they saying?' demanded my father, and during the long pauses, I interpreted. Yes, said the cook, he had been making medicine, and he returned to his hut and came back with a small cooking pot full of leaves which he showed us. His brother Philemon was sick with fever, he added, and he had been lying in his hut these many days and showed no sign of getting better. Time had remembered that certain herbs grew some miles away on the banks of the river and he had gone there this afternoon to gather them and had brought them back to make an infusion for his brother to drink. I told my father all this, and then one of the garden boys stepped forward into the circle of light and asked 'If it is as this man says, why then did I find that thing over there lying at my door?' and he pointed to something lying in the grass. We walked over and my father bent down to pick up the carcase of a small, dead kitten, its front paws tied and its lips sewn together with what we first thought was cotton, but on closer inspection found to be strands of black hair.

'Strewth,' cried my father, 'What the bloody hell's going on 'ere?' Time looked away, stonyfaced, and the garden boys huddled closer together, shivering in the night air, and I felt a chill as I stood watching. 'Bring that lamp 'ere,' cried my father, 'we'll see what else Mr Time's got in his room.' But Time leapt forward to stand at his door, barring any entry, his eyes flashing and his breathing rapid. The garden boys were called to seize the cook and to hold him and my father lifted the lamp as he entered the dark hut. The rough bed stood in a corner and a string was run from one end of the room to the other. On it were heaped clothes of the cook's and a blanket had been thrown over the petrol box which stood in a corner. My father lifted it and we saw spread out on the surface several items which we could not at first identify, but when we looked closer we saw a dead frog, some animal teeth, a snakeskin, several pebbles, white chicken feathers and what at first sight, appeared to be bundles of fluff. Carefully my father lifted them to smell and then he hurriedly put them down. 'It's hair,' he said and he turned to Stella, 'Your's and your sister's,' and he turned to flick at a small pile of white shards, 'and these are fingernails or perhaps, toenails,' he said. There was a deathly silence in the hut as my father gathered together all the impedimenta of the witchdoctor.

'Now boy', he said, 'you've got exactly ten minutes to clear orf, pack your things and go, otherwise me and the boys'll tie you up and take you to the police station. I know its late, but we'll do it and you'll be charged for practising witchcraft, and its against the law; but first, I'll give you a few lashes on me own account,' and he called to one of the boys to run up to the house and fetch his sjambok from where it hung in the kitchen. The garden boys brought wood which they heaped onto their fire and the tied and trussed Time was laid on the ground and thrashed; I had repeated my father's words to him only to be met by a stony glare and silence, but I shivered with fear, feeling that somehow my sister and I were implicated and might suffer harm from this man. Before the thrashing had ceased, my father told me to tell Time that each man would give him an extra lash to counter any ill-effects or curses which lay in wait for them. 'Make it sound good,' urged my father, 'scare the shit out of the sod.' Slowly I advanced to stand before the cook. 'Time,' I said softly, 'you are a wicked man, you have brought evil to our house and to these men here, your brothers. You wish them dead and for my sister and I, you were ready to punish us. We have done you no ill and are innocent. You must go as my father says, this very night, but if you do not, he will call the police and they will catch you.' I trembled with fright and longed to be far away from this malevolent influence and regretted it had been my lot to speak with my father's words. Each man came forward and summoning all his might, he brought the whip down on to the defenceless victim.

Slowly the fire burned down as we stood in the dark under the syringa trees and at last Time came out of his hut with his clothes bundled into a blanket; the petrol box and the loathsome artifacts of his calling were heaped onto the dying embers of the fire and without a backward glance, the servant disappeared into the darkness towards the river. But where were they to sleep? asked the garden boys. Did the Inkoos expect them to return to their huts, where this very moment, many evils were waiting for them? They could not set foot over the doorway, they insisted, and they sat down on their haunches spitting through their teeth in disgust. 'I've cleared out me old house,' agreed my father after some minutes thought, 'you lot can sleep there tonight, but tomorrow first thing, we'll burn down these huts and then you'll have to start building others.' Horrified looks came from the men and one stepped forward to ask 'Here Inkoos? We cannot build over the old huts, we will have to move from this place, we cannot build here.'

After many minutes of argument and speculation, it was decided that they would move a few yards away and would re-build their homes nearer the hedge, and at last, weary and still afraid, we went back to the house and went supperless to bed. But my father was not finished, there was still the matter of Philemon to settle and at first light when we heard the boys shouting and calling in the compound, I ran with my father to see what was happening. Wood and sticks had been piled against the huts and the men stood around with all their belongings lying in heaps, asking each other if these too, were to be consigned to the flames. 'Tell them I've got some of me own magic to do, I'll make their things safe but I can't do the same for their huts,' and he went back to the house, running as fast as he could.

He re-appeared several minutes later carrying an old army bugle in one hand and in the other a horse-tail fly whisk and a glass jar half full of grey powder. 'It's gunpowder outa them old cartridges I've had for bleedin' years,' he said, and then he added, with a wry smile, 'now just watch carefully and when I stop blowing me bugle, I want you to walk in front of me and wave this 'ere horsetail over them bundles but fer Gawd's sake, don't laugh.' I kept a straight face but found it hard to do

240

so when he stood before each heap of clothes sprinkling the contents of the jar a few feet in front, and then he stood between the huts, looking quizzically up at the sun, shifting his position several times and then at last he raised the bugle to his lips. The eerie, strangled sounds rang through the clear morning air, the boys gazed at him in awe and I solemnly advanced to make passes over each pile of clothing as the last trembling notes died away. Tip-toeing carefully between each bundle my father applied a lighted match to the gunpowder which fizzled and burst into sparks to the cries of 'Auw!' and the solemn clapping of hands.

'Tell 'em there ain't a curse left between 'ere and the Hunyani', said my father triumphantly, 'but we'll have to think up some other rigmarole when they've built their new huts.' Well pleased with himself, he gave the men the day off to go into the bush and cut down trees for their huts and to fetch mud and clay from the river to complete the plastering. 'Will Time try something else?' I asked. 'Not now,' said my father. 'His brother Philemon's been watching. I'll shift the bleeder', and he strode towards the cowering boy who had crept out of his hut which stood away from the others. 'D'ye want a taste of your brother's medicine?' I was told to ask. 'No Inkoos, I am going,' said the frightened Philemon and he picked up his blankets and bundles and fled in the same direction his brother had taken last night.

The new huts were built and the only concession my father made to the spirits was to allow the boys to brew a few petrol cans of the native beer and to allow them to kill a black cockerel. They sprinkled the blood from the unfortunate bird at the entrance of each new hut and moved in, Time forgotten; but they often sat around their fires at night, laughing and chortling as they reminded each other of the Inkoos' powerful medicine.

As the days passed, a new servant was engaged but Stella became more and more discontented. She had many invitations from her boy-friends but often, one visit to our house was enough. 'What's 'e want?' my father would ask and when Stella explained they had come to take her out, he grumbled and groused and asked who they were, what did their parents do, where did they work? 'A Civil Servant is what you want to set your sights on,' said my father, 'a feller with a decent job, social standing and a pension after thirty years.' If any of the gallants wore scruffy clothes, had dirty fingernails or innocently admitted they were motor mechanics or railway workers, he was openly rude to them, saying 'Me daughter's too good for the likes of you,' and as they mounted their bicycles and rode away, he shouted insults and threats at their diminishing backs, promising more than words the next time.

Some were more persistent than others and either sat in their cars and hooted for Stella, or joked with my father as they buttered him up, passing their cigarettes and laughing at his every observation, and were later declared to be 'jolly nice blokes, real gentlemen'. Stella became braver and accepted every invitation despite my father's grumbles and complaints.

Among her more persistent admirers was Tommy. He had a long dark green car in which he drove up with a flourish, scattering the hens pecking in the yard and lolling back as he pressed the hooter to summon Stella. When she joined him, they drove off in a cloud of exhaust smoke and she would return late, carrying parcels of stockings, underwear and lengths of material which she told me they had bought at the Indian store on their way to the race course, where Tommy kept a few horses. They had stopped at some of the more grand hotels for 'a drink', which she declined to define, and she was back for just a few moments to change, they were going out for dinner. Tommy sat in the car waiting for her, ignoring my father who prowled around clearing his throat, and at last when he could bear it no longer, he sidled up to the car to ask 'What make?' Tommy stepped out to discuss the car with him and my father grinned ingratiatingly at his every remark.

'There's a first-class gent for you,' he would tell me later, 'a real corker, not afraid to spend his money on a decent girl,' but I had seen the calculating eye, and felt his look of appraisal as he watched Stella approach the car. 'He's old,' I retorted, 'and bald, and fat,' but his only reply was: 'You're just a stupid kid, jealous too.' But I wondered why my sister went out with Tommy.

Suddenly he came no longer. Stella cried a lot and stood anxiously at the gate watching every cloud of dust as it approached and then turned dispiritedly away when she saw it was not Tommy. As we rode to work in the mornings, I longed to ask her why she was so unhappy, but her wretched face warned me not to broach the subject and we parted, promising to meet as usual to ride home together later. As the days passed, and other young men appeared she cheered up and soon Tommy was forgotten. 'Why doesn't he take you out any longer?' I asked eventually. For some minutes she was silent and then she said, 'He tried to get fresh with me and when I said I wasn't that sort of girl, he asked me why had I taken all his presents? I told him I thought he loved me and

242

wanted to marry me, but he just laughed and said he wasn't the marrying kind.' 'Did you want him to come back? Is that why you stood at the gate looking up the road?' I asked. 'Yes', she admitted. 'He's rich and I would have done what he wanted me to, if he'd promised to marry me.' I was shocked to think that she was prepared to commit a sin such as that, and when I said so, she laughed and asked, 'You don't believe all that stuff about purity and chastity the nuns were always talking about, do you?' 'Yes,' I told her, and I also believed in marrying for love, but she laughed all the more scornfully and said: 'In that case, you're a fool, look what happened to poor Daddy, look at what our mother did to him and he loved her. No thank you, if a feller's got money I'll marry him, there's no such thing as love, as you call it.'

As though in answer to my father's dearest wishes, four young men who worked in the Department of Customs and Excise moved into the empty house nearby where the Samuels family had lived those years ago. A notice was hung on the front gate announcing that the house was now 'Customs House' and below were the names of the residents. The wounds that Tommy had inflicted were soon healed when one of the young men came to our house to beg a loan of a few chairs. 'We're having a party tonight for our friends in town, would you like to come?' they asked Stella, and my father who was lurking nearby, preened himself and answered for her, saying what time and yes, of course, she would love to go.

For a long time I lay in bed listening to the music which drifted through the still night, hearing the shouts and yells from the exuberant guests, and at last I heard whispering on the front porch, then giggles and Stella crept into the room. 'Tell you about it tomorrow', she said as she got into bed, but when the next day came, she said very little except that they were very nice young men and that there had been lots of girls there. 'Snobs, all of them,' she volunteered. 'Some of them were those kids we were at school with and they kept calling me Saddlebackie, I felt so embarrassed.'

Although her new friends never took her out or included her in their picnics, she was always welcome at their house and she appeared to enjoy the company of each young man for the space of a few weeks at a time. Later and later she would creep into bed, and one night she confessed that she thought the men had steady girls in town and that they were just playing with her, but she persevered as she worked her way through them. My father became more and more angry and sat up waiting for her, a practice he had recently resorted to when he'd discovered she was not at home one night when he'd come in to turn out my light, and then decided to walk over to Customs House and to fetch his errant daughter home. The house was in darkness except for one pink light and he stumbled around the garden searching for the front door, where he stood banging and knocking and calling 'Is Stella there?' For some time there was no answer, then he saw the door of the pink lighted room open and heard the hoarse whisper 'Can't you see the signal?' Baffled, he strode in to the room, where Stella was lying on the bed, her clothes in disarray and her admirer hiding behind the door.

He marched in and pulled Stella to her feet, and without a word he dragged and pulled his recalcitrant daughter back home. He demanded an explanation, shouting and swearing, but she sat silently in her chair, snivelling and wiping her eyes. 'You'll get yourself into trouble, if you ain't careful,' he said, 'you know what I mean, don't you?' She looked at him sullenly. 'He was only kissing me, and I was tired and just lying down, we weren't doing anything.' 'Kissing?' roared my father, 'with yer bleedin' clothes orf?' 'I didn't want to crease my dress, and Len said the bed was more comfortable.' She looked innocently at my father, daring him to say what was in his mind.

Had he been mistaken, he wondered? Was it only a picture in his mind? 'Bleedin' civil servants,' he snorted, 'they oughta know better.' 'Well,' said Stella, 'you said they were the best, didn't you?' 'It don't matter who they are,' he admitted reluctantly, 'if any of 'em get you into trouble, you'll have to get married. Gawd Help us, you're not nineteen yet, you don't want to be pushing a pram at your age.' 'I don't want to get married either,' she retorted, her spirits rising as she realised he was already repenting his hasty action. ' 'Ere,' said my father, 'what did he mean when he said didn't you see the signal? What signal?' 'Dunno what you're talking about,' replied Stella as she rose from her seat. 'I'm going to bed, you've been making a fuss about nothing, it's late and I'm tired.' She got up and put her arms around him and with her cheek against his she whispered, 'Don't be cross with me, I know what I'm doing.' They kissed and stood for a long time and over her shoulder she saw me standing in the darkened doorway. She crossed her fingers as she winked at me and then freed herself and followed me into our bedroom.

I looked at her with admiration, partly because she had emerged unscathed from what I saw as a dangerous situation with Len, and partly because she had got the better of my father. 'What did he mean about a signal,' I asked. 'Oh that,' she laughed. 'When one of the men has a girl in his room he throws a red scarf over the light to warn the others not to

244

come in.' 'Were you really just kissing?' I persisted. 'Don't be so wet,' she said as she smiled to herself.

Her discontent grew and nothing in the house pleased her. How, she asked, could we invite anyone, girls even, to our house when there was hardly enough furniture in it? Why did we have to wind up buckets of water from the well, straining and striving at the windlass like niggers, why was there no bathroom and why couldn't I also go out with boys and men? She hoped I would be her ally, but when I replied that I didn't want to join her or to go out with men she laughed all the more and said: 'You're stupid, lots of blokes ask about you, they want to meet you and take you out.' But I was afraid and had little self confidence and shook my head saying, 'I don't want to.'

Suddenly, quite unexpectedly, a letter arrived with a Portuguese stamp on it. It had been re-addressed several times and from the date we saw it had been posted in Beira three weeks earlier. It read 'Dear Bill, I will be in Salisbury on 30th and would very much like to see you and your family if at all possible. I will be staying at Meikles Hotel and would be glad if you could come to dinner with me on that night. Please leave your answer at the hotel for me. Yours sincerely, George Williams.'

'Bleedin' cheek,' snorted my father, 'who does he think he is?' But the more he pondered the invitation, the more attractive it seemed. He could ask in a round-about way for news of Charlotte – without them kids knowing of course, it would have to be done on the sly – and he could show off his daughters in a posh place and get a decent meal as well. From our pay packets he extracted an extra note, telling us to get ourselves some decent stockings, not them thick ones we usually wore, and some material to run up a couple of new dresses, and he wrote his acceptance to George Williams.

Stella and I feverishly cut out and sewed our new dresses, full length as fashion demanded, and with our new white shoes and first pairs of fully fashioned stockings, we presented ourselves at the hotel. Standing in the foyer was the usual collection of farmers, business men, young bloods and smartly dressed and coiffed women, and amongst them was the tall figure of our uncle, dark, with shining black hair and eyes, almost Portuguese to look at, and as he advanced to greet us his brilliant white teeth flashed and I noticed he sported one or two gold ones.

George Williams was the eldest of the Williams's sons and although he had been to university in Cape Town, his father had hoped that he would follow in his footsteps and take over Rockingstone Farm. But when George had instead been accepted by the Rhodesia Railways as a cadet, Grandpa had not minded, and the task of managing the farm fell to their youngest son, Rhodes. George had worked in every department of the railways and when the line was extended into Portuguese East Africa the Rhodesia Railways had been nominated to administer the line eastwards into Moçambique and Nyasaland and George was appointed to be manager in charge of the new line, as yet unbuilt. The trains went no further than Umtali, the most eastern town in Rhodesia, and here the work started.

For five years the men cut through the bush, bored tunnels through the granite hills and died like flies from malaria and yellow fever, and then came to their first staging post, Macequece, where a depot was established. George moved his office further east where the line would branch off to cross the Zambesi River at a point where the Shangaan tribesmen lived and which was named Dondo from the name given by them to the sloping valley which lay ahead. Ten years later the line was completed at Beira on the coast, where the rivers Buzi and Pungwe flowed into the Indian Ocean, and Dondo was the nickname given to my uncle who had lived under canvas for those ten years, directing the men in their work, supervising the building of the bund on which the line was built, organising patrols to capture and punish the tribesmen who descended in their hordes onto the line and stole the sleepers, fishplates and bolts to make into spears and knives, and arranging shooting parties to prevent the elephants from tearing up the lines. Building the four hundred miles of line had taken many years and cost many lives and a great deal of money. The men who had done the work became heroes in their own life-time and had many stories to tell.

Now we stood shyly with my father as Dondo came to greet us, looking admiringly at Stella and me in our white and pink organdy dresses. When he led us into dinner I was stricken with panic at the array of cutlery on the table. Dondo and my father chatted amiably and then our uncle said, 'I've really come to Salisbury to arrange for my wedding at the Catholic Church in a month's time.' I saw my father freeze at the mention of the Church, but he pulled himself together to ask, 'Ain't you married then?' 'No,' said Dondo, 'never had the time, spent all those years in the bush, but it's not too late, and she's very nice, you'll meet her just before the wedding. We would like the two girls to be bridesmaids and you to be the best man, Bill. I don't know anyone in Salisbury.' 'Why don't yer get married in Beira,' asked my father. 'They're all bl—, they're all Catholics there ain't they?' 'It's a long story, I'll tell you some other time, but Molly wants to get married here.' 'Can't think why,' grumbled my father, already seeking obstacles to put in everyone's way. 'If yer ain't got any friends here, Beira seems the better bet.' 'No,' said Dondo, 'she insists on the Cathedral here, and we've all got to please the little woman, haven't we?'

He dug into his pocket and extracted a sketch of the dresses we were to wear. They would have to be made, he said, and he would pay for everything, hats, gloves, shoes and flowers, and he drew out a large bundle of notes which he passed to my father. 'There's twenty pounds there, ought to be enough,' he said, 'but only the best mind, and if you need more, let me know when we both come back.'

'Twenty bleedin' quid,' breathed my father as we bowled home in his old lorry, 'all to spend on frocks and stuff! What couldn't I do with twenty quid.' Deftly Stella leaned over, snatched the money from him and stuffed it into her purse. 'Oh no you don't,' she laughed. 'I'll look after that.' 'But what about me suit?' said my father, suddenly inspired. 'You can wear your navy blue,' replied Stella. 'This is for just us two, Dondo said so.' Glumly he looked ahead, he felt an injustice had been done; best man or no, he would have to make do with what he'd got, there wasn't going to be any twenty quid handed to him just like that. 'Bleedin' Williams,' he muttered.

Resisting any impulse to make the dresses ourselves on the hand sewing-machine we had bought on Hire Purchase, we found Magdelena, a coloured dressmaker who lived in a dingy little room near the Masonic Hotel, and patterns and materials were discussed. Hats at Barbours, the prestige shop in the main street, and everything else that was necessary, were bought and what remained, we shared. 'We'll need that when we leave here,' said Stella. I looked at her in astonishment. 'Leave?' I asked. 'You don't think I'm going to stay here any longer than we have to,' she said. 'Stuck out here in the bush, we don't ever see anyone, can't ask friends to come and when we do, he's so darned rude to them. And he takes all our money,' she added finally.

Did she perhaps realise that if we both left, my father would find it harder to get us back? We were still under age and we had often heard him tell people that he had legal custody of us, but we had not been fully aware of what it meant. Feelings of guilt overcame me and I was not sure I wanted to run away with her. 'Let's see what happens after the wedding,' we agreed.

Another letter arrived from Dondo, asking us to come again for dinner and to meet the bride the day before the wedding so that last minute details could be discussed. 'This is Molly', he said. 'Mrs Molly Haynes, who's brave enough to take me on,' and he laughed heartily at his own joke. She was little, and beautiful, like a small Japanese doll, her short dark hair expertly cut close to her head and her high cheek bones and almond eyes giving her an exotic, oriental appearance. She seemed shy and spoke quietly and obviously adored her large handsome bridegroom, but I knew my father's brain was buzzing with curiosity. 'Mrs did you say? Widow?' he asked. Molly flushed and looked at Dondo for reassurance. He took her hand in his and patted it, saying, 'Yes, poor little darling, you wouldn't think she has a six-year-old son, would you? We left him in Beira with friends, he wouldn't understand what was happening,' and he leaned forward to kiss his little bride.

There were only five of us in that vast cathedral for the wedding service; Molly looked radiant in oyster crepe, Stella and I stood dutifully in our places, my father constantly loosened the unfamiliar stiff collar and there was only one slight hitch. When the priest held forward his prayer book for the coin, which would signify Dondo's worldly goods, to be placed on it by the best man, my father frantically searched through his pockets knowing quite well that he had not a penny on him. Reassuringly, Dondo drew out the necessary coin from his own pocket and the service proceeded. 'Didn't 'arf feel a bloomin' fool,' confessed my father afterwards, ' 'e should have told me I had to put money on the prayer book.'

We stood waiting for the train to leave for Victoria Falls where a short honeymoon was to be spent; kisses were exchanged and then Molly asked 'Wouldn't you girls like to come and stay with us when you get your leave?' We nodded our heads in agreement but told her we would only be able to go after Christmas, our brother would be home then and we hadn't seen him for almost a year. 'Well, just let us know when you get your leave and we'll send you your train tickets. George will see to everything and you'll only need pocket money.' We thanked her profusely but my father seemed ill at ease and drew Dondo aside, asking him to walk a few paces up the platform.

'I suppose you know I've got custody of my kids,' he asked Dondo, who looked puzzled at the turn of the conversation. 'The court give me custody when the divorce went through and they're mine until they turn twenty-one.' 'Why are you telling me this,' asked Dondo. 'Because I can't let 'em go swanning off any-old-where', said my father. 'I was the injured party and Charlotte deserted me and her kids, and I've struggled to give 'em a good education and I ain't going to just let 'em go now, I

248

spent everything I earned on 'em,' and he sniffed and wiped the all-too-ready tear from his eye.

'We're only asking them for a holiday,' replied Dondo, 'not to stay or leave home, only a holiday.' 'And what about Charlotte?' asked my father, 'is she in Beira too? I don't want 'er to think she can take the kids away from me now. Not when I've worked me fingers to the bone, keeping 'em at the Convent. I deserve something back.' Dondo was appalled. 'Perhaps you don't know it Bill, but Charlotte has been in South Africa for years, you must have known that at the time of the divorce.' 'Well,' said my father, 'I don't want my kids to have anything to do with her, in fact, I told 'em years ago she was dead. It was the disgrace y'see, the Convent would never have took 'em and we've always told people that their mother is dead.'

'If it wasn't my wedding day, I would tell you what I think about that,' said Dondo. 'Do you mean to tell me that your children don't know where their mother is? You ought to be ashamed for telling them such a terrible lie.' 'It was the best I could do,' my father said. 'I didn't want people talking about it and taking it out on the kids. And now, they're both working, I need their money. I've given them everything I ever got. I ain't ready to see it all vanish.' He stared defiantly at Dondo who could only shake his head in amazement. 'We'd better join them, the train is due to go in a few minutes', and they strolled back to join us, as though nothing was wrong.

Tom towered over me and I could not get used to the fact that he was that small, puny, crying boy who had left us a year ago to join the training ship. 'Do you like it?' I asked as I followed him around the house. 'It's all right,' he said and he took out a packet of cigarettes and matches and lit a cigarette. 'Are you allowed to smoke? Does Daddy know?' 'Don't care if he does,' he replied off-handedly, 'I'm my own boss now, I can do what I like.' 'But you're not yet fifteen,' I reminded him. 'Where do you get the money to buy those?' 'I worked for it on the ship, it's my own money. No one asked me if I wanted to go to sea, I was just told I was going and the longer I've been away, the more I've realised what a tyrant Dad is. And look at you,' he said contemptuously. 'Were you asked what you wanted to do? No, but you were always reminded how much it was costing him to keep you at school; and now he takes all your money from you, it's as though you have to pay him back.'

But my father was overjoyed to have his son home and took him with

249

him every evening on visits to the Beer Hall, the Posada Bar, the Grand Hotel Bar and other places where his cronies hung out. He boasted of Tom, never disclosing his age to the barman in case the boy would be ordered out, and he gave him spending money and denied him nothing. 'Put yer uniform on and we'll drop in and see yer aunty,' he would ask and sulkily Tom would get dressed and go out to be paraded as a trophy.

Christmas came and went and Tom returned to his training ship. We stood once more on the station platform chatting to him through his carriage window, and my father ran to the buffet to buy some sweets and fruit for the traveller. 'How much longer are you staying with him?' asked Tom. Stella and I looked at each other, amazed that Tom should have guessed our intention and wondering if we had inadvertently said something which indicated our plans. 'You want to find somewhere in town to live and try and get better jobs,' he advised and he passed a slip of paper towards us. 'This is my address, so write and tell me what happens,' and guiltily we stuffed the paper into Stella's handbag. 'Easter,' she said to Tom, 'we're going to Beira for a holiday to stay with Uncle Dondo at Easter and we'll do it then.' 'Good for you,' he said and gave us a thumbs-up salute. 'Don't go all soft.' Desultorily we chatted when my father joined us and yet again we stood waving at the departing traveller as the Cape Mail steamed out of the station for its two thousand mile journey to the coast.

Winter came early that year and my father insisted on coming to share our bedroom, saying it would be warmer for him, he was too cold sleeping on the verandah. To Stella that was the last straw. 'What does he think he's up to?' she asked angrily. 'Have to get dressed and undressed under the blankets and then he walks around with nothing on! It's disgusting.' I too was deeply shocked, I had never seen a naked grown-up man before and I began to dread bedtime. 'What will people say,' was Stella's constant cry as we lay in bed with our arms around each other. 'Let's go and sleep on the verandah,' I said. 'I'm frightened, please don't go out, please don't leave me alone.' She never did, but even so I had to shut my mind against how he tried to behave. We made a pact that we would ignore him, that we would stay together and that come Easter, we would leave without regrets.

Without saying a word I applied for another job at a grocery store in the main street, to start in a month's time, and the week before Easter I gave a week's notice and asked for my leave pay, and Stella took an hour off

250

from her job and rode up the avenues, looking for an address which had advertised a Room to Let. Every day when we rode to work, we took some of our clothes with us in paper bags strapped to our carriers and Stella gave the servant five shillings to carry our sewing machine to her office, telling my father it was going in for repair. There were only our holiday clothes at the house and the morning we were due to catch the Beira train, she sat down and wrote my father a short note telling him that we were not coming back to his house after our holiday, that we would be staying in town and would let him know our address then. If he insisted on making a fuss, we would both be prepared to tell the magistrate, before whom we knew we would have to appear, that we considered we were badly treated, that I had had to forfeit all my money to him for the past year, and that his insistence on sharing our bedroom with us had been the last straw.

My father drove us to the station, unaware of our plans, and when he told us that he was taking the morning off and would rather like to get off home right away, we were both thrown into a panic, knowing that he would have time to read the letter and return to remove us from the station; the train was not due to leave for another ninety minutes. 'Don't go,' Stella urged. 'What's the hurry, let's sit and talk for a while. You haven't told us about your new lady friend, what's her name?' He beamed with pleasure and shepherded us towards the station buffet. 'Doris,' he said, 'old Mrs Kemp's daughter, she works at the *Herald*, she's a reader there, has to read the paper from top to bottom every day before it goes out. Looks for mistakes and things like that before they print. It's a job for a clever girl, she's a bit of all right, is Doris,' and he smiled as he blew smoke rings into the air. Then he turned to me. 'Haven't you forgotten something?'

When I had left the United Tobacco Company the day before, I had been handed my pay envelope with sixteen pounds in it, representing a month's pay and a month's leave pay. Carefully I had opened it, by running a pencil along the glued line and had extracted half of the money and then re-sealed the envelope just as carefully. I hid the extra money in the top of my stocking and later transferred it to the pocket of my clean pyjamas now packed in a shabby suitcase with my other clothes.

'No I didn't forget, thanks for reminding me,' I said as I opened my handbag to take out the envelope. ''Ere, I'll have that', he said snatching my bag from me. He opened it and rummaged about, throwing out a handkerchief, comb, powder puff and a pencil and small pad, and the small brown pay envelope. 'Thought you'd get away with it, did you?' he asked as he ran his finger along the seal. My heart beat rapidly with relief, he hadn't spotted the re-glued mark. ' 'Ere's a coupla quid for you to spend', and he threw two pound notes at me. 'Don't want your posh relations to know you're a poor-white, do we?' he asked archly. Afraid that he could still stop us from going, I meekly replied 'I'm not a poor-white, I wish you wouldn't call me that.' 'Oho, all hoity-toity are we, just because we're off on holiday with our rich uncle. Bleedin' Williams, who do they think they are,' he asked as he counted out the remaining six pounds and stowed them in his pocket. 'Have a good time', he said heartily. 'Think I'd better get orf, have a shave and have a wash before I go and see me new girl friend,' and he made ready to go.

'Oh! I nearly forgot', said my quick-thinking sister. 'One of the garden boys was looking for you before we left. I forgot to tell you. He said there was something wrong with that pump you bought the other day, the one down by the river, he said it wasn't working properly, he wanted you to have a look at it.' It was a lie I knew, one she hoped would prevent him from going into the house, yelling for the house servant, who was now quite probably riding her bicycle into town and leading mine beside him to deposit them in the backyard of her office near the station, and finding the letter.

'Christ Almighty! I'd better get along, it's only ten minutes before your train goes so I'll go; better see to that pump, them bleedin' niggers'll be sitting around on their backsides having a good loaf,' and he made ready to leave. Stella put her arms around his neck and held him close. 'Goodbye Daddy,' she said, 'have a nice weekend, and don't do anything I wouldn't do,' and she held him for a few minutes longer. ' 'Ere, people'll think we're sweethearts,' he said jokingly, ' 'arf a mo,' as he freed himself. To me he merely said 'Ta-ta then, bring us some sea sand for me sweetpeas', and then he was gone without a backward glance. Stella and I scurried to our compartment, noting the station clock hands pointed to ten minutes to the hour. 'Pray he can't start the lorry', urged Stella, 'or that someone's parked in front of him,' and we locked the door and sat quietly trying to gather our wits, terrified that he might come storming in to drag us back home, although we knew he had a twenty minute ride to his house. Earnestly we besought our guardian angels to take care of us, to make our father run straight down to the river to look at the pump instead of going into the house, and we begged forgiveness for implicating the innocent garden boys who no doubt were, at this moment, lolling about, smoking and gossiping, as the pump did their work for them.

The train had only travelled a few miles and had slowed down to negotiate the bridge which we had been able to see from our house when Stella jumped up to go out into the corridor and stand, peering into the distance. Then I saw her shoulders shake and realised she was crying. 'What's the matter?' I asked as she sobbed into her handkerchief. 'I wish we hadn't done it. I can see him now, reading that letter. What will he do? Poor Daddy, I wish I hadn't written it. We shouldn't have done it, we shouldn't have run away, he'll have no one to look after him, Oh God, what have we done?'

I was flabbergasted. I put my arm around her and said, 'It was your idea, you've been talking about it ever since we went to live with him, you know we couldn't have gone on living there, he's been really rotten. I'm not a bit sorry, I'm only worried that he'll make trouble for us when we come back.' But she would not be comforted and sat crying for a long time in the corner of the compartment. After some time she asked 'Do you think he might kill himself? He might cut his throat or shoot himself. What shall we do? Shall we get out when the train stops at Bromley? Do you think we ought to try and get a lift back to town?'

'Now you're being silly', I told her. 'It's done. He's not the sort of man to do anything to himself, you know that. Worse things have happened to him before; he'll probably go straight around to Aunty Betty's like he did when he and Bob had that fight years ago. You remember don't you?' I asked, hoping to reassure her. She started to cry again, saying, 'Don't talk like that, don't, I can't bear it.' 'The conductor's coming,' I told her and immediately she reached for her handbag and took out her powder puff to try and hide her tear-sodden face. 'What's going on here?' asked the big, jovial man, 'not quarrelling are you?' 'No,' I said surprising myself at my initiative, 'she's just said goodbye to her sweetheart.' He looked sympathetically at Stella, clipped our tickets, made a mark on the door indicating we were to have beds made up at night and told us that we would reach the border near midnight.

'What did you do with your money?' Stella asked. 'Hid it,' I replied and she opened her bag and took out the money Dondo had given us before Christmas. 'Here's another five pounds for you and the same for me, there was more left over than I realised. I'm glad Daddy didn't know about it, he'd have taken it for sure.' 'Do you feel better now?' I asked. 'No, not really, but I'll write to him from Beira', she said. 'You're a fool',

I said. I had absolutely no regrets, only a feeling of great relief, tinged with fear for the future.

As we sat there and the train puffed up the steep gradient, I looked back at the past, remembering all my frustrations and disappointments at school, the neglect I had suffered, that awful feeling that nobody really cared about me and the pains and humiliations I had endured at my first job. I didn't really like my father, I concluded, and now I deeply regretted that I had never stood up to him and that I had helped to make him the man he was. 'Honour thy father and mother,' said the fifth commandment, and this I had tried to do in gratitude for the gift of life they had given me, but surely they too, owed me something? But nagging away in the back of my mind was that question which constantly haunted me. *Why* had my father so openly disliked me? It would be many years before I knew the answer.

The train whistled as we hurtled through the Amatongas Forest, and we marvelled at the depth of the trees and clutched each other as we rushed down the steep gradient, knowing that we were approaching the Customs Post where our passports would have to be shown. The traumas of the day seemed to have been forgotten and Stella had been flattered by the attentions of a young man at our dining table; he was returning to his office in Beira after a holiday in Rhodesia and he hoped we would meet on the beach at Ponte Gea, he said. 'Where do you live?' asked Stella. 'At Johnson's Private Hotel,' he said. 'And you? Are you going to friends or relations?' We told him our uncle was Dondo Williams, the Station Master in Beira, and we too would be staying in Ponte Gea with him. 'Dondo Williams?' mused the young man. 'Yes I know him, everyone does, and his wife, we all know her,' but he refused to say more and quickly changed the subject.

Nervously we waited for the Passport Control when the train stopped at Macequece. The official and his minions, when they came, were accompanied by a soldier. Our documents were scrutinised, stamped and handed back to us with a flashing smile and a salute. They left – but just as we were settling down there was a knock on our door and the soldier re-appeared. Looking over Stella's head, he beckoned to me and said 'You come', and he stood aside as I stepped outside. What had I done, I wondered? 'We have coffee, yes?' he asked and I followed him to the saloon car and sat down. Curious looks followed me. 'Is there anything wrong?' I asked nervously. He smiled and I noticed that he didn't look quite like the usual Portuguese. Straight black hair, very white skin, those black Mediterranean eyes which glittered and sparkled. 'No reason', he said. 'Only that I ask you to have coffee with me. You are not English?' 'Yes', I told him 'I am.' 'I see from your passport that you are with your sister', he said. 'You are not like sisters.' What had all this to do with him, I thought, but he continued: 'You are so different,' and he offered me a cigarette and passed the sugar. 'You have been on this train before?' he asked. 'No', I replied, 'we are going to Beira for a holiday, and to stay with relations there.' He looked at me steadily with those dark, impenetrable eyes. I began to wonder what I was doing, sitting in the restaurant car with a man I had never seen before, and then he leaned forward to take my hand, which I quickly put on my lap. 'You are young, menina, you must take care, many men will admire you, myself included,' and he sat back, blowing the smoke of his cigarette through his nostrils. Terrifying thoughts of white slave traders came to my mind and in my consternation, I rose to leave. He reached forward to press me down in my seat and said gently, 'I am the Intendente at this post, I do not wish to harm you. Only to talk. I like you,' and from his jacket pocket he drew out an embossed leather cardcase, extracted a visiting card and passed it to me. I read 'Rui Alonzo Anta, Tenente de Infantaria'.

'I am here for three years more', he continued. 'When you return to Rhodesia, you will look for me here. Perhaps we will take coffee again? Perhaps we will be friends.' He rose, reached for his cap and escorted me back to my compartment. At the door he took my hand, smiled as he raised it to his lips, and said 'I will see you again, menina,' and as the train slowly drew into Vila Pery, he saluted and stepped off. For a long time I stood watching as he stood there, and then he faded into the darkness and I turned to see Stella standing by the door. 'Made a conquest I see?' 'No, not really, I think he just wanted someone to talk to', I told her, 'he was very nice.' She snorted. 'Those sort of men must pick up dozens of girls on the train, but how could you have anything to do with a Portuguese?' she asked. 'I didn't have anything to do with him, we just had a cup of coffee and he asked who we were, that was all.' 'Your first beau,' she said mockingly. 'You would choose a dirty foreigner, wouldn't you?' Her remark was lost on me, I could see no reasoning behind it, but I remembered the touch of his hand on mine, his dark eyes, and I hoped I would see him again.

The first sight of Beira took my breath away. The bright, white buildings which fringed the busy harbour, the palm studded esplanade, the white clad people of many nationalities mingling freely, and the ships lying at the mole. Sydney, Hongkong, Bremen, Barcelona, London, read the names on their bows. Cargoes of cement, copra, dried fish and maize were being loaded and unloaded by stevedores, and everywhere, at every quayside and street corner, were policemen in drab khaki, revolvers in their holsters.

Dondo met us in a taxi and pointed out places of interest as we drove to the northern suburbs of this small town. There was the Savoy Hotel, owned and managed by the Rhodesia Railways, where he would bring us for our first taste of Pimm's Cup which was served on the stroke of eleven o'clock each morning, and where English Tea Dances were held every afternoon. The main avenue ran the length of the town, through a long row of white bungalows, their blinds drawn down early against the fierce morning sun and every wall garlanded with brilliantly coloured bouganvillia. The dazzling white beaches fringed with casuarina trees and the blue sea, were clean, cool and inviting. 'What's that place?' I asked, leaning out to look at a two storeyed house where many young people were sitting on the flight of steps which led to the upper floor. 'That's Johnson's Private Hotel', said Dondo. 'That's where I met your Aunty Molly.' He said no more and we drew up at his front door and saw we were only a short distance from the beach at Ponte Gea.

Although Dondo had been in Beira for many years and spoke Portuguese fluently, he appeared to have very few friends; many acquaintances bowed in greeting, but they paused only for a few minutes to be introduced, and Molly never ventured into the town. The household staff shopped and went to the market and the only guests were our other two uncles, Harry who was married, and Rhodes who lived in a number of rooms at the top of the Post Office building. Harry with his wife and two small boys spent days on the beach with us, but they were virtual strangers and our conversations were always guarded; we carefully skirted our private lives and past years, only speaking of the immediate present and what we hoped for in the future. We said nothing about our father, the subject seemed almost taboo, and we gave only the sketchiest account of our jobs and where we lived.

'Let's you and I,' said Uncle Rhodes, 'have a picnic on the beach tomorrow, just the two of us, Stella's taking Peter to Harry's for the day.' Peter, Molly's little son, was quiet and shy, a pretty little boy who spent all his days on the beach but who now attached himself to Stella and followed her wherever she went. 'We can go to the old wreck up the coast,' said Rhodes, 'and I'll bring the lunch.' On bicycles, we rode along the sandy dunes and came at last to the carcase of the old tramp steamer which had been blown ashore in one of the hurricanes which were a feature of this coast. Its rusted shell stood where it had been stranded, the timbers long gone but the framework provided shelter from the burning sun. Barnacles grew on the plates and small fish swam in the deeper pools in the lower decks and holds. We stood our bicycles against the wreck and unpacked our lunch.

'I thought you were staying on the farm,' I asked Rhodes when we lay on the sand after our swim. 'Not yet', he said. 'The old people are managing for the present, but when it gets too much for them they'll send for me. Your grandfather is nearly eighty.' For a moment I had a feeling of guilty regret that I had not seen my grandparents for so many years, but I dismissed these thoughts from my mind. 'Why aren't you married?' I asked. He sat up and laughed. 'There are so many, I do not know which one to choose. Would it be fair to ask someone to live on the farm with me? Miles from everywhere? It would be very lonely for any woman.' Thoughtfully, he looked towards the horizon where several tramp steamers were heading for the port.

'Look how long Dondo waited for a wife,' I said. 'Perhaps you'll find the right one too.' He laughed again. 'You don't know the half of it,' he replied. 'You ought to know the truth about Molly, this is a small town and most of the English and Portuguese know what happened.' 'Tell me,' I asked, wondering how the exquisite Molly could have been involved in anything scandalous. 'I know she was a widow. What happened to her husband? How did he die?'

'He was killed,' said Rhodes, 'by another white man, a Portuguese. It was about five years ago. Molly and her husband lived up country and he had to spend a lot of time away from home. She wasn't lonely, she had a lover, a young Portuguese. He came one night but found her husband with her so he waited outside the house and when her husband came out, the Portuguese shot him. He was arrested on the border, I suppose he was trying to escape into Rhodesia but he was brought back to Beira for the trial. He got a life sentence and was sent to Fort Jesus right up the coast. It's an island like Devil's Island, there's no possibility of escape, he'll simply rot away, it's a fever-ridden hell hole.'

'Poor man,' I said after some minutes. 'Yes,' agreed Rhodes. 'The people here all said the wrong person had been shot, they had little sympathy for Molly.' 'She's a Catholic,' I said, 'surely she must have known she was committing a sin, adultery is a mortal sin.' 'When the blood runs hot,' said Rhodes, 'who stops to think?' I shivered and

257

replied, 'She looks so innocent, who would have thought there had been such a tragedy in her life.' 'Not in hers,' said Rhodes. 'Don't forget there were two victims, one is dead and the other as good as. You women have a lot to answer for. The Catholic church says you possess all carnal knowledge; you are so desirable, so enticing but yet so treacherous.' I did not answer and we sat silent for some minutes. At last I asked: 'Do you think Molly is happy now? She was very lucky to find someone like Dondo. How did they meet?'

'She was completely ostracized,' he said, 'so the Augustinian nuns took her in and when all the fuss had died down, Molly took Peter and they left the convent. She got a job at Johnson's Private Hotel, as a waitress, but she never spoke to a soul and kept to herself. Dondo had lived at the hotel for years and the next thing we all knew, he announced he was to marry her.' 'They seem happy together,' I said. 'I'm sure they are,' said Rhodes, 'but who knows what goes on in her mind when she's alone?' That would be her penance I thought, the knowledge of what she had done, and then I heard Rhodes say, 'So now you know why I hesitate about marriage.' 'But it would be different for you,' I replied. 'I think you distrust all women and if you had a wife, you would not leave her alone.' 'I am quite happy as I am,' he said smiling at me. 'Lots of girl friends and a niece I can always rely on to keep me on the straight and narrow.' 'Too late for that,' I assured him.

Our holiday passed in a flurry of beach picnics during the siesta hours with Rhodes and his many friends, bank clerks from the British bank, French and Italian officers from the ships in port, Swedish engineers from the electrical company who were installing a power station, and handsome blonde Germans masquerading as construction engineers but strongly suspected of setting up a spy station on the ship they lived on, anchored out in the bay. There were visits to the British Club, we called at the Savoy promptly at eleven o'clock to enjoy their Pimm's cup and we danced at the Penguino Night Club when the day had passed. It was a life I had only read about, and I began to see at last that there was another world where men were polite, considerate and undemanding. My fear of them started to fade.

'But where are all the Portuguese girls?' I had asked. 'They're very carefully guarded,' I was told. 'They cannot go out like you English girls, not even with their novios, unless the chaperone goes with them. That is why you always see them with their aunties or grandmothers, never alone with a man.' 'Are they not trusted?' I asked. My friend laughed. 'It is we men who have to be watched, our parents choose our wives for us but in the meantime, we enjoy ourselves with the foreign girls like you.'

The day we left Beira, we discussed our plans with Dondo and Rhodes but we did not elaborate our reasons for leaving my father's home and moving in to town where we would have to fend for ourselves. I was too ashamed to tell the two men of my father's attitude to me, his intolerance and neglect. Perhaps I had imagined it all? But so many little incidents came to my mind, so many crises I had been forced to deal with myself: they were real. My uncles had been brought up in a different world and I was afraid of their disapproval. 'I am arranging with my bank to pay you a small allowance each month,' Rhodes told me and when I stammered my thanks he added, 'I'm a lonely old bachelor and entitled to spoil my niece,' and he laughed but I knew he was not lonely. I had heard many stories of what went on in those rooms at the top of the Post Office building, of his many amours in the town and of his affairs, but I did not like him the less for all the talk. How much easier it all seemed if you were a man, I thought.

'Do you know the Intendente at Macequece?' I asked as we stood waiting for the train to leave, and I drew out the visiting card from my purse and passed it to Rhodes. He looked at it for a few moments. 'I've met him at the Portuguese Club,' he said. 'I go there to play billiards. How is it you have his card?' I told him of my meeting and he raised his eyebrows. 'I don't know much about him, but I heard that there was a family scandal back in Portugal, and he was posted abroad. Like the English remittance men in Kenya. But no one knows what really happened, he never speaks about it. But be careful, officials like him often pick up girls on the trains, the men don't intend it to be serious, just a little flirtation, but the girls often take it seriously and get hurt. I'm not saying he's like that, please don't misunderstand me. He may be seriously interested in you. Perhaps you remind him of a little sister or a relation – you look Portuguese.' We both burst out laughing at this suggestion, and I thought I was probably making something big out of a trifle.

But Rhodes was still thinking it over. 'If he gave you his card and address, I don't think he was being frivolous, but if he does pester you, you can always report him, you have the number of his regiment. The Portuguese are very proper and I know that he comes from a good family, well-born, not a colonial. But don't worry, just be friendly. The poor man was probably lonely and wanted someone to talk to and thought you looked interesting.' 'I don't want his or any man's interest,' I retorted; but I knew how flattered I had been by his attention and his insistence that we meet again, how excited I had felt at the touch of his hand on mine.But as I thought of that sensation, there flooded into my mind the memory of that other hand which had touched me. I heard again the heavy breathing and felt the weight of a body on my side of the bed, the searching hand as my nightgown was stealthily lifted and then the probing fingers. Screaming, I had flung myself towards Stella, who lay beside me in the bed. She had sat up groping for the light, crying 'What's the matter? what are you doing?' and I had seen my father standing only a few feet away. He was naked but he stood there blinking in the flickering candle-light. 'You were touching me,' I cried, 'it was you.' 'Me?' he shouted. 'I wasn't anywhere near you, just going for a drink of water. You was dreaming, yer don't know what you're saying,' and he bent down to retrieve his shirt lying next to the bed. 'Silly bleedin' kid,' he muttered.

I had huddled against my sister crying in terror, doubt already beginning to seep into my mind. Perhaps it had been a dream? Was it really his hand I had felt? Why was his shirt lying so near to my side of the bed? And why was he naked? I shivered with fear as I clung to Stella and she drew me close saying, 'Don't cry, you're all right now, I'm here, go back to sleep.' From the other side of the bedroom came the angry voice. 'Stone the bleedin' crows! Can't a bloke get a decent night's sleep? Work all day and then have to put up with stupid bloody kids' yelling and screaming because they was dreaming.'

I emerged from the remembrance of that night to hear Rhodes asking, 'Are you all right? I thought for a moment you were going to faint, you've gone quite pale.' 'It's the heat,' I mumbled, 'and I was thinking of something else.' He patted me. 'Be nice to the lieutenant,' he said. 'I'm sure he only wants to be friendly. Remember you live hundreds of miles away in another country, it would be difficult for him to compromise you, unless you lose your head of course.' He smiled quizzically at me and suddenly in my mind I saw the soldier again, in his faultless khaki, his black hair smooth and immaculate, his eyes twinkling as he stood laughing and joking with his fellow officers and saying 'She fell into my hands like a ripe peach, I picked her up on the train, she was young, no more than seventeen, and ready for everything I suggested.' His friends would laugh delightedly and tell him what a rogue he was. 'What of her family?' they would ask. 'Family?' he would reply. 'We never got to that, there was no time to speak of families.'

No, I told myself, that was not the man I had met under such strange circumstances, who had asked 'When you return to Rhodesia you will look for me here?' and he said 'I will see you again'. The train had been full of girls and he could have chosen any one of them if he had wanted to while away a dull hour or so. 'I'm being silly,' I said at last to Rhodes. 'Of course I'll be nice to him if we meet again. It will be exciting to have a friend of my very own; and quite an old man too.'

We joined the farewell party and kisses were exchanged, our uncles hugged us, the bank clerks and officers begged us to come back, the Scandinavians bowed low, the German engineers raised their fists in salute and the train steamed out of Beira, over the Pungwe Flats and slowly gathered speed as it began the long climb up to the plateau of Rhodesia.

Late in the afternoon, when the train slowed and braked and came to a stop at the water tank of Vila Pery, I glanced down the line and noticed the three uniformed men climbing on board. The Passport control was once again with us. 'Looking for your friend?' Stella asked. 'No,' I said. 'He's not with them.' 'What did I tell you?' she replied. 'He's probably holding some other girl's hand.' Formalities were completed, smiles exchanged and we resumed our places at the window. I was relieved. There was no demon to confront me, to try to get me alone, to do unspeakable things to me in broad daylight, to stifle my screams or to say it was all my fault, I had led him on. Then I heard the sound of footsteps in the corridor and a voice said: 'You are here, I thought I had missed you.' The Intendente, standing in the doorway smiling at me, was in civilian clothes, when I had been looking for a uniformed figure. In that instant I almost fainted from fright, but I gathered my scattered wits and blurted out 'I didn't see you get on the train,' and I was suddenly conscious of my bare arms and legs, my low-cut cotton dress and my sandals, and I blushed with embarrassment, knowing what thoughts had just passed through my mind.

'Come,' he said as he stood aside, 'they are serving English tea in the saloon,' and he turned to Stella. 'Perhaps you will join us?' 'No thanks,' said Stella offhandedly, 'I'll have mine here.' Knowing of her prejudices against those she termed dagoes, which encompassed Frenchmen, Spaniards, Italians, Portuguese, Greeks and Jews, I left her to a solitary tea tray.

'How did you know we were on this train?' I asked. 'I knew you had three weeks holiday. I left Macequece last night. I hoped to find you at Vila Pery, it is my sueto, my day-off today. So, you looked for me?' he asked, leaning forward to take my hand in his. 'You look very nice.' I giggled and said, 'I think you mean 'well', nice means something

261

different.' He turned my hand over and asked 'You are happy to see me?' 'Yes,' I said, 'I am always happy to see friends.' He raised my hand to kiss and smiled broadly. 'So we are friends, it is my pleasure,' he said and we sat in silence for a few minutes waiting for tea to be served. I was beginning to feel more at ease, but when I glanced at him, I found his eyes fixed intently on me. He looked away and would not meet my eyes.

'Are you travelling as far as the border,' I asked eventually. 'I am,' he told me, 'travelling to Umtali with you. We will have dinner there at the hotel, the train has to wait for two hours for changes. We will have a short time only, but we will talk. But alas, I must return on the mail train tonight to Macequece. I can go no further. I am unhappy it is such a short time, but I have seen you.' I was almost overcome at what I thought was flattery, and as I looked around the saloon car, I noticed curious eyes were fixed on us and one or two couples were whispering and looking at me.

We returned to the compartment as it grew dark. 'If you are taking me to dinner at the hotel, should I not change my dress?' I asked, my mind hurriedly searching through my suitcase, knowing everything had been folded and packed and would be creased. 'Please do not do so, you look very nice,' and we both laughed together, remembering my earlier definition of the word. Stella was not prepared to join in the conversation and gave only short replies to Rui's questions, but she smiled slyly at me from time to time and winked, and then she asked, 'Does your wife also live in Macequece, Senhor Anta?'

'I am not married,' he replied. 'Many years ago I was engaged but I was very foolish and behaved badly. There was a scandal,' and he shrugged his shoulders, 'so I requested an overseas posting. I have not been home for many years. Nor is it my custom to mislead where truth is asked for,' but his eyes were hard as he watched Stella, and she smiled shamefacedly at us both. I wished she had not been so tactless.

He turned to me 'And your holiday?' The conversation continued in a lighter vein as I recounted our stay in Beira. 'My uncle Rhodes Williams says he has seen you at the Portugeues Club where he plays billiards,' I prattled on, but I could see he was not listening to me, his eyes were fixed on Stella and presently he rose and held out his hand. 'We are almost there menina,' and he turned to my sister. 'You have no objection if I take your sister to dinner? In the town? I will return her to you safely, before the train departs,' and he smiled at her but with his mouth only and pushed me out into the corridor.

Our conversation progressed slowly over dinner. Other than the usual colloquialisms, I knew very little Portuguese, but once I had become accustomed to the guttural H and to his particular brand of English, I was able to say more about our holiday. My sister's question still hung heavily in the air between us and I felt I should apologise for her, but by now I felt comfortable in his presence and did not want our meeting to end in explanations and apologies. 'It is of no account', he told me when I had said how sorry I was that my sister had been rude. 'She is angry because she is alone. She has many friends?' 'Yes,' I told him, 'it is usually me who stays behind, not my sister.'

He sat watching me through the smoke of his cigarette and asked, 'You too, I am sure, have many admirers in your home town?' 'No,' I replied. 'I don't know anybody there I like enough. I read a lot and play hockey and tennis at a club, sometimes I go to the dances there but always in a crowd.' 'But is there not one who is especial?' he asked. 'None' I replied, 'no, no one.' 'You surprise me,' he said drily, 'but no matter. You will give me your address, and when I come to Salisbury, we will meet, yes?' 'Do you often come to Rhodesia?' I asked. 'Not before, but now, yes', he said laughing at me.

We were back at the station which lay in partial darkness, only the lights from the train casting a glow under the canopy over the platform. The engine had not been connected and stores were being loaded, water tanks filled and bedroom boys were counting out the required number of beds to be made up. 'I am happy to have seen you,' said Rui 'but such a short time. Tell me, I believe you are afraid of me?' 'I was, but not now,' I said, 'you are the first strange man I have been alone with and I was nervous.' He put his arm around me and drew me close saying, 'I have told you, I like you, I mean you no harm, you have nothing to fear,' and then I felt both arms around me, his face against mine, his breath on my cheek and I thought, as my heart began to pound, 'What am I doing here with a man I barely know?' At the same time I could not deny that I enjoyed his embrace, the sound of his voice and the smell of him and then he kissed me and held me tightly before he released me saying, 'Your sister is watching, what will you tell her?' 'If you kiss me again, I will tell you,' I said brazenly and when he did, I longed for the moment to last but wondered if I had been too bold, or too sure that this interlude was merely another holiday flirtation.

'There's not very much to tell,' I said at last. 'We had dinner, we talked, we kissed goodbye, that is all.' 'But it will not be all', said Rui. 'In a few minutes your train will go and you with it, but we will meet again, be sure of that.' I stood on the observation platform for many minutes as his figure became smaller and fainter in the darkness of the station and at last I rejoined my sister. 'Fancy letting that Portugoose kiss you,' she said.

'Are you going to see your boy-friend again?' she persisted as we got ready for bed. 'He's not my boy-friend, we're friends and I like him,' I said. 'Yes. I probably will see him again, but I don't know when.' 'These damned dagoes', she muttered as she struggled into her nightgown, 'they're everywhere these days, I suppose he'll come hanging around but I don't want people to know my little sister's got a Portuguese for a boy-friend.' Infuriated by her tone, I stormed out to sit on the observation platform to cool off. When I returned she was lying in bed and held her hand out to me saying, 'I'm sorry I made you cross', and she sat up and put her arm around me. 'It's you and I against everyone else, I don't want anyone to take you away from me, we must stick together, whatever happens', and at that moment I realised I had broken the emotional tie which held me to her, that she would use me for her own ends without any consideration of my needs and hopes.

'Before you go to sleep,' I said from my bed, 'I don't want you to think or tell anyone what doesn't concern you. Lieutenant Anta is not my boy-friend as you keep saying, though he may turn out to be just that, because I do like him and will see him again if I can.' 'But he's Portuguese,' she insisted, 'a foreigner who can't even speak proper English.' 'I don't care if he's a two-headed Apache Indian,' I told her. 'There's nothing more to say, it's my business and no one else's so goodnight.'

We stood on Salisbury station in the cold wind of an early winter, waiting for the native porter to find a taxi for us, and then we were driven to our new home; one double bedroom in a family house, where we would share the damp little bathroom with the family. Two large notices were brought to our attention. 'No Cooking in Bedrooms' and 'No laundry allowed in the bathroom', and the tight-lipped lady of the house, on the pretext of clean towels, reminded us that 'no men are allowed in the bedroom either, you can sit on the verandah with them or in the lounge'. 'What about my dad?' asked Stella. 'I can't keep him out on the verandah.' 'Fathers and other male relations are all right', we were told and I almost laughed as the ridiculous thought of our three uncles and my father facing each other, two on each bed.

In Salisbury and throughout Rhodesia during the early thirties, there were many more men than girls and when word got about that we were available and unattached, invitations to parties and dances followed. Sunday picnics were organised to Mermaids Pool and Hunyani river, tennis parties at the more affluent homes were arranged, and in large groups we packed the cinemas on Saturday nights. But soon enough pairs formed and drifted away from the circle, leaving a nucleus of many unattached young men and very few girls who wanted no more than light-hearted friendships or merely a friend on a platonic basis, and this is where I found myself. We discussed our hopes for the future, the state of the world, the Gold standard, and the new party in opposition in the Legislative Assembly, and here my aunt's name was mentioned. She had donated a large sum to the Reform Party and was a tireless worker for its election to Government. Most of all, we talked about Communism, then considered such an outrageous and unlikely doctrine. 'It'll never catch on here', exclaimed the pundits amongst us, as though it was a fashion or contagious disease. 'Can't see the nigs sharing with everyone else.' 'But,' I volunteered, 'they already have the extended family system, surely that's very near to communism?' An appalled silence greeted this pronouncement. 'You don't know what you're talking about,' they cried, but I wondered who amongst us all had the most right to speak.

I made my own friends among the office and shop girls near the store where I worked and we met at lunch times to stroll around the town and view the shop windows. We stood with our noses pressed against the glass, as we eyed those unattainable dresses, hats and shoes, but my eyes were also drawn to the natives sitting on the edges of the pavements. They laughed and cackled at their own jokes, passing loaves of bread they had bought for their midday meal, tearing out hunks and cramming it into their mouths, sharing the tea they had appropriated from the office tea pot when the boss had not been looking, and sweetened surreptitiously while the small Inkossikaas had not been watching. They seemed to have such fun over the most trivial occurrence and they slapped each other on the back as they discussed their day's events. What have they got to be so happy about? I wondered.

We discussed our jobs, where we lived, our bosses and most of all our boy friends. There were those who were going steady since their school days, those who accepted favours from their superiors in their offices or shops and those who played the field. 'And you?' someone asked me. How could I explain that my only contact with any man had been a few hours with a Portuguese soldier, a foreigner whom I barely knew and whose intentions, if he had any, were as yet unknown to me. Could I admit to a few hours spent with a stranger whose background, career and language were a mystery to me? 'No,' I said at last, 'I don't have a boy friend, no one special, I only left school eighteen months ago.'

The grocery store where I worked was a small family firm, soon to be swallowed up by the large departmental complex across the road, but in the meantime, it catered for the more discerning customers who preferred the fawning attention of the elderly salesmen who manned the counters, drew forth high backed chairs for them to sit on, listened attentively to their complaints and took their orders, clicking their fingers and calling 'Boy' to fetch a pound of sugar, a jar of imported conserve or a bottle of sauce. Other men in long white aprons hovered over the bacon counter, slicing hams and hand-slicing bacon or skilfully weighing and patting up pounds of best butter between wooden paddles, always accurate to the ounce.

Diligently I kept the accounts in order, rang up money, gave change, and typed threatening letters to delinquent customers reminding them that their accounts were now overdue. I scrutinised the Debtor's Gazette to see who had been charged with fraud or jailed for passing dud cheques or failing to honour their Hire Purchase agreements, and I studied the Police Register to see who had been black-listed for drunkenness and to whom it would be an offence for any store to sell liquor. I answered the telephone and took orders for groceries to be delivered, placated those angry customers who had received the wrong items and, after I had passed on the telephone number to friends, engaged in light-hearted chatter about the latest man I had been seen out with, or rebuffed those who asked for dates.

Depending on her mood or the list of her engagements for the evening, Stella and I met after work to wheel our cycles along the streets, only stopping to peer into the dress shop windows and to speculate on how the month's salary was to be spent. We bought lengths of material and sat sewing in our bedroom at nights, and we reverted to our diet of meat pies, bread and jam and cups of tea. The height of our expectations was to be invited out for a meal either to someone's home or to one of the many restaurants which had sprung up in the city, and it became an art to see how long an admirer could be kept dangling on a string in the hope that we would agree to 'go steady'.

Weekend hockey or tennis matches were arranged and we piled into cars to drive to the outlying small towns, many miles from the capital, for the Saturday evening 'hop' in the village hall or the farmhouse verandah, and we spent the next day chasing the hockey ball and relishing the whistles and cat-calls from the onlookers as they stood, beer glasses in hand, urging us on to victory. Tennis matches were played on hastily rolled and marked stretches of levelled earth behind tobacco barns, and picannins were conscripted to pick up tennis balls or to search for the mis-hits in the dense bush. Friendships were formed with our hosts, and invitations to come again were extended, and we returned late on Sunday evenings with baskets of mangoes, guavas and peaches, telephone numbers and addresses. But there was a restlessness about everything I did, and I longed for something more, something different, escape perhaps. I began to find myself more and more with the same young man until his groping in the darkened cinema or his foot in our door and his urgent question 'Is your sister out?' drove me to quarrel and abandon him.

It was in this restless mood that I came out of the shop one late afternoon on my way home, to find standing looking into the doorway, an elderly, swarthy man whom I recognised as Mario Gomez, a wholesale fruit dealer whose business offices were near the railway station. 'I was searching for this number please missy?' he said and he held out an envelope to show me. On it was written in a fine, sloping, foreign hand, my own name and the street number of the grocery shop. 'It is for me, Mr Gomez,' I told him, 'this is my name and the correct address. How do you come to have it?' 'Every two weeks or so, I take my lorry and we drive over the border where I buy fruit for my store. It is cheaper that way you understand, than if it comes on the railway. My cousins live at Vila de Manica so I spend a few days with them. When I passed through the Customs post the Intendente saw my name on the truck and he asked me to deliver this letter to you.' He smiled as he spoke and then he asked 'Do you speak Portuguese?' 'No,' I told him, 'only very little and I cannot read it at all.' 'I wait,' he said, 'perhaps I can help you.'

I opened the letter and found only a single sheet of paper and two or three sentences. Only my own name and the signature I recognised, and I handed it back to Gomez and waited while he studied it. 'It says very little', he said. 'Shall I read it to you? "I will be in Salisbury on the 30th",' he read, wrinkling his brow and pursing his lips, ' "please meet me at the Grand Hotel at noon for lunch. I hope you are free to do so." ' Gomez looked at me. 'It is signed, that is all. Do you wish me to write a reply?' he asked, but I thanked him, saying that it was not necessary and that I was grateful for his help and glad he had found me. I walked with him to his cycle at the edge of the pavement and took the outstretched hand. 'Thank you Mr Gomez, you have been very kind.' 'non faz mal', he replied and he waved as he cycled away.

'What shall I do?' I wailed at my sister. 'The 30th is next Saturday, old Hampson will never give me the morning off.' 'Surely you're not going to meet this friend of yours?' she asked disapprovingly. 'People will talk about you if you're seen with a Portuguese, everyone knows who we are.' 'What difference does it make if he's a foreigner?' 'Girls like us don't go out with dagoes and in any case he's too old for you. And you know what they say about foreigners? They like to get hold of English girls to fool about with, it means nothing to them, they end up marrying their own kind, girls their parents choose for them.'

'But he's only asking me to lunch, nothing else,' I answered. 'So how am I going to get the morning off?' 'Do what I do, just don't turn up, you can always say you weren't feeling well on Monday morning. But it will probably get back to the Old Man and then there'll be hell to pay.' I thought for some minutes, dreading the consequences should my father hear that I had been seen at the Grand Hotel in the company of an older man, and not an Englishman at that. 'He doesn't really care what I do,' I told Stella. 'I know he doesn't,' she said quite calmly, 'but you know what he's like. He'll force us both to go back and live with him and once he does that, you can say goodbye to your money, it'll be the same thing all over again.' I was terrified at what might happen and sat for some minutes thinking of a way out of the impasse. Then suddenly I had the solution. 'If I meet anyone I know or if Daddy gets to know about it, I will say I was with Uncle Rhodes, he's only four or five years older than Rui and no-one knows Rhodes.' 'Poor fellow,' laughed Stella, 'I wonder how he'll feel, being passed off as an uncle.' 'He won't know,' I told her, 'if I speak quickly, he won't understand.'

'Is Mr Anta staying here,' I asked the supercilious receptionist at the desk, when I presented myself there on the last day of the month. She looked up from her work 'Who shall I say?' she asked but before I could reply, I heard his footstep behind me and the next moment he had seized my hand and was saying 'I am very happy you came.' I was overcome with shyness and could say nothing for a few minutes, but gradually I began to feel at ease as he told me of his overnight train journey from the border and that he had arranged a lift back with a Rhodesian Customs officer tomorrow afternoon. 'Do you have business in Salisbury?' I asked. 'No', he replied, 'I have no business here. But I wanted to see you again and it was not difficult to arrange.' Dare I ask him why, I thought. Shall I ask 'Have you designs on me lieutenant?' or 'Are you hoping for a dirty weekend in a foreign town with a seventeen-year-old who is as green as grass?' What would his answer be? And how do I translate a 'dirty weekend'? What would he say if I told him my sister is quite sure he has evil intentions towards me and that I am foolish to think we can have a chaste and platonic friendship? And does he know that there can be no carryings on in places like the Grand or any other hotel in the town. Porters sit by the staircases to see all is legal and above board and that there is no smuggling of girls into upstairs rooms. My mind wandered to the Ardbennie Hotel with its closed and curtained back rooms where discretion and silence could be bought for a few pounds and I smiled to myself, realising that my imagination was running away with me.

'You are happy to see me?' he asked. I nodded. 'Do you have any other friends in Salisbury?' I asked. 'Portuguese friends perhaps?' 'I know no one only you,' he said. 'I told you when I first saw you that I would see you again. So I am here. We will have lunch now, dinner tonight and then we will meet again tomorrow for lunch. I have arranged it all.' He looked very pleased with himself.

For a long time after lunch, we sat in the cool and darkened lounge and when the waiters drifted outside to chat to passing friends, Rui drew me closely to his side and said, 'I think of you many times menina, you trouble me.' 'I am sorry,' I replied, but he drew me closer and said, 'Do not apologise' and he rose to his feet pulling me up beside him. 'We will walk and you will show me where you live with your sister, and tell me about your parents.' I told him that only my father was alive, that I had been to boarding school for eleven years and had left school eighteen months ago. 'And your mother?' he asked. 'She died many years ago,' I told him, 'and we live in town because my father and my sister have quarrelled.' 'So you have no one?' he asked, 'but perhaps many boy-friends?' 'No boy-friends, but I know many young men who sometimes take me out,' I said, 'and there are my uncles who live in Beira.'

'You will have to sit on the verandah,' I explained when we reached the house. 'Madam does not allow us to have friends in our bedroom,' and I went in to change into the obligatory long dress which the Grand Hotel would insist upon.

'I thought it was only lunch,' hissed Stella when the greetings were over, 'now you're going out again! You'll get into trouble, he'll think he owns you, foreigners are very possessive and jealous, he'll think you're easy and try to keep you out all night. You're asking for trouble.' But I ignored her and only paused to remark, 'for someone who professes to despise all foreigners, you do talk a lot of rubbish, you don't even know any, and for heavens sake call him by his name,' but she was determined to have the last word. 'Does he know you're a virgin?' she asked, but I was too angry to reply and I joined Rui and we walked slowly back to the hotel.

I sat at the cocktail bar confronted by a White Lady cocktail which had been ordered for me while Rui went upstairs to change, and presently I heard the sound of many voices and a party of young men surged into the bar, to seat themselves on stools and chairs, discussing the motor cycle races they had been to see. A hand reached over and picked up my glass. 'Can I taste?' he asked and I turned to see Malcolm, the local motor-cycle champion, a young man whose wealthy parents owned a large motor business and who had asked me many times to go to the races or to dances with him, but I had heard of his reputation and had always declined. 'Waiting for someone?' he asked as he looked me up and down. 'Yes,' I said, 'I'm waiting for a friend', and as I said it, Rui walked into the bar. He ordered a drink, ignored me, nodded to the assembly of young men and when his drink was placed before him, he took me by the hand and led me outside into the palm court.

'Who is your friend?' he asked at last. 'Just a man I know, he is not a friend, I do not like him,' I said but Rui said nothing and for some minutes was silent. His eyes were angry and he turned away. 'What is the matter?' I asked timidly. 'I can see you are angry with me, why?' I asked.

'I do not wish you to speak to other men when you are with me,' he said indignantly, 'I do not like it.' His face was white and his eyes blazed. 'But he is not even a friend,' I tried to explain. He looked coldly at me and said 'How is it he called you by name?' 'He has invited me out many times but I have always refused, I do not like him,' I repeated, and then I picked up my handbag and coat and stood up. 'I know many people in this town. I have lived here all my life, you are not my novio. I enjoy your company, I like you and I am sorry if I have offended you, but I am free to do as I please.' Angrily I stalked out of the hotel.

So Stella is right, I told myself as I fumed, he is possessive and jealous. I have given him no reason to be and I do not wish to be dominated by a man I hardly know; but then I remembered the difficulties he had experienced in making the journey to spend such a short time with me, of finding himself in what he considered an alien society in a situation which presented so many problems. I slowed down, and when I heard him striding along the pavement behind me, I stopped. He took my hand, turned the palm upwards and kissed my hand saying, 'You are right menina, I have no right to speak so to you. Come back and we will say no more.' 'But we must,' I insisted. 'How will I know what to do when I am with you if you are so angry about such a small matter?' The event had clouded the night, and I said at last 'If we are to be more than friends, there are many things to speak about,' and we turned to walk back to the hotel.

After dinner, we sat in the open courtyard as he told me about his family and his years of service in the army, and we watched the crowds who drifted in for the Saturday night dance; family parties with mothers, fathers and their children and friends, large groups of young people – many of whom I knew but hardly dared to glance at – middle aged foursomes and newly engaged couples trying to ignore the catcalls and jeers of their unattached friends. 'You too, come here?' asked Rui. 'Sometimes,' I replied, 'in a party like that over there, or with the rugby club. But this is the first time I have been here with only one man,' and I smiled at him as he held out his hand and asked, 'We too will dance?' and we joined the crowded dance floor.

No more was said. The excitement of being held so close, the nearness of those glittering black eyes and his breath on my face drove all other thoughts from my mind and I longed for the moment to last and already dreaded tomorrow when he would be gone. 'I am very happy to be with you', he said at last. 'Let us not think of tomorrow,' as though he had read my mind, and he held me closer and asked: 'And you?' 'I do not want you to go, Rui,' I told him.

'Let us walk,' he said, 'there are too many people here and so much noise.' 'Goodnight,' called the motor cycle fans, adding roguishly, 'Don't do anything I wouldn't do,' as they collapsed over each other in their mirth. 'What do they say?' asked Rui, perplexed at their behaviour and not understanding the quickly delivered phrase. 'They are being foolish,' I told him, and I asked, 'if I learn to speak Portuguese we will not have to speak English to each other, do you not agree?' He smiled down at me, putting his arm around me, saying 'Talking is not always necessary querida. I am happy to be silent with you.'

It was late when we returned. The hotel was in darkness, the dance was over and the ball-room was empty; paper streamers hung forlornly from the upstairs balcony, the partygoers had left and only the dim light

271

from the boot-boy's cubby-hole lit the lobby. The porter was despatched to summon one of Salisbury's two taxis and we drove through the deserted streets where only the policeman walked his beat. All was silent and dark. 'Your sister, the duenna, will commend me for bringing you home safely,' said Rui and before I could stop myself, I said 'She has gone dancing at The Ace of Spades, it is a night club out of town. She will come home very late.' 'We will sit on your verandah until then' he said. 'I will be very correct,' and he laughed at me.

It was late when he left, but before doing so, he said 'Tomorrow we will meet at early Mass?' 'But I am Protestant,' I told him. 'No matter,' he said, 'it will be a good start, we do not have long together. You must go in, I will look for you at the church.' What a strange man I thought, so different to any other man I knew, so correct, none of that fumbling and groping I had experienced with those who took me out, his natural good manners and his concern for me such a contrast to the boorishness and ungraciousness of my partners from the rugby club or those men who whistled and called after me in the street or blew their hooters at me when they passed, calling out as they went, 'What you doing tonight darling' or 'Let's get together.'

'Where are you going?' asked Stella, when she awoke early to find me almost fully dressed. 'To church,' I told her and she sat up in bed and asked, 'Whatever for? Have you been a naughty girl? Did that wicked man do something he shouldn't? Tell me?' 'No, I'm sorry to disappoint you,' I told her, 'he was charming, delightful and very nice to me.' 'But what did you do?' she persisted. 'After dinner, we went to the dance but we almost had a quarrel, he got annoyed because Malcolm spoke to me, but we made it up and went for a long walk around the town and then we sat on the verandah for ages just talking.' 'Is that all?' she asked. She sounded disappointed. 'Yes,' I said, 'he also kissed me a lot.' 'Well, one thing will lead to another so don't say I didn't warn you,' and she fell back into bed and lay there picking at her nail varnish. 'And now you're off to church with him and then what?' 'He's leaving after lunch,' I said, 'but he said he would come again soon,' and I left her. But will he? I asked myself, and why? Our conversation had skated over our thoughts and I had been too afraid to ask why he had sought me out and then travelled more than two hundred miles to spend only a few hours with me. Would I go to so much trouble to see him at his post, in a foreign country where I barely understood the language? I asked myself, but I knew what the answer was and I dismissed the doubts from my mind, anticipating only the pleasure of being with him again.

272

I hardly noted the beauty of the rows of exotic flowers and the shrubs in the public gardens where we walked after breakfast and church and already my mind was full of dread at the thought of his going. We left the gardens and went back to his hotel and when it was almost time for him to leave he said 'I will give Gomez a message for you. He will tell you when I come to see you again, perhaps in three weeks' time,' and then he paused and looking very serious he added, 'but perhaps no. I will arrive and the duenna will tell me you are out with that man you spoke to the other night. Your sister will be happy, no?' 'And you?' I asked 'What will you do then?' 'I will kill him,' and he burst out laughing, but he became serious and said 'I cannot ask you to remain at home every night but you must not forget me. Do not forget the many things we have spoken about and later, who knows, there will be many decisions to be made.' 'You say many things I do not understand,' I told him but he held me in his arms and kissed me and then he left.

For many months this was to be the pattern of my life. Rui's weekend visits were announced by Gomez whereupon there was a frantic cancelling of engagements previously arranged, but no longer did we dine and dance at the Grand. It became possible to hire a car and we drove out to Hunyani to picnic on the river bank where so many years before I had swum with my brother and helped Jorbey load my father's lorry, but I did not speak of it. He did not wish to hear of my childhood, Rui said, he found it distasteful, and he expressed no desire to meet my father when we spoke of our parents. Nor did we always dance after dinner at the Grand. Instead we went to the cinema to improve his English, he said, and where his elegant good looks drew admiring glances. In order to prolong the pleasure of being together, we went on to the Ace of Spades when the band at the hotel had packed their instruments and left, and we danced on that smoky, crowded floor or sat quietly in the gloom of the night club oblivious to the crowd.

Stella was puzzled. 'Do you really expect me to believe that he's never tried to get fresh with you,' she asked. 'He's old enough to have had lots of experience.' 'No,' I told her, 'apart from kissing me a lot and always putting his arms around me, he's very proper. Perhaps Portuguese men don't get fresh, as you call it, perhaps they have more respect. And don't forget what happened to poor Annie, I don't think Rui would ever do that to me; I wouldn't let him, it would be immoral.' 'You are so naive,' she laughed at me, 'I think he wants to marry you. Has he asked you?' 'He has asked me,' I confessed to her, 'but it's my age. He says we have met three years too soon. Perhaps I ought to just run off with him.'

'The old man would have a fit,' she said. 'There would be hell to pay if you did.' 'But why?' I asked. 'He doesn't care two hoots about me, it would mean nothing to him if I did.' 'It's what people would say that would worry him', she said. But the possibility of that happening never arose.

Mario Gomez stood in the doorway of the store, twisting his cap in his hands looking anxiously for me, and when I had joined him, he said: 'There is no letter senhorinha, but I have spoken with the Intendente, not more than two days past. He asked me to say that you are to take the mail train on Sunday to Umtali. He will meet you there, it is a matter of great urgency. He has been recalled to his regiment. He is anxious to see you.' I was struck with horror at what Gomez was saying, but thanked him and rode home to tell Stella and two days later she went with me to the station, saying she would come with me if I wanted her to. But I told her I would return on the Beira mail the next day and would be away for no longer than necessary. 'I'm sorry I teased you about Rui,' she said, 'and said all those rotten things. I'm sorry too that I wasn't very nice to him sometimes.' 'It doesn't matter,' I reassured her, 'he didn't take you very seriously and most of the time, he didn't understand what you were saying.' 'No, I know,' she replied. 'He only had eyes for you.'

He was standing on the platform when the train drew into Umtali station and as we walked up the street towards the hotel, he told me his news. His regiment stationed in Lourenço Marques had been posted to the Far East, to Macao, for a five year tour of duty. At midday he was to leave on the very train I had arrived on for Beira where he would join his regiment on the s.s. *Duque de Teceira*. He had spoken many times of his desire to return to regimental life but the suddenness of the order stunned us both. Summoning up all my courage I tried to make light of it, saying, 'You were right, we should have found each other in three years' time, not now, it is too soon. You are fortunate, you will have a better life than the years you have lived in Macequece. You will be with friends and officers you have known for long and there will be new places to see and many things to do.' 'And you?' he asked. Lightheartedly, I replied 'I shall change my job, go to another town perhaps,' but I didn't say 'and I will think of you every day and wish you had never left.' 'I will send a letter to Gomez for you,' he said, 'I cannot say more now. I have booked you a room at the hotel and tomorrow you will return to Salisbury. I must report to my post at noon.' His face was white. In silence we drank our coffee and when a car drew up under the portico, he stood up and took me in his arms and kissed me and said, 'Adios menina, do not forget me,' and then he was gone.

I returned to Salisbury the next afternoon, thoroughly wretched and feeling that the world had come to an end. The sun still shone, the streets were alive with people and I could think of nothing but the sight of Rui's misery and the suddenness of the last three days events. Perhaps it was better this way, I told myself, I could not have endured a long-drawn-out parting as inevitably there had to be one. The likelihood of our being married was so remote. I was under age and still in the custody of my father who would never have given his permission; officers in the Portuguese army were almost obliged to make good marriages, and I was a Protestant and I knew that mixed marriages were frowned upon by the Mother Church. It had been doomed from the outset.

But I could not sit in that cheerless little bedroom wrapped in my grief and thoughts, and I returned to the store to placate Mr Hampson and to make up my mind about my future. Stella too, had not been idle. Contact had been made at last with my father. After leaving me at the station she had ridden out to see him and spent the day with him. 'He looks so miserable,' she told me, 'living there alone with only his boy to look after him, but he put my bike in the car and we drove out to see Doris, that girl he's been seeing. She's very smart in an old fashioned sort of way, different I suppose. Wears waistless dresses and little hats, she's only twenty-nine. But what about you?' 'I don't want to talk about it, I'll tell you some other time,' I said but she persisted and at last I said 'Rui's been transferred overseas, he left the day I arrived, I only saw him for a few hours. He was too upset to say much. His regiment has gone to Macao, it's in China, and he'll be there for five years at least, so I won't ever see him again.' 'I'm sorry,' she said, 'but you'll get over it.' 'You're not half as sorry as I am,' I told her, 'and I probably will get over it. But not yet, so don't let us discuss it any more.'

We rode out the following Sunday to see my father, and as we passed Aunty Betty's house, we saw her standing in the garden speaking to friends. We slowed down and called out to her and she came to the gate. 'How you getting on then?' she asked. We could see we were not going to be invited in and made ready to cycle away. 'So yer dad's thinking of getting married again,' she called after us and we turned back. 'To that Kemp girl, her wot works at the *Herald*.' 'Yes, we know,' said Stella, 'and a good job too.' 'He ain't been the same since you two kids cleared orf,' said our aunt. 'Thinking of going back to him, are yer? He can make yer, yer know.' Stella grinned at her sheepishly. 'He won't want us around when he's got a new wife, we'd be in the way.' My aunt was quiet for a moment. 'Hope he has better luck with this one,' she said. 'We'll have to keep our fingers crossed, won't we,' said Stella, and we waved as we cycled up that old familiar sandy road. 'Just let him try getting us back,' she muttered.

'Wotcher,' said my father when we had parked our bicycles on the verandah. He took Stella's arm to lead her inside the house turning to say: 'Got the pip 'ave yer? Didn't want to come and see yer old dad, did yer.' 'Leave her alone,' said Stella, 'she's been sick with malaria this last week, had to stay at home and had terrible headaches, didn't you?' 'Yes,' I agreed, silently thanking her for the lie.

'We bin invited to the Kemps this afternoon for you to meet Doris,' announced my father, 'so see you behave proper, mind yer p's and q's and no bleedin' sulking,' and then he went on to tell us of his last meeting with the formidable old lady whose permission to marry her twenty-nine year old daughter he had sought. He had realised at the first meeting with the mother that it was she he had to impress, he was already sure of the girl.

'She ain't 'arf a card,' he told us gleefully. 'I put on me best suit and me noo bowtie and took her six bottles of stout and yer know what she said to me? "Why did them two kids of yours go orf and live in town on their own? What did you do to them? Didn't you treat 'em proper?" "Treat 'em proper?" I asked. "Course I treated 'em well, sent 'em to the best school in the country, give 'em a good eddication, starved meself to do it, went without for bleedin' years, I did." I told her you both got decent jobs when yer left school but I didn't want you riding in and out of town past all them niggers, through the brickfields, so I let yer go orf on yer own like you wanted to. Then she says to me, "I wouldn't let my daughter live in town, she's a good girl and don't mind riding seven miles each way to work." I bleedin' told the old cow that you two kids wouldn't do anything without me permission, that I got custody of you both till you're twenty-one and if any little whippersnapper came sniffing around wanting to marry you, I'd have 'im up before the judge before you could say knife.' Yes, I thought to myself, Stella was right, but how I regretted my lack of courage to defy him, and Rui's insistence that we wait until I became of age.

'My word,' cried the old beldame when we eventually arrived at her

276

home, 'you two girls don't look like sisters at all but I can see your dad in you,' she beamed at Stella. 'And who do you look like?' she asked me. 'My mother,' I told her looking at my father for his reaction. 'Must have been foreign?' asked Mrs Kemp. 'You're so dark, and your sister so fair.' My father was nervous and hastily changed the subject, calling to his lady-love as she came down the front path. She was tall and thin, with different coloured eyes, one brown and one quite blue, giving her a slightly exotic appearance, but she was very shy and blushed when we greeted her and to put her at ease, I said 'What a lovely dress, did you make it?' 'No,' she replied. 'Mother makes all my clothes for me, come and see my trousseau,' and she blushed again as though she had said something improper.

I felt sorry for Doris Kemp, but then perhaps if I also had to wait until I was almost thirty before I got married, I too would have married the first man who came along. She had never been out with a man, she told me as we examined her beautifully sewn underwear. 'Mother wouldn't let me at first, and when my sisters got married, she wanted me to stay with her. But when Bill, your father,' and she blushed again, 'met us that day in town and asked if he could come and see me, mother didn't seem to mind. She told me she was glad he was that much older, she said young men do awful things,' and she put her hand over her mouth and hurriedly packed away her pretty clothes. 'Haven't you been to dances in town?' I asked, 'or to the cinema?' 'Oh no,' she said quite innocently. 'Mother wouldn't let me, your father is the first man I've ever been out with.'

'When are you getting married?' I asked. 'Mother says we can when Bill's finished his house, he's building on some extra rooms so that she can move in with us.' I didn't know who to feel sorriest for and wondered how they would get along. 'She's a sap,' said Stella when I retailed the conversation to her, 'and I can't see the old lady minding her own business, but thank heavens, he won't want us along,' and then she added: 'What a pity this didn't all happen a year ago, you could have married your soldier and been thousands of miles away by now.' But it was all too late to have regrets I told myself. Out aloud I said: 'It was exciting while it lasted but let's talk about something else.' 'Shall we talk about those three?' she asked as we dissolved into giggles. 'Have you seen the old dragon's pantry? It's stacked to the ceiling with all sorts of stuff, hope she gives us some,' and we went into the dining room where a feast awaited us. My father looked fondly at Doris who sat eyes downcast, fiddling with the tablecloth and Mrs Kemp shifted the plates of sandwiches, sausage rolls, pancakes, buns, cream horns, chocolate cake and fruit cake to insert yet another plate of home cooked delicacies. At least he'll get plenty to eat, I thought to myself.

Suddenly I found myself included in Stella's round of parties, dances and visits to the cinema, and the phone at our office and at home rang constantly, much to the annoyance of our landlady. We were pursued by bank clerks, police cadets, civil servants, wealthy young farmers from the bush, men who spent all their time on the borders manning the Tsetse Fly Control, boys now grown up whom we'd known at school and some of the married men in our respective offices who assured us that their wives didn't understand them and that only we could lighten their dreary lives. We ignored the invitations from the railway employees or the motor mechanics or those who did not as yet possess a motor car, and any invitation to go for a walk around the park was treated with derision.

Parties to go to the Show Ball were made up and I found myself with Malcolm, who had so familiarly addressed me at the Grand Hotel. 'What happened to your boy friend?' he asked me. 'Which one?' I asked, having heard my sister use the same ploy. 'That foreigner,' he said. 'I often saw you out with him.' 'We were going to get married,' I told him, deciding the truth would be far less trouble than any fantasy I could concoct, 'but he had to go away, he was a Portuguese soldier and there's no chance he'll come back.' He whistled and put his hand over mine before I could draw it away. 'I'll marry you then,' he said. 'No thank you,' I told him, 'you're far too young,' and I laughed as he tried to puzzle out what I'd said.

More and more I went out with him and my sister looked on approvingly. 'His people are rich, they've got bags of money. They own both those new garages in town and he's very generous,' she said as she fingered the tweed coat he'd given me and turned to switch on the imposing radio set he'd installed in our bedroom while our landlady kept watch at the doorway. 'He's an oaf,' I told Stella, 'even if he is the champion motor cycle racer.' But I went with him everywhere, to the races, to dances, to parties – and then he asked me home to meet his parents. 'Why?' I asked. 'They want to know who I spend all my time with,' he replied.

The long, low, rambling house stood well back from the road and was surrounded by a lush garden watered all day during the hot weather and throughout the dry winter months by overhead sprays fed from the borehole pump. Cattle grazed in paddocks and a flower-fringed bowling green had been laid out at the side of the house, and every weekend crowds of friends came to play bowls with the parents or to partake of the sumptuous meals. Many white-suited servants were in attendance and the drive was littered with the latest model cars, but Mrs Johnson was a suspicious and enigmatic woman, a member of the Womens Institute, chairwoman of many committees and a pillar of the Presbyterian Church where she sang in the choir. Her husband was a fat, jolly man, kindhearted, but he wore a puzzled expression as if he constantly asked himself what he'd done to displease his wife and bring such a discontented sneer to her face. 'Malcolm told us he's known you quite a long time,' she said in her complaining voice, and I replied, 'Not long really, only a few months, it's my sister he's known longer.' She questioned me repeatedly about my background, my job and my friends, her disapproving look deepening as I recounted it all, glossing over facts which I thought did not concern a comparative stranger. 'I heard you were engaged? At your age?' she asked. I thought for a few moments and then replied: 'No, I met someone who wanted to marry me but he went overseas and probably won't come back to this country, we weren't engaged.' 'All decent girls get engaged if they're going to be married,' she reminded me. 'He was a foreigner, I believe?' she persisted. 'Yes,' I said but I did not give her the benefit of any further information to discuss with her friends over the tea table, and excused myself.

'The old lady is nosy' said her daughter Marjorie. 'She thinks every girl Malcolm brings home is dying to marry him, she thinks you're all designing hussies.' 'You can tell her he's quite safe with me, I have no intention of marrying him or any other man, I only left school less than two years ago,' and before she could continue on that theme I asked, 'Which team do you play hockey for?' She was a large, pudding-faced girl, very popular, but she had a louche reputation and her liaisons and affairs were the talk of the town.

Most evenings and weekends I found myself in Malcolm's company, sometimes with others but more and more often alone, and soon it was taken for granted that we were a serious twosome. 'I won't take you out again if you accept invitations from other fellows,' he would threaten me, and when I replied 'Just as you like' he sent his servant to the shop with notes asking me to join him for lunch or he hung around the store after work to wheel my cycle along the pavement, sitting on our verandah until the pangs of hunger forced him either to invite me out or

279

to take me home; but I made many excuses not to go to that cold, unprepossessing house to face his mother and her questions. He sent me embarrassing gifts – a wrist watch, boxes of stockings which I shared with Stella, the handsome tweed coat, boxes of sweets and chocolates which we gleefully ate and the large mahogany-cased radio set which he stood on our bedside table. Driving lessons were offered, and he owned two permanent seats in the cinema which he generously gave to my sister and me when he could not use them. He frequently asked 'You do like me, don't you?'

'You'll never guess who's here at my office,' said Stella on the telephone. 'Who?' I asked, my heart missing a beat and my hands beginning to sweat. 'Uncle Rhodes, he's on his way overseas to fetch the old Williamses, he's taking the Cape Mail tonight, he wants us to meet him at lunch time. Can you sneak out for a few hours? Tell old Hampson you're not feeling well, you want to go home, and I'll meet you in ten minutes, I'll say I've come to fetch you.' 'Yes, you don't look too good,' said poor, gullible Mr Hampson. 'Take the afternoon off, hope you feel better in the morning,' and I joined Stella and Rhodes who had been waiting around a convenient corner.

'Where shall we go?' he asked, linking arms through ours as we walked up the street. 'Meikles,' I said before Stella could answer. I did not wish to resurrect any ghosts at the Grand Hotel. 'The food's good and it's not so crowded at midday.' We dawdled over lunch, asking about the grandparents' holiday and telling Rhodes about our jobs and our lodgings, and then, during a pause, he drew a small package from his pocket and passed it across the table to me. 'This is for you, Rui Anta asked me to give it to you. I saw him by chance on the dockside, with several other officers, watching the men embark. But there was a hold-up for a few days and they had been discussing what they were going to do during the time with a ship full of men. I asked him to dine with me at the Terrace, I remembered you had met him and I was curious.'

'How was he?' I asked. 'Desolate,' said Rhodes, 'very downhearted. He told me he came to see you every free weekend he had. For him it was a coup de foudre, love at first sight, but when he found out how young you were, he was devastated. He wanted to marry you, he said, and after waiting years to be posted back to his regiment, when it finally happened, he was almost destroyed.' 'Yes,' I agreed, 'he sent a message to me to come to Umtali and I got there the day he left. It was like a bad dream. I felt sorrier for him than I was for myself. It was such a shock, his sudden leaving, I don't think I was fully conscious of what was

280

happening.'

He turned to Stella. 'Did you like him?' he asked. 'Oh yes,' she said airily, 'he was very nice, always polite, in fact a perfect gentleman but not my cup of tea. Far too possessive, but very keen. You should have seen the flowers he sent, our room looked like a florist shop,' and she laughed at the memory of it.

'Why didn't you marry him and put him out of his misery?' asked Rhodes, his eyes twinkling and his tone teasing. 'How could I?' I asked. 'Our father would never have given permission and I was under eighteen at the time. He reminds us every time he possibly can that we are in his custody until we turn twenty-one. We couldn't have gone to Moçambique and got married, there are no civil marriages there, Rui had enquired, and then there was the difference in religion, it would have taken ages for me, and my father's permission, to change mine. And then there was the Army.' 'Yes,' said Rhodes, 'it's too big a machine to fight. He knew that.'

'But you're over it now?' asked Rhodes. 'I try not to think about it,' I told him. 'I was crushed and miserable for a long time but I remembered how wretched he was that day in Umtali, he could hardly speak to me and I wished I had never gone, it was awful.' 'What are you doing now?' he asked. 'Biding my time,' I told him. 'I'm going to look for a better job, in fact I've had a few offers, then I'm going to save all my money and travel and see the world, I don't want to be stuck here for the rest of my life.' 'Any special boy-friends?' asked Rhodes. 'No,' I said, 'but plenty of them,' and we all laughed. 'Open that little parcel?' asked Rhodes as he pushed it across the table. I did, and there lying against the velvet of the small box, were two plain gold ear-rings and a ring set with garnets and river pearls. I turned it to catch the light and saw they were pale grey, pale pink and cream coloured and on the inside of the band was engraved one word. 'Querida' read Rhodes, 'what a lovely old-fashioned word, "beloved".'

Goodbyes were exchanged and promises given to keep in touch and we rode home along the quiet avenues. 'Let's finish our dresses,' urged Stella. 'We've got the rest of the afternoon off.' I wore the ear-rings constantly and the ring whenever I was invited out, and every time I went near the Grand Hotel I prayed that Rui remembered me only as a transient passion and to my mind came Rosalind's words to Orlando: 'Men have died from time to time and worms have eaten them, but not for love.'

* * *

281

We were in that lovely month of April, the start of the African winter which in the northerly climates would have been designated autumn. The leaves on the trees which marched up each avenue turned russet, dried and blew in drifts along the strees as the cold wind whistled and moaned around the houses, clouds of dust whirled into the skies and veldt fires festooned the horizon as the flames rippled through the dried bush leaving a wasteland of charred tree trunks, blackened grass and scorched earth. Bleached bones and skeletons lay in the dried-out river beds where animals had come in search of water, and in the native kraals the women and children searched for grubs, caterpillars and termite nests, to augment their dried mealies and millet. Their husbands and fathers rode to work in the cities wrapped in anything they could beg or filch, old jackets, discarded overcoats, unravelling jerseys, hessian sacks draped over their heads and shoulders, fingerless gloves and outsize shoes or mismatched boots, all gleaned from the municipal rubbish dumps. Their skin lost its lustrous shine, turning dull grey as the air dried and the humidity vanished. Garden boys searched and found thickets of elephant grass which crackled and whispered as they cut it to build shelters around newly planted hedges, flower beds and precious vegetable gardens, glad they lived in their masters' native quarters where water flowed freely from the taps and where they could huddle around the fire which heated the household water supply.

City workers, household servants and factory employees retained their well-being, content to be fed and housed as Government decreed, but amongst the delivery boys at the store it became a joke that the city jail was the best place to be during winter, out of the cold and with regular meals throughout the day. They arrived at the shop early in the mornings to collect their orders for delivery and begged the remaining hot water in the electric kettle which they drank from old jam tins or pickle jars, relishing the warmth but stamping their feet against the cold of the yard.

'Why,' I asked Mr Hampson, 'can't the boys have the tea that's left over? They have to leave home early when it's still dark and it's so cold.' 'I don't want to spoil them,' he said, 'but if none of the men want any more, give it to the boys, but watch the sugar, they'll take the lot.' I doled out a ration of sugar and milk and debated as to whether I should ask for the unsold, stale bread to give the boys; but no, said Mr Hampson, it's for sale to the coloured men who come to the back door. I had seen their wives trailing around the town with droves of children clutching at their skirts, their eyes bright and intelligent as they looked longingly at the goods in the shops, their mothers' faces bitter and resentful, knowing that they were not welcome in the white men's stores and that the Indian quarter catered for their needs.

Silently they stood in the doorways, their eyes begging for attention, but they were shouted at: 'Yes? What do you want?' 'Got any pieces for tickey? Please master, my kids is hungry,' they cried as they eyed the bacon counter where succulent hams sat oozing pink jelly, rolls of gammon glistened and sides of smoked bacon gleamed. 'Got some bones, would make good soup,' said the sympathetic younger assistant. 'Bits of skin with lots of fat if you want it,' and gratefully they would reach out for the newspaper-wrapped parcel, fumbling through their decrepit handbags for that elusive tickey and bobbing their curtseys of thanks. But the older assistants were not so obliging. 'Clear orf, voetsak,' they would shout, 'you've got plenty of shops down Charter Road, what d'ye want to come here for?'

The delivery boys where more cunning. Paraffin for lamps or stoves was diverted into empty liquor bottles to be carried home disguised in rolled up clothes or coats, bags of sugar were mysteriously spoiled and flour and meal bags torn or burst on arrival would be scooped up in the twinkling of an eyelid, hidden and then borne home in triumph. I aided and abetted their actions by turning a blind eye as I checked incoming merchandise or reported that I suspected the paraffin drums had sprung leaks or that the vegetables and fruit arriving from the farms were over-ripe or spoiled and not fit for sale.

I stood late one afternoon checking a new delivery when I glanced up to see a strange African standing by the gate. He was not one of the delivery boys but his face was vaguely familiar. It was the voice, however, which drew me back into the past and I suddenly remembered where I had seen him before. 'Aren't you the man who used to sell bread by the railway line a long time ago?' I asked. He turned to me and when he grinned, I knew instantly that my surmise was right; my first instinct was to reach out to shake his hand and I asked 'What are you doing here?' He was embarrassed by my action and released his hand saying 'You remember me?' and he turned to explain to the silent onlookers that he had known me when I was so high, when I used to run through the brickfields with my little brother, on our way to the town.

'Come into the lane where we can talk', I said. 'If the boss catches me loafing he'll make trouble.' He had had to give up his bread-selling business he said, the police had moved him away from the railway line and he had applied for a licence and a designated pitch; he spat between his teeth and said there were so many rules and regulations now, not like it was long ago. Now he had to ride to the Harare location to his customers, but it was directly opposite to his former stand, and further from his home at Epworth. Then his brother Elijah, who worked in the hatshop, had told him that Mr Hampson was taking on extra delivery boys, 'and here I am, I have been signed on and start tomorrow morning.' 'What is your pay?' I asked. 'Ten shillings a week and three shillings ration money,' he said.'When I know the job, there will be more money.' 'It's not much,' I commented. 'It is hard madam, I have a wife and three children, but my wife she grows vegetables and brings them on her bicycle to town. She takes the older children to her mother and puts the baby on her back and rides around to the white ladies' houses. She has many regular customers. But it is hard. But I have much luck' he added. 'I have my own hut at Epworth and I have my family.' 'What is your name?' I asked him, realising that I had only known him as the bread-seller, and then I asked 'not your tribal name, what do they call you here?' 'Sorrow,' he said, and we both burst out laughing, but there was only time to say hurriedly 'Come to me if you are in trouble' and I left him there to scuttle back to the telephone and my invoices.

How, I wondered, can a grown man, his wife and three children live on less than three pounds a month? Do they have enough to eat, are there enough blankets to share in the cold weather? And clothes, what happened when they wore out, they were cast-offs to begin with, and what did they do if they got wet; did they ever dry out properly as they hung over the wood fire in the middle of the hut? But there were thousands of other Africans living in shacks, disintegrating huts, lean-tos, dormitories and servants' quarters, much worse off. At least Sorrow had his family around him.

As the winter drew to a close, and almost overnight the days became hot and humid, Tom suddenly arrived for what was to be the last vacation from the *General Botha*. A post as midshipman had been allocated to him by the Clan Line on one of their tramp steamers, carrying cargoes all over the world, and he would be based in England. No more would he make that long journey from the Cape for his holidays, and for the first time in his life he looked happy. At sixteen he had filled out and was a handsome young man, dark like our Uncle Dondo, solid and full of self-confidence, and he made it quite plain that he had litle feeling for my father. He spent all his days cleaning his shoes and seeing to his uniforms which he would later don before meeting me at the store.

On Saturday nights we went to the Meikles dance; he was a sensation amongst the young girls of the town in his walking-out dress, and they clustered about us asking for introductions, knowing that we were so alike, there could be no question that we were not brother and sister. Assignations were made, liaisons formed and my father turned a blind, if slightly jaundiced eye, when Tom returned at midday after a night out. 'You should have seen his face,' he laughed as he told me. 'He was dying to know where I'd been, but I never said a word.' My father quite plainly adored his son and would deny him nothing, handing out money and buying him presents, but Tom treated him coldly and ordered him about or told him to mind his own business when the all too-ready question hovered between them.

Stella too, complained about his behaviour to his father, saying that at least he should not get himself talked about. 'You're a fine one,' he had retorted. 'You're pretty notorious around the town yourself, I've heard lots of stories about you,' and very soon they were arguing furiously, shouting at each other until Stella burst into tears and ran into the bedroom. I looked at them both with different eyes, wondering why the wrath of the heavens had not descended on them, why they did just as they pleased without any thought of everything we had been taught and why they were not punished. I thought too, of Rui, always so correct and proper, of our chaste relationship, of our observation of the rules of his church and my Convent and of the frustrations and unhappiness we had both endured. Life seemed very unfair. But could I behave as my sister and brother did, I asked myself, could I succumb to the amorous Malcolm and the others who besought my favours, and still have any self-respect? Was remaining virtuous worthwhile? Was I merely a coward and a prude? I pushed all these thoughts to the back of my mind and prayed earnestly for guidance, strength and the assurance that my mortal soul remained inviolate. I knew that I would not change my views.

The day for Tom's departure drew near and everything stood packed, ready to be taken to the station the next day, and my father looked glum as he inspected the labels. Tom was nowhere to be seen, he had borrowed the garden boy's bicycle and ridden off into the bush where he had joined a crowd of natives on their way to the town. In their midst stalked a very angry male baboon, with a thick dog collar and chain around his waist and who had been a captive since the day his mother had been ambushed with her troop by the farmer whose mealies they were ravaging. He had been kept tied up outside Barnabas's hut; hunks of cold mealie porridge had been thrown to him, calabashes of soured milk left at a safe distance and gradually he had been tamed and then trained to walk with his owner. Frequent beatings had reduced him to an obedient and fawning pet but now, just over four years old, he had become bad-tempered and violent, frequently attacking the children in the kraal, and Barnabas had decided to get rid of him.

'How much do you want for him?' asked Tom when he learned he was for sale. 'Ten shillings, inkosi,' said Barnabas. 'I'll give you seven shillings', said Tom, 'for the monkey, the collar and the chain.' Barnabas looked at his friends as they shuffled their feet in the sand. 'Did you hear what he offered?' he asked. 'Seven shillings! This bobbijan has been with me for many years. He has been like a child of my family. I have given him the best food and milk and this inkoos offers me seven shillings!' And he spat with disgust. 'Ten shillings, Inkoos, nothing less.' Tom wheeled his cycle onto the road and prepared to mount. 'Seven shillings Barnabas, that is all I have. If I take him, you will not have the trouble of taking him further with you. You will have to go from house to house offering him for sale and it will be many hours before you find anyone foolish enough to give you ten shillings for such an animal.' He put his foot on the pedal and prepared to push off. The baboon rose to his feet and with a nimble spring, alighted on Barbabas's head where he proceeded to inspect his scalp in the hope of finding a flea or a louse to crack between his teeth.

Barnabas spat with disgust. 'Eweh!' he grunted as he loosened the animal's grip from around his neck and swung him around onto his chest. He looked at the baboon, who raised his eyebrows and began to chatter at his master, and then he said. 'Seven shillings inkosi as you say, but I am a poor man to sell one who has been as a child in my hut', and he quickly deposited the monkey onto the handlebars, shortening the chain which he handed to Tom. Quietly and earnestly the animal inspected the cigarette end Tom had handed him, before stuffing it into his mouth, money changed hands and Barnabas and his friends went off without a backward glance at their erstwhile family friend, dancing and shuffling down the road, happy to be rid of their burden.

When my father arrived home late that afternoon, Tom had installed the baboon in the back yard. A nine-foot pole had been sunk into the ground and an empty paraffin box had been nailed at the top. The chain had been looped over the pole allowing the animal three or four yards of freedom, but most of the time, he squatted on top of the box scanning the treetops and inspecting his immediate surroundings. My father was enchanted with him and they soon struck up a friendship. 'Wotcher mate', my father called, the baboon eyed him coldly when he saw he was empty-handed, but his churlish look turned to joyous expectation when my father brought out a plate of small cakes the cook had made for afternoon tea.

'Ta son', said my father to Tom. 'When he's settled down, I'll let him off the chain, he can run with the dogs and scare the shit out of them bleedin' niggers.' To this end, he encouraged the garden boys and his house servant to tease the baboon, which they did with reluctance. Bowls of food were placed just out of reach, sticks were brandished every time they passed his pole and tit-bits were offered and snatched away before the strangely human-like little hands could grasp them. The baboon bared his teeth, showing the long canines, his eyes turned red and he jumped up and down in fury screaming with rage every time he saw a black face; 'auw, auw, auw' he grunted as he lunged to the end of his chain. The boys scattered and ran, my father stood laughing at the antics of his newest possession and the baboon, forgetting his tormentors, earnestly searched the sand for some mislaid tit-bit. 'Why do you let the boys tease him?' asked Stella. My father explained that he didn't want the baboon to become too friendly with his servants, or to remember he had been brought up by natives; he hoped the animal would deter any strangers and especially those who came to pass the time of day with his garden boys when he was not there to watch them.

When the time came for us to say goodbye once more to Tom, I did not know that I was never to see him again. As we stood waiting for the engine to be connected to the train, he told me that he had no intention of ever returning; he had made a career for himself in the Merchant Navy and would be based in England and there he intended to live. 'Won't I ever see you again?' I asked. 'What about leave?' 'No,' he replied, 'I'm going to live the way I want, I'll buy myself a little house somewhere in England but of course, if we ever call at Beira and there's time, I'll try and come and see you all.' It was a hollow promise.

During his childhood he had been cruelly neglected and ignored and he felt he owed loyalty to no one. He had never known the love of parents or the security of a family home and in turn, he cared nothing for others; even his own father he despised, taking everything he offered and giving nothing in return. He went out of his way to embarrass my father and he did this by associating with natives and coloured men, joking and laughing with them in the streets in the days when no white man ever spoke to an African or a half-caste other than as a master to a servant. 'It's only a phase', my father would explain to his friends, but he was ashamed and appalled at his son's behaviour. 'You should see the totties in the Cape,' Tom would tell us, 'some of them can pass for white, and they give themselves Italian or Spanish sounding names and pretend they're from Europe. Some of them are beautiful, they dye their hair and you'd never know they're half-castes.' 'How do you know?' asked Stella coldly. 'Because I've taken them out,' he replied, enjoying her disapproval.

'You're the only person I ever think about,' he told me on the station platform, and I remembered the many escapades we had shared and how we had shielded each other from the wrath of my aunt and her household. I recalled the day he had accidentally shot me with his pellet gun, the pellet embedding itself an inch from my eye, in the soft tissue of my cheek. We had prised it out with a piece of twig and then stopped an ice-cream boy to beg a piece of ice to stop the bleeding. Ice-cream was kept cold by rock-salt which was packed around the container and the boy had misunderstood us and handed me a large piece of salt which I had held to the wound. The bleeding had certainly ceased and the injury was cauterised, but the pain had been excruiating and I had doubled up screaming from the agony of the cure. 'You won't say I did it?' begged Tom. 'They'll beat me and Billy won't lend me his gun again,' and he cried and sobbed with me. Slowly we walked home, concocting a plausible alibi. 'What have you done to your face?' asked Aunty Betty. 'Fell on a sharp stick when we were playing,' I told her. 'Serve you bleedin' right, you kids're always in the bush.'

Then there was the morning we stood watching the cattle being dipped on the bank, just above the river. Herds came from all over the district, the herdboys had risen before dawn to drive the multi-coloured cattle through the outskirts of the town, raising clouds of dust whilst the populace still slept in their beds, deaf to the thundering hooves and the bellowing cattle. We stood watching, fascinated as the boys ran about cracking their long whips, keeping their own herds together and bringing them into line before they were driven down the ramp to plunge into the dark green, oily, manure-laden water. The frightened beasts surged forward, to hesitate on the brink before a lash from their minder sent them plunging into the dipping tank, their eyes rolling in terror and their horns clashed together as they bellowed in fear, trying desperately to reach the shallow incline and the warmth of the sun.

A slight push from Tom was all that was necessary to send me flying into the churning water, amidst the melée of hooves, horns and sodden bodies, but as I surfaced, a black arm reached down and dragged me clear of the terrified animals and I was deposited at the feet of the boss-boy, crying and spitting out the foul water. Others had run to catch Tom and head him off from the river and he was brought back for the boss-boy to give him a thorough beating. 'Mompara,' cried Phineas who was in charge, 'are you trying to kill your sister? Indeed you are a fool, she was almost trampled to death. But go now and help her wash in the river,' and he turned to me saying I had better wring out my dress and spread it on the bushes to dry. 'Please don't tell on me,' sobbed Tom. 'I didn't mean it, honest I didn't.'

There were many other occasions when I had protected him, when I had stolen out of bed during the night to raid the kitchen or steal sweets and fruit from the dining room, or when I had hidden his torn clothes – a crime which merited harsh punishment – and when I had lied and stolen for him. Had my protection made him the person he now was? I asked myself. Had I been wrong to try to take my mother's place in his life? But I knew now that this was what he wanted; complete severance from his family and all that had brought him so much unhappiness, and I felt bereft as though some part of me was being cut away. 'Try and write to me,' I asked as I kissed him goodbye and when the train steamed away, Stella and I remounted our cycles and rode home, debating whether to finish our newly sewn dresses or whether to indulge ourselves and have a look at the newest items displayed in the shop windows. I knew that the last link with the past had been severed with Tom's departure; I had felt closer to him than to any other member of the family in spite of the many years' separation we had endured.

Soon a new star swam into Stella's orbit. 'How did you meet Stanley?' I asked. 'Margie, you know that girl who works in the bakery, she introduced us,' said my sister, looking very pleased with herself. 'He's from South Africa, very rich, got pots of dough and a snappy little two-seater, he's been begging Margie to introduce us.' 'Margie's hardly a girl,' I said, 'she's quite old,' but I did not add that I'd heard that she was also divorced. Her jolly nature and ever-present laugh and sophisti-cated clothes hid her past, and she never spoke of it, but she was always seen in the company of a very rich white farmer, also reputed to have come to the country from South Africa.

'He's asked me to go to the Film Star's Ball next week,' Stella told me proudly – it was the social occasion of the year. 'Who are you going as?' I asked, intrigued to know who she thought she resembled. 'Jean Harlow of course, stupid,' she said. To accomplish this necessitated a great deal of bleaching of her already fair hair and the purchase of a length of plum-coloured satin to be sewn into a glamorous long dress, backless and decolleté and encrusted with diamanté. Feverishly we cut and stitched and glued on the rhinestones and at last the gown was finished. Skilful makeup and cleverly combed and arranged white hair completed the ensemble and she won the first prize easily and returned with Stanley in tow, jubilant with her trophy, a brush and comb set tastefully encased in a satin-lined box.

From that day on, and despite Stanley's ever present attendance on her, she was courted by all the young men in the town. Flowers arrived with invitations, boxes of Cape fruit and sweets were delivered to our room, gifts of perfume in expensive boxes, silky underwear in tissue paper and gift-wrapped parcels of stockings, scarves and jewellery arrived at her office, and although she accepted them all as her due, she refused the invitations. Stanley took precedence, making a foursome with Margie and Mr Surtees, they dined and danced at all Salisbury's best places. It seemed strange to me that Stanley should choose to spend two months on holiday in Salisbury when we were always being told by visiting South Africans that we didn't know we were born and were twenty years behind the times; that life in the Golden City was hectic, sophisticated and fast, everyone had money to burn, all the girls were beautiful and highly paid and all the men rich and handsome.

I was disappointed in Stanley. He seemed so old, forty at least I surmised. There was something false about that well-groomed person, his sleek Brylcremed hair and the flashing all-too-ready smile. He wore well-cut navy blue suits but his shoes were slightly down at heel and his shirt cuffs frayed at the edges which did not match the image of an elegant man about town. He sang sad Victorian songs about dead brides, abandoned children, the Poor House, Mother and jilted lovers, but he appeared to fit the description of a typical South African white male as he lavishly spent money and chauffeured Stella around the town.

'What does he do?' I asked. He was, I learned, something very important in the Johannesburg City Council and had a lovely home in one of the nicest suburbs of that city and – most important – was a bachelor and had asked Stella to marry him. Plans were made to ask my father's permission for the wedding to take place in South Africa, and at first my father hesitated. 'Me leave ain't due for another four months,' he said, 'I can't get away any old time, me job's not the sort I can drop at a minutes notice, they'll dock me pay,' he complained; and then he added: 'He's a real toff is Stanley, a gent not afraid to lash out a coupla quid on a beautiful girl like Stella.' Of course, he would re-imburse Stanley for the cost of the wedding and he was heartbroken he wasn't able to be there, but he wasn't his own boss and so on ad infinitum.

Stanley got into his snappy little two-seater and drove off to the south, leaving a gap in Stella's life, but soon letters full of postal orders arrived from him, with instructions to set herself up with a first class trousseau, and instead of feeling miserable, she shopped at the best stores in town; packages and parcels piled up in our bedroom, magazines were searched for dress patterns for Madeleine the dressmaker to copy, and a pale ivory satin wedding dress and veil were bought. 'You told me pearls were for tears when Rui sent me that ring,' I reminded her, 'so I hope that pearl headdress doesn't bring you bad luck.' 'They're imitation so that doesn't count,' said Stella smugly.

Immersed as we were in her preparations to leave at the month's end, I had not forgotten that I would soon have to find somewhere else to live. The prospect of being completely alone frightened me and I tried not to think about it; I dreaded our eventual parting and knew I would be very lonely without my sister. She made friends easily whereas I found it difficult to do so, and she seemed to have a permanent itch to go out, to be seen at every event, but I preferred my own company and spent all my spare time reading. I cried as I rode through the avenues looking for signs saying Room to Let, and I wondered how I would fare, would I be able to manage on my own money without getting into debt? Would I be branded as that 'fast girl's sister', and how could I repel the advances of Malcolm once my sister had gone and I was alone? I was even uncertain of where I wanted to live and was afraid of formidable landladies who might try to turn me out or to overcharge me for their rooms. Meals, too, would be a problem. Stella and I had often gone together for our Sunday lunches to the restaurants in the town, but could I go alone? I had never seen lone girls eating in public places, it just wasn't done.

My father came to take Stella and her luggage to the station and once again I found myself standing there saying goodbye and wondering whether one day I would be in that happy situation of knowing that I was heading for greener fields and happier times, but I could think of nothing but my own misery. 'Cheer up,' said Stella, 'I'll write to you and perhaps you'll come down and see us at Easter. Get Malcolm to bring you in his car, you'll be very welcome.' Whistles were blown, bells rang and the train puffed out of the station taking with it all that remained of our childhood together, leaving me at last, alone and desolate.

My father's voice drew me out of my reverie. 'I'll be getting along then,' he said. 'Gotta see Doris, having lunch with her and the old lady, ta-ta, then,' and he pushed his way out of the crowded forecourt, got in his car and drove away. I walked the three miles back to our room to spend the rest of the day sorting out the debris of a year's stay there, bundling up Stella's discarded clothes for the boys at the store, and considering my future.

PART SIX

It was the Godley sisters who told me there was a vacant room to let at Kenthurst where they both lived, and as I only had a few more days of the month left in which to find somewhere, I met them after work and we cycled along the quiet avenue and came to the house. 'It's not wonderful,' Letty told me, 'but it's very cheap and the old girl doesn't mind about boy-friends or cooking, she's usually tight by five o'clock and doesn't interfere. But she's always sober on pay-day, that's today, so perhaps she can fix you up.'

'Yes,' said Mrs Gibbons as she carefully sized me up, 'the room's still empty, it'll cost you two quid a month, it's at the end of the verandah,' and she shouted 'Jeremiah! Come here you lazy sod.' From the back of the long row of bedrooms ambled a large African dressed in tattered shorts, a lady's pink blouse and down-at-heel tennis shoes. 'Show this madam the end room,' she commanded Jeremiah who turned without a word to escort me down the verandah as he quietly muttered to himself. 'What is your tribe?' I asked, using the usual preamble to any conversation with an African. 'Mashona madam,' he replied, as he unlocked the bedroom and stood aside for me to enter. 'Have you worked for Mrs Gibbons for many years?' I asked in the vernacular. He looked at me with surprise. 'How is it you speak my tongue?' he asked and I explained I was born in the town and had spoken Shona long before I could speak English. His face cracked into a broad grin as he slapped his knee and said, 'I have never heard the Makiwa speak Shona before,' and he excused himself to impart this piece of information to the other boys who were standing by the back gate, gossiping. He returned and said, 'you must ask if I can clean your room, I will take care of your things if you come to stay, I will be your friend.' 'Thank you,' I replied, 'I am fortunate to have a friend here, there is no one I know other than the two girls in number two.' I left and returned to Mrs Gibbons.

295

'I will take the room,' I told her, 'and Jeremiah says he cleans it every day, will that be all right?' She swept the tangle of greying hair out of her eyes and looked at me. 'You can pay me now,' she said. 'It's only a couple of pounds but it's nice and clean and it's just been painted. I'll get the boy to see to the window, you can't open it, it's nailed down.' We walked back down the verandah and went in. It was crammed with furniture; a bed, a wardrobe, a washstand, a triple-mirrored dressing table and three rickety little tables; shelves made of cheap boxwood were fastened on the wall and a fireplace had been bricked up. I was a little perturbed by the nearness of the servants' quarters and the two lavatories which served twelve bedrooms. 'The boys won't bother you,' explained Mrs Gibbons, 'nor will the people going to the lavatory, this 'ere partition is thick, you won't hear nor see nothing.' She gazed complacently around.

It wasn't really what I wanted, but all my other enquiries had been unsuccessful and after tomorrow I would be homeless. My eyes strayed towards the window. Nailed down, she had said and I wondered why. I looked closer and saw that six inch nails has been driven in obliquely so that it was impossible to open the window and I thought of the long summer nights ahead, thundery, stifling nights when the corrugated iron roof would make the room even hotter.

'Sorrow,' I asked the next day at the store, 'I have to move my things after work, can you help me?' Willingly, he said, as I handed him the bundle of Stella's old clothes, he would borrow his delivery bicycle and would return it before he went home, no one would know, and so it was arranged. The move went ahead and when the precious radio set had been safely installed and I walked to the back gate to say goodbye to Sorrow, Jeremiah appeared to ask if he could remove the nails from the window sill, and I saw he carried a claw hammer. 'Why was it nailed down?' I asked. Jeremiah scratched at his chin, rubbed his hair, shifted his feet and looked over my head, and instantly I knew he was going to tell a lie. 'Please tell me what happened. The truth, no lies Jeremiah,' I asked him. He looked at Sorrow and said, 'It was two months ago, in the night. A lady older than this one awoke one night when a stranger climbed through this window. Not one of us heard him enter the gate. He raised the window while she slept and struck a match to see what he could steal. The curtains caught fire and she saw him bending over her. Auw! there was much trouble. The police came and the lady was taken to hospital.'

Sorrow and I looked at him in horror. 'Then what happened?' I asked.

'Did they catch the man?' He turned to me. 'Yes Madam, they caught him when he ran out into the garden. He was naked and had smeared grease over his body, but they caught him.' He sighed. 'Now that man is in the jail, waiting for the hangman. It is a bad thing he did,' and he shook his head.

'Why did you not tell me of this when I came yesterday?' I asked. 'I am afraid to stay here, but I have paid for the room, now what shall I do?' Sorrow, Jeremiah and I searched each other's faces for a solution and then Jeremiah spoke. 'There is nothing to fear,' he said. 'Madam has had the gate repaired and you can see there are new bolts and barbed wire across the top. I keep the key in my room and lock the gate at night; it was kept by madam before the time of which we speak and many times she forgot to lock the gate.' He sighed again. 'There is also a ma-johnny and his askari who patrol the lane. There is nothing to fear, I am here and I sleep at the door of our room, I will hear instantly someone tries to break in.'

It was too late to search for another room so I thanked Jeremiah and said goodbye to Sorrow and unpacked my clothes, but I changed the room around, moving the bed away from the window, and joined the Godley girls for a sandwich and a cup of tea. 'Tell me what happened when that man broke into my room?' I asked. 'It was awful,' they said. 'Grace here woke up first. It was Miss Cotton's screaming and then we smelt fire so we leapt out of bed and when we got to her door, that nigger was on top of her, the curtains were on fire, bits of them dropping on to the bed, on to her hair, and the smell! All her neck and parts of her face were burnt, but the worst part of it was that the nigger was stark naked and covered in something slippery. Some of the men caught and held him, Mrs Viljoen down the verandah phoned for the police and Ma Gibbons covered poor old Cotton up and tried to quieten her and find out what had happened. She was screaming not because he had raped her but because her pillow, her hair and the curtains were on fire. When they got her to hospital, they had to dig bits of the curtain out of her skin. It was awful,' and they shuddered at the memory of that dreadful night. 'Where is she now?' I asked and they told me she had left and gone down to live in South Africa. The doctors had told her she might find a doctor there who could perform a skin graft and repair the damage to her face and neck. But what about her state of mind, I wondered, every time she looked in the mirror she would re-live the terror of that fearful night.

But I would have to make the best of the situation and I soon settled down. I made friends with the other tenants, with down-trodden Mrs Viljoen and her four small children, with Mollie and her cousin Betty who lived across the dingy courtyard, with Gordon and Maria Panyakis recently arrived from the south, and with the four young men, brick-layers and plumbers, who earned big wages but lived on tins of sardines and bottles of beer and who sent all their earnings home to their families in England. All these friendships were born of propinquity, but Carrie, who like me lived alone in the only other single room, was my real friend.

Although she worked in a large solicitor's office, she also sold cinema tickets at the Palace at nights, sitting in her little cubbyhole, ticking off seats, giving change and warding off her leering admirers as they leaned over to get a better view of her low cut dress and bosom. 'Men are beasts,' she told me as she related their most recent efforts, but she only had one intimate friend who had been taking her out for the past four years. 'Are you engaged?' I asked. 'Sort of,' she replied, 'but I wish he would name the day. He shies off whenever I ask him about it.' Clearly she was unhappy about it, but she confessed to be madly in love with Paul and had told him so many times. 'But when you give in to a man,' she told me, 'he's got what he wants, and it's usually not marriage.' She sighed with unhappiness, but I was shocked at the casual manner of her admission. 'How can you?' I asked, but it was her turn to look surprised and she asked, 'but doesn't everyone?'

'But it's a sin to do that before you get married,' I remarked, and she lay back in her chair and laughed until the tears ran down her face. 'You're a prig,' she accused me, 'you don't really believe all that stuff about hell-fire and damnation and going as a virgin to the altar, do you?' Yes, I told her, I did. I believed in purity, in chastity and everything I had been told as a child, and the beliefs were so strong in me, I could not change now. 'What about Malcolm?' she asked. 'I'll bet he doesn't think the same way as you do, does he?' I said nothing, and got up to go, but I was ever conscious of his demands, of his insistence, of his saying if I loved him at all I would do as he asked. He would take care of me he said, we would get married; but when he saw I would not agree he grew angry and shouted that he would not take me out again, there were plenty of girls in the town who were crazy about him, I would be sorry for treating him so scurvily. He reminded me of the many presents he had given me, of the time and money he spent on me and of how much he loved me.

I recalled the girls I had known who had suddenly had to marry their sullen and unwilling boy friends and had then found themselves bringing up their babies singlehanded as their new husbands stayed out after work, drinking with their unshackled friends at the rugby and cricket clubs; of those who had been forced to marry and live with resentful parents and of those who had abruptly disappeared from our midst to return months later looking drawn and betrayed and avoiding those men whose company they had always enjoyed. There were those too, who were reputed to have suffered at the hands of the local abortionist or had been victims of knitting needles, overdoses of previously unheard of remedies and suicide attempts; two of my former classmates had died and I recalled reading their death notices in the newspaper, wondering if 'died suddenly' meant from an accident, heart failure or a sudden illness.

'No,' I told Carrie, 'Malcolm and I have a peculiar friendship. He says he'll marry me if I agree to do what he wants but I don't want to get married. Not to him at least, I like him, but not enough and I have told him over and over but he says he'll change my mind. But he won't you know, I've known too many girls who have got into trouble and I'm not going to be one of them.' 'You don't always have to land up with a baby,' said Carrie. 'There are ways of avoiding that,' but I did not wish to hear more and shunned her for some days.

I applied for and got another job with a firm of wholesale importers at the bottom end of the town, quite near the infamous Queens Hotel, and so great was my determination to save money that I went without meals, made my own clothes and stuffed pieces of cardboard in my shoes when the soles wore out. When my bank balance reached one hundred pounds, I would throw all my clothes away and start again, I told myself as I gave the office boy a shilling to buy my lunchtime sandwiches; and then I would leave this town and go either to the Belgian Congo in the north or to Beira where Rhodes still lived. Letters from him arrived infrequently. Although Stella had been gone for some months, neither my father nor I had heard from her. I decided I would ride out to see him after work one day to ask if he had any news.

His house looked different and I realised he had built on a two-bedroomed wing at the back, and the garden hedges had been removed and in their place was a green lawn bordered by flower beds. A smart little car stood by the front gate and tubs of lilies and ferns were displayed on the deep verandah. I walked through the front door and found him sitting at the tea table presided over by Mrs Kemp, and when he saw me he called out, 'I was wondering when you were coming to see yer old dad, think you're too good for the likes of us, do yer?' Smiles were exchanged and then I asked 'Have you heard from Stella at all?' 'Nah,' he said, 'probably too busy with her noo 'usband and 'ome shouldn't wonder, always was one for the best of everything.' This seemed completely irrelevant to my query and I was invited to join them for tea.

'How's Doris?' I asked Mrs Kemp, 'is she here?' 'Of course, she's bleedin' 'ere,' interrupted my father, 'we bin married for three weeks, where else did you think she was?' 'I didn't even know you'd got married.' I told him, feeling hurt that he had not even thought of telling me. 'Just decided on the spur of the moment to get it over with,' he said. 'You shoulda come, we had a slap up do after the registry orfice,' and he grinned. 'But why didn't you let me know?' I asked. 'Of course I would have been there but I didn't know.' 'Well, it's over and done now,' said my father, 'and I've got two of 'em to look after me, Gawd it don't 'arf make a change.' As he said so I heard a door close behind me and Doris came forward to join us. 'I'm sorry, I didn't even know you had got married,' I told her, wondering why I was apologising for their oversight. 'It don't matter,' she said, blushing to the roots of her hair, 'but the house is finished now and we're very comfortable here, come and have a look around.'

There was everything necessary for a comfortable life and I was happy for my father who had for so long lived in that shack, and then in this house, but when I saw there were two spare rooms, I thought of my urgent search for just such a room and wondered what would have been the response had I asked if I could have moved in. I was glad I had not asked.

'Have you still got that baboon?' I asked. 'Yes,' she said, 'we call him Pogo, he ain't 'arf a card and your dad spoils him, always bringing him sweets and chocolates,' and we walked out to see the baboon. I was surprised that Doris now spoke like my father, imitating his very words, dropping her aitches and adopting a Cockney twang to her words.

Pogo sat at the top of his box staring into the distance but when he saw us approaching, he skidded down his pole, and baring his teeth, he raised his eyebrows and gibbered. My father squatted down and stroked his coat, speaking quietly to him while the baboon searched through his jacket pockets until he came to a few paper-wrapped sweets. In a flash they were in his hand and he dashed up the pole to sit tearing off the paper and stuffing them into his mouth. 'Ain't he a beaut?' asked his fond owner. Pogo ignored him, but when he saw the garden boy coming up the path from the river, carring a bowl of cooked mealie meal, he leapt up and down on stiffened legs, grunting with pleasure. The food was placed near by and the boy retreated to a safe distance but the animal took no notice until a pigeon fluttered down from a nearby syringa tree and advanced to peck hesitantly at the hot food. There was a flurry of grey fur, white and blue feathers and squeals of triumph as Pogo scampered back up his pole carrying the dead bird. He tore the feathers from it and bit into the plump body, blood dripping from his chin mixed with the feathers and bone and he licked his fingers with pleasure. 'Did you ever see anythink so quick,' asked old Mrs Kemp from the verandah, and then in a more serious tone she said: 'You shouldn't let him eat raw meat, it's bad for him, it'll make him fierce.' My father and his new wife put their arms around each other and grinned self-consciously but their eyes were full of admiration. I was revolted and as soon as I could, I left.

Despite the new friends I made at Kenthurst, I was desperately lonely and missed my sister; I fell ill with malaria and what were called 'sick headaches', now more correctly diagnosed as migraine, and a visit to the doctor confirmed that my constant sore throats were due to poisoned tonsils. They would have to come out and this would require several days in hospital. 'I see from your card that you are eighteen,' said Dr Jacobs. 'Who is your guardian, he will have to give his consent,' and he handed me the form asking me to bring it back signed and he would make the necessary arrangements.

'I see that I'll be copped for the fees', said my father when he had read the form and remarked on my general appearance. 'Ain't yer eating proper?' he asked. 'You're so thin, you'd better ask the doctor for a tonic,' and he handed the form back to me unsigned. 'What about giving your consent?' I asked. 'Not bleedin' likely,' he retorted. 'You earn a good salary, you can pay it yourself.' 'I don't have much left over each month,' I told him, 'by the time I've paid for my room, food, meals and washing there's only a few pounds over.' 'Well, yer'll just have to go without something,' he replied. 'I got a noo family to look after and haven't finished building the house, no, I can't afford to pay for you to spend time in horspital.' 'Does that mean that you are no longer my guardian then?' I asked. 'Can I do what I like, even get married, leave Salisbury, go south or whatever, and it won't concern you?' 'Don't you give me any of that lip young lady,' he shouted. 'I kept you at the Convent for bleedin' years, giving you the best education and you lived a damn sight better than I did, now you got the bleedin' neck to cheek me, go on clear orf.'

I left, determined never to ask him for anything ever again. How could he, I asked myself, insist that I was in his custody, which implied that we both had obligations to each other, if he was not willing to meet his? He would withhold his permission if it involved money but he was quick to remind me of my duty to him. He took a malicious delight in denying me the most elementary aid or support and it was almost as if he did not admit to being my father. I remembered the money he had lavished on Tom, who had given him no thanks for his efforts, and I still felt resentful that he had not even bothered to tell me of his wedding. I wondered why I had been such a fool and always deferred to him, and momentarily I remembered Rui, wishing now that I had been sufficiently worldly-wise and had compromised him, forcing him to marry me. But I knew in my heart of hearts that Rui would not have allowed such a situation to develop, he was too deeply bound by the tenets of his religion, as I was to my Convent upbringing.

Riding home in the late afternoon, I debated about Malcolm, and considered giving up the ensuing battle and surrendering to his demands, but there remained that lingering doubt and I asked myself, was it worth it? Did I really want to be like everyone else, to join the herd, to get married simply because everyone else was, or worse, to find myself in trouble and deserted? And would Malcolm, like Paul, evade the question of marriage and be content with a liaison, despite his assurances? There was no one I could turn to for help, I had to resolve my future myself and be responsible for my own actions, and I knew that there was no alternative but to tell Malcolm that he was wasting his time with me, I did not want him to make love to me nor did I wish to marry him.

'What will I tell my mother?' he shouted angrily. 'We've been going out for six months, I've given you lots of presents and asked you to marry me and now you're giving me the push, it's not fair.' 'But I am being fair,' I told him. 'I don't want you to waste your time with me and I'm tired of all the quarrels and wrestling matches we have, I don't want to go to bed with you or anyone else.' 'Who is he? Who?' he shouted. 'Has your Portuguese friend come back, is that it?' he cried. 'I wish he had,' I said, 'but no, I've told you all along that I don't want to get married or have an affair. Please leave me alone and find someone else.' He looked stunned and was still very angry. 'Let's leave it until after Easter,' he said. 'Margie wants to make up a party to go to the Falls and I've already told her we'll go. I'll pay for you,' he added. 'All right,' I relucantly agreed, knowing that the argument would rage for hours and sensing that by that time, he hoped I would have come to my senses and agreed to all he demanded. 'Can we just be friends then, without any ties?' I asked and we parted on that understanding.

Carrie laughed as I recounted the quarrel to her, over Sunday lunch in the town. 'I see he still comes around,' she remarked. 'Perhaps he's still hoping', but I noticed she toyed with her meal and did not seem to be her usual cheerful self. 'Are you all right?' I asked as I scooped off her portion on to my plate. 'It's nothing,' she said, 'I'm just a bit worried,' and then she quickly changed the subject saying 'I've never seen anyone as skinny as you are eat such a lot; you're the only person I know who can go through the whole menu, you certainly get your money's worth.' 'It's the only hot meal I have in a week,' I reminded her. 'The rest of the time it's meat pies, bananas or oranges and buns from the tea shop.' We laughed but she seemed distracted and pale, and then she asked, 'Shall we walk through the park, the flowers are beautiful at this time of the year and there's nothing to do for the rest of the day.' We made our way past the closed shops, past the groups of bored families out for an afternoon stroll and past the couples hand in hand, speculating about the three piece suites, the rows of saucepans and mounds of household linens in the shops, and we came to the park, where we found a bench.

'If I tell you something,' said Carrie, 'promise you won't tell anyone or think any less of me.' She was near to crying. 'Tell me,' I said. She bent down and began to cry. 'I haven't seen Paul for two weeks. I've been feeling rotten and when I went to see the doctor he did a test and says I'm in the family way. I phoned Paul and we met at Meikles and I told him and he said I wasn't to worry, he would fix everything. I thought he meant the wedding but no, he's arranged for me to see Mrs Grey,' and she put her hands up to her face and cried bitterly. 'What am I to do?' she asked. 'He hasn't been near me since and I'm scared.'

'Who is Mrs Grey and what has she got to do with it?' I asked. 'You really are naive,' sobbed Carrie. 'She's the abortionist, you must have seen her often, she drives around in that smart car of hers, always dressed up to the nines. For a hundred pounds she'll fix me up, but I'm so scared I don't know what to do.' 'Won't he marry you?' I asked. 'You always told me he wanted to.' She wiped her eyes and tried to compose herself.

'He always said he would but now he doesn't want to although he hasn't said so in as many words. But I know him. And to think he's prepared to spend a hundred pounds on an abortion when all I want is for him to spend that on a wedding for us.' She could not stop crying. 'But Carrie, you can't do it.' I said. 'It's tantamount to murder, you'd be destroying a life, it is a worse sin than what you've already done.' She drew herself up. 'There you go again, all that religious nonsense, you're not in the Convent now you know. It's me in trouble, and praying about it isn't going to do any good.' I did not say it might have helped her in the first place if she had held on to any moral values she may have had; she was in such distress that I could only feel pity for her.

Mrs Grey I thought – that name rings a bell. The picture flashed on to my mind, almost as though on to the cinema screen, and again I saw the tall well-dressed lady riding her bicycle up the long avenue of blue gum trees, my mother standing at the door shading her eyes against the setting sun and calling out 'You're a month too early, it's not till after Christmas,' and Mrs Grey's chuckle as she dismounted and called out 'Never mind, put the kettle on and give us a cup of tea.' The scene shifted and I saw her standing in the candlelight of my mother's bedroom drying her hands on the thin towel and saying 'you'll be all right now, I'll call and see you tomorrow.'

'I know who you mean,' I told Carrie. 'She used to be a midwife, she came to our house when my brother was born. Is she the same lady who you're going to see? Has she given up delivering babies, and destroys them instead?' At this Carrie burst into loud sobs, crying, 'Stop it. I thought you were my friend,' and she got up to walk away. I followed her. 'I am your friend,' I told her. 'I wish I could help you, but I can't, but I wish you would think what you're going to do. It will be murder,' I said again. Furiously she turned on me. 'Don't you think I don't know that, but how can I have a baby when I'm not married. How am I going to manage? Do you think Ma Gibbons will let me stay at Kenthurst? Where am I going to get the money from to bring up a child on my own?'

'But surely Paul will give you some?' I said. 'Paul,' – she spat out the name – 'is only prepared to pay me off now. But you know, if he said he would marry me, I would be the happiest girl in the world. I love him although he's behaved like a scoundrel and I just want to be married with a home of my own. If only he would say let's get married,' she repeated, 'and I didn't have to meet this woman. What am I going to do?' Slowly we walked home in the cool of the late afternoon, through the crowds, through the lovely park, both of us wrapped in grief as if in a mantle of winter's rain.

The next night the air was heavy and thunder rumbled in the distance and I heard the heavy raindrops beat on to the corrugated iron roof and gurgle down the gutters. From the boys' quarters came the soft strumming of their mbira and their soulful singing, and flashes of lightning lit up my room, but I could not get the picture of Carrie's misery out of my mind. What would I do if I were in her place, I asked myself? Would I be prepared to suffer the struggle and shame of bringing up an illegitimate child, without a job, living on savings in bleak and squalid rooms, unable to get work, tied to a child? I swore to myself that such a problem would never confront me. Fitfully I slept, Carrie's dilemma uppermost in my mind, but I felt ill at ease and uncomfortable, and at last I got out of bed and switched on the light.

There was a strange, heavy, foetid smell in the room and looking upwards, I saw little brown specks emerging from the cracks in the ceiling, from behind the board which had closed the chimney, marching in long threads across the wall and on my bed; bed bugs, thousands of them seduced from their hiding places by the humid air. I pulled back the blankets and saw them in my bed and when I removed my nightgown I saw the weals where I had been bitten and where I had scratched when asleep. Frantically I picked up as many as I could before they scuttled away, scraped them off the walls and caught them in the bed and drowned them in the tooth mug, shivering with revulsion as I did so and impatient for the light of morning.

'Yer always get bugs at this time of the year,' said Mrs Gibbons as she held unsteadily on to the back of her chair. She tipped a little more gin into her glass and asked, 'Perhaps yer brought 'em with you?' Furiously I reminded her I had been here now for some months and I asked if she would have the room and all my clothes fumigated right away. 'I'll see what I can do', she mumbled, and called for Jeremiah. 'Yer'll have to get all your things out so the boys can scrub everything down,' she said. 'Yer clothes will have to be put on the line and you can't sleep there tonight, the room will have to be sealed.' 'Have you a spare room?' I asked. 'Nah,' she said, 'get one of them girls, Grace or Letty, to let you sleep with them tonight and you can move back tomorrer.' She tipped more gin into her glass, gave Jeremiah his orders and staggered to the doorway with me. 'Don't worry dear,' she said. 'We've had 'em before and Jeremiah knows what to do. Plenty of Jeyes fluid and a couple sulphur candles will do the trick.' I got on my bicycle and rode off to my office feeling defiled and dirty.

'Have you seen Carrie these last few days?' asked Grace as we strove to make ourselves comfortable in her single bed, that night. 'She's around,' I told her, 'we had lunch together on Sunday and she didn't say she was going away.' 'Perhaps she's sick,' volunteered Letty from the other side of the room, 'I saw her go out early yesterday morning to work but when I came for my hockey stick for practice yesterday afternoon, I saw her bicycle standing on the verandah, she must be feeling ill or something.' 'I'll call her tomorrow,' I said, 'perhaps she had the afternoon off.' We said no more but I lay there wondering about Carrie and then suddenly I climbed over Grace and knelt by the bedside. Irritably she sat up. 'Now what's the matter?' she asked. 'I'm just saying my prayers, I nearly forgot,' I said. 'You damned Convent girls,' she cried, 'always praying, nagging at the Saints and bothering God, d'ye think it helps?' 'I've got to believe it, haven't I?' I asked. 'I've got no one else to look after me.' Grace turned over. 'Say one for me then,' she asked. 'I need a better job than this ghastly one I've got. With better pay too, please.'

It was the timid knocking that woke me. I looked at my watch and saw it was five thirty in the morning, still dark, a heavy drizzle still falling, and I wondered why Jeremiah was so early with the tea. He stood at the door wearing only a blanket and he put his finger to his lips and leaned forward to close the door behind me. 'Come missy,' he asked. 'Miss Carrie's in the lavatory, I heard her making a noise but she will not open the door. She is sick perhaps, but she has been there for a long time. All through the night I heard her walking up and down the verandah but she has been in there now for many hours. She is crying. Come quick.' 'Go back to your bed', I told him, 'I will see to her.' 'Shall I call madam?' he asked as he turned away. 'No, I'm sure it is nothing serious. Say nothing to anyone else please.'

After many minutes of fruitless knocking, Carrie opened the door. She was doubled up, her face was drawn and white and I saw her hair too, was wet and she was sweating in spite of the chill of the morning. 'What's the matter?' I asked. 'Thank God you've come, I wanted to call you earlier but your room's locked. I haven't been to sleep all night. Oh God. I'm in agony,' she cried as she doubled up in pain and I led her as quietly as I could back to her own room and switched on the light. I was appalled. Her room looked as though some unfortunate small animal had been slaughtered there. Streaks of blood were smeared over her bed, a blood-soaked towel lay in the wash basin and her bed was soaked with blood. There were gouts of blood on the floor, on the chair and on her clothes which lay in an untidy heap on the floor.

I helped her strip off her sodden gown and nightdress and while she sat shivering on a chair, I removed all the bedding from her bed, turned the mattress over and spread the discarded newspaper over it. Together we rubbed down her blood-stained legs and when she had bathed her face and combed her hair, I helped her wrap herself in one of the rough blankets. She was still shivering, her lips were blue, but the moaning and whimpering had ceased and she lay down on the bed and closed her eyes.

'Is that better?' I asked. She nodded. 'Are you still in pain?' I asked. She reached out for my hand, opened her eyes and said in a whisper 'No.' 'Shall I run down to the call box and call a doctor?' I asked again, bewildered to find myself in the role of rescuer and frightened that she was going to die. 'Can you make a cup of tea,' she whispered and she sat up and reached out for a roll of cotton wool which lay on the table. I turned to find the kettle but more so to spare her the embarrassment of having me see what she was doing. 'Shall I find a doctor?' I asked again. 'Can you tell me what happened and what's the matter with you?'

She had dozed off and when the tea was made, I shook her gently and asked again, 'Carrie, let me fetch a doctor.' 'Please don't, please,' she said. 'She said that was the last thing I must do, call a doctor. She said no one must know, that I must cope by myself, not tell anyone.' She closed her eyes again and lay back in bed. 'Don't go to sleep, drink your tea and tell me what happened; tell me if there's anything else I can do?' She drank her tea, sipping it slowly. She was deathly pale and exhausted. 'I'm so tired,' she repeated over and over again, and remembering the first aid I had learned so long ago as a Girl Guide, I asked 'You're having a haemorrhage, aren't you?' She nodded. 'More than that,' she whispered.

I began to feel more frightened but she put out her hand and said, 'Stay with me today, don't go to work, don't let anyone come in. Stay with me, please.' 'Are you losing a lot of blood?' I asked. 'No,' she said 'not so much, I'm just so tired.' 'Go to sleep,' I urged. 'I'll lock your door and take the key with me. When I'm dressed, I'll get Jeremiah to get me some clean sheets and I'll come back. I won't be long.' I was overwhelmed with pity for Carrie as I thought of her walking up and down the verandah while we all slept, of the agony she had apparently endured to reduce her to such a pale, trembling wreck, and of the state of her bedroom.

'Carrie's ill,' I told the Godley girls as we sorted out our clothes, and tried to dress hurriedly. 'I saw her on my way to the bathroom, she's got a terrible sore throat and thinks she's got the flu. Keep well away from

307

her or you'll catch it.' And then I added another lie. 'I'm going to make her some tea but I think we'd better leave her alone, I'll call the doctor on my way to work.'

I waited until half past eight and then ran down to the corner where a telephone box stood. 'Please tell Mr Crombie I can't come in today,' I said, speaking in a strangled whisper. 'I've got a terrible cold and headache, a bit of flu but I'll probably feel better tomorrow.' 'I'll tell him', sang the cheerful junior and I hurried back to Kenthurst.

I knew Mrs Gibbons would be at her breakfast of gin so I found Jeremiah and persuaded him to unlock the linen cupboard, saying I needed clean bedding and that I hoped my own room would be unsealed so that I could straighten it out. 'Give me some sheets for madam in No.9,' I asked. 'Miss Carrie is still sleeping and I might just as well change her bed too.' He gave me a knowing look and asked 'She is better now?' 'Yes,' I said. 'She ate something that gave her very bad pains in her stomach,' and I reached into my handbag and drew out a ten shilling note. 'She asked me to give you this Jeremiah, if you had not called me, she would have sat in the lavatory all night, she was in great pain.' He clicked his teeth and spat. 'It is good to have friends,' and he carefully tucked the note into his pocket. 'I am here if you need anything else,' he said and he smiled as though we were conspirators.

On the pretext of seeing to my own room and shaking out all my clothes which still smelled strongly of sulphur, I waited until everyone had gone to work, or taken their children to school and then I went in to see Carrie. While she slept I wiped up the blood, hung up her clothes, emptied the basins and tidied up. It was midday before she woke. 'Are you feeling a little better?' I asked. Her face was drawn and pale and while she sat in the chair and I remade the bed, complete with the newspaper on the mattress, she told me of the horrifying three days she had endured.

She had gone to see Paul at his boarding house after we had parted on Sunday. She had pleaded with him to marry her, but he was adamant, saying he did not wish to be tied down at his age, his career would be ruined, he did not earn enough to support a wife and child. 'I felt humiliated,' she said, 'but as I listened to his excuses I began to see him for what he was. Selfish, conceited and utterly despicable, letting me think all those years that he had meant for us to get married. I made a doormat of myself, I never looked at another man, I sat about waiting for him when he stood me up, I lent him money which he never repaid. In fact I've been a complete fool. But in spite of all that, I still wanted him to marry me and then I asked him "Do you still love me Paul?" And do you know what he said? He said he'd got used to me.' Her face was hard with bitterness and she began to cry again.

I waited for a few minutes. 'And then what happened?' I asked. She began to fiddle with her handkerchief and resumed her story. 'I realised then how stupid I had been so I asked him to give me the money and I would do as he asked. No, he said, he'd already paid Mrs Grey, he'd made all the arrangements. When it was all over, he said he would come and see me again and perhaps we could go on as before.' I was astounded at what she was telling me and burst out 'But you can't, can you?' She was silent for a while and then said, 'Do you know, if he'd said then let's get married, I would have agreed; whether it would have been because I couldn't face the abortion, or because I loved him, I don't know.'

For many minutes we sat in contemplation; I was appalled at what she was telling me but I was saddened by her distress and did not wish to add to it by my criticism and lack of sympathy. 'Please don't say any more,' I asked her. I searched about and found a packet of biscuits and made some tea and we sat, in silent companionship, each busy with her own thoughts, until she spoke again.

'She was waiting for me when I got to the address. She said nothing until she had done what she was paid for and when I was getting dressed, she picked up her handbag and said I was to wait for ten minutes so that we weren't seen together and then I could leave. It was humiliating and I wished I could die, I felt so ashamed. When she got to the door, she turned and said, "Whatever happens, don't call the doctor, phone me at this number," and she handed me her card with just her telephone number on it, no address. "What will I do if something does go wrong", I asked. "You'll have to do what you can, but if you mention my name, I'll deny ever having seen you." Then she left and I waited and then I cycled home.'

'You know the rest,' she continued. 'All Monday night and yesterday I was having terrible pains but I just walked about in my room, trying not to make a noise, hoping they would stop but not really knowing what to expect. Last night was awful and when it got worse, I suddenly had a kind of brainstorm. I wanted only to see Paul, to ask him to help me and I got dressed and ran out into the road to walk up to his place. But I hadn't gone more than a few yards when everything seemed to happen at once and there was blood everywhere; I staggered back here and tried to call you, but your room was locked and there was no answer.' 'I wasn't there,' I interjected, 'I had to have my room fumigated and was sleeping with Letty and Grace, if I'd known what was happening I would have come to your room, you should have called me when I came home after work.'

She looked downcast and started to cry again. 'I rushed to the lavatory; that woman said I was to be sure not to leave anything around, blood stains and that sort of thing, and I sat there for ages. I heard Jeremiah knocking and asking if he should call someone, and then I whispered through the door that he was to call you. Then I think I fainted and the next thing I remember was when you opened the door.'

'What are you going to do now?' I asked. 'Is there anything else I can do? Get you something to eat? I suppose you've had nothing since our Sunday lunch together?' She nodded and reached for her handbag. 'I've got a week off, so if nothing goes wrong, I'll be all right,' she said. 'And Paul?' I asked. 'What will you tell him when he calls?' 'I'll have to think about that,' Carrie said, 'but it will never be the same again, never. I'm not even sure I'll stay here, I could ask for a transfer down south, even Bulawayo if there's a vacancy in the office.' 'Will you let me know if there's anything else I can do,' I said as I got up to go. She sat up in bed and asked, 'Please don't say a word to a soul, if anyone asks, just say I've had malaria. Promise me you won't tell anyone what I've told you? Please?'

'Of course I won't,' I said trying to reassure her but knowing that something had gone from our friendship and that like her relationship with Paul, things would never be the same again. Was I feeling self-righteous I wondered, because I had resisted the temptation she had succumbed to? I would try not to let Carrie know that I thought less of her. After all, I told myself, if I were a true friend, nothing would matter and I chided myself for my unworthiness.

It was some weeks later that we met for lunch. 'What's happening?' I asked, 'have you had a rise in pay? We don't usually do this in the middle of the week.' Carrie was excited and momentarily I wondered if she had met a new man. 'I've got a transfer to the Bulawayo office,' she told me, 'more pay in a smaller firm and I'm leaving at the end of the month.' My heart sank as I thought once again I was being deserted. But I was glad for her and asked, 'Is that what you really want?' 'Yes,' she said, 'a new start, new people in a different town, a new beginning really, I'm so excited,' and she reached across the table to take my hand. 'Why don't you make a move too,' she asked. 'We could find a flat and share, it would be marvellous. I believe the Bulawayo people are very

310

friendly, not like this lot here, all civil servants and cliques.' Why not, I asked myself, but I said 'I'd have to ask Mr Crombie but he's just raised my pay and given me an office of my own and besides, I've promised Malcolm's sister to go with a big party she's organised to the Falls at Easter. Perhaps you could meet me at the station during the two hour wait and we could discuss it again. But it's two months away, lots might happen.'

We walked out of the restaurant to where our bicycles stood against the kerb when Carrie suddenly said, 'Come back, I've left my coat behind,' and darted back indoors. But we had not worn coats, it was January and still midsummer. I followed her and found her standing in the doorway trembling, with her hand to her mouth. 'What's the matter?' I asked.

'Didn't you see her?' she asked. 'That woman in the red dress, coming along the pavement?' 'Yes,' I said, 'what about her?' 'It's Mrs Grey,' she said. I looked up the street and saw the tall, elegant figure strolling leisurely towards us, a half-smile on her face as she surveyed the passing traffic. Carrie's arm reached out to draw me inside and she hissed, 'I don't want her to see me, someone might see her smile at me. They'll know she knows me.' We stood in the gloom of the doorway and saw Mrs Grey walk past, and when we thought it was safe, we took our cycles and rode up the street in the opposite direction. 'It's like the Roman Games,' I told Carrie. 'Mrs Grey's smile at you would be like the Emperor's nod, a signal to the executioner.' 'But in this case,' observed my friend, 'it would be my reputation that would be destroyed.'

At the end of that month, Carrie left Kenthurst and all the friends she had made there. She called Jeremiah and handed him the safety chain and licence for her bicycle saying, 'I want you to have my cycle, I have written a note to say I am giving it to you, it is yours.' Jeremiah took the papers and the chain and looked at the bicycle. 'For me?' he asked, overcome at owning such a splendid machine. 'It is for me?' 'Yes,' said Carrie, 'you looked after me when I was so sick, if you had not called my friend, I don't know what I would have done.' He clapped his hands and touched them to his forehead and bowed. 'Indeed you are my good friend,' he said.

The days passed quickly after Carrie had left and the arrangements for the four day visit to the Falls were complete. There would be ten of us in the party, five men and five girls, but the hotel had been fully booked for many months and two of the girls would have to remain in the carriage which would be shunted into a siding to await the return journey after the holidays. The other compartments would be occupied by the arrivals from Northern Rhodesia. Rhoda and I, who had travelled together from Salisbury, were the ones excluded from the hotel, although we would enjoy all the privileges of that august establishment. 'All meals and bathrooms, and everything else the hotel has to offer,' Marjorie had told me as we sorted out tickets at the start of the journey.

Malcolm and I stood in the corridor as the train steamed south. He slipped his arm around me and said, 'Ask your friend to move in with her boy-friend tonight. We could spend the night together, just you and me.' He smiled engagingly at me as he looked for signs of hope in my face. 'I don't think it would be a good idea. We've had this conversation dozens of times before. Can't you accept the fact that I can't and won't change my mind?'

He drew away sulkily. 'I don't know why I waste my time with you,' he said. 'It's not as though you're anything special. Your Dad tars the town streets, your sister had quite a reputation and you think you're too good for the likes of me, don't you?' 'Don't you dare to criticise my father and my sister,' I shouted angrily, 'your own sister isn't exactly a shining example. Nor do I think I'm better than you or anyone else. It's not that at all,' and I turned away irritably. 'We've been over this so many times; I wish I hadn't agreed to come.'

Instantly he was apologetic, and when he saw my room-mate coming down the corridor towards us, he bade us both goodnight and said 'See you tomorrow morning then, when the train stops in Bulawayo?' 'No,' I said. 'Carrie's meeting me there, we arranged it ages ago before she left Salisbury. I'm dying to know how she likes Bulawayo but I'll see you sometime during the day.'

'Rhoda,' I asked as we lay in our bunks listening to the sound of the train as it clicked and rumbled over the lines, 'if I'd asked you to stay with your boy-friend all night so's Malcolm and I could have this compartment to ourselves, what would you have said?' She looked astonished. 'I'm very glad you didn't, my mother would kill me if she thought I'd get up to something like that. She only agreed to my coming when I told her we would be sharing all the time. But did you want to – you know what?' 'Of course not,' I replied, 'but Malcolm did ask. It was the hundredth time I think.' I leaned down and took her outstretched hand and she smiled up at me and asked, 'Is there something wrong with you and me?' 'Yes,' I said, 'I think we're out of step with everyone else.' I turned out my light and went to sleep with the sound of Rhoda's laughter in my ears.

It was late afternoon when the train finally arrived at Victoria Falls. Carrie had not been on the Bulawayo station and I had looked in vain for a message on the board. I had found the rest of our party and when we resumed our journey, Rhoda and I joined them and spent the day playing cards, or sitting about talking. Malcolm appeared to have forgotten our contretemps of the previous evening and when at last we drew to a stop and waited for our coach to be shunted to the siding, the rest of our crowd departed for the hotel which we could see nearby, calling out that we would all meet for dinner later. Plans for the next day were discussed, a visit to the small town across the border, a walk through the Rain Forest, perhaps a trip up river in the launch. Rhoda and I made our way back to the train, tired after our day's journey and secure in the knowledge that we were here to enjoy ourselves.

'There's a dance tomorrow night,' said Rhoda. 'Did you see all those fellows who got on the train in Bulawayo? Masses of them,' but I had been too occupied with the passing landscape to notice the constant stream of people who had passed our compartment. Mimosa trees in their full glory of yellow blossom stretched to the horizon, but although it was the end of the rainy seeason, the veldt was dry and brown, evidence of the encroaching Kalahari Desert which covered more than a hundred thousand square miles. It stretched from the Orange river in South Africa to this part of Matabeleland, marching relentlessly on-wards with the passing of time. Groups of scrub trees and the spindly branches of the baobabs loomed in the distance, but there was no sign of human habitation.

Suddenly I sat up in bed and started to dress. 'I'm going down to have a look at the Falls,' I told my sleepy room-mate. 'Coming?' Together we made our way through the hotel grounds and on to the sandy road which led down to the bridge which linked the two Rhodesias and which we could see dimly through the thick trees. A mighty cloud of spray rose from the escarpment where the river fell thousands of feet into the silent pools beneath. Our voices were drowned by the thundering roar of the river and soon we found ourselves on the path into the Rain Forest.

Tall trees loomed over us and only the glimmer of the moonlight showed us where the path led, winding between bushes and clumps of dense undergrowth soaked, as we were, in a fine dense spray. We came out into the moonlight and found ourselves only yards from a sheer drop, looking at the magnificent splendour of the foaming white river where it fell over the precipice. Lunar rainbows glowed in the mist, leaves shone like silver and for a long time we stood in awe. Slowly we returned to our train, our clothes and hair soaked, but overjoyed that we had witnessed one of the wonders of the world. 'Those men in the bars don't know what they're missing,' observed Rhoda as we dried ourselves and climbed back into bed.

We repeated the excursion the next day, but although the sight was magnificent, it lacked the aura and mystery we had witnessed at midnight; parties of sight-seers crowded through the Rain Forest, gaped at the volume of water hurtling down to the Silent Pool, speculated what would happen to the foolhardy who ventured too near the brink, and bartered and bargained with the curio sellers for their carvings, skins and clay pots. Hordes of baboons scampered onto the lawns of the hotel to await their tit-bits and to perform for the guests, and our party gathered to discuss the night's dance. Malcolm sat quietly beside me, his head in his hands and his face pale and haggard from a night's heavy drinking. 'I'll see you later,' he told me. 'I feel sick, but I'll be all right after a sleep. I'll see you at dinner tonight,' and he carefully wove his way between chairs and tables to his room.

I sat on the vast verandah engrossed in my book, Lin Yutang's *Importance of Living*; the others were either swimming in the pool, sleeping or seeing to their dresses and hair for the night's Grand Ball. My own dress hung in my compartment and I relished every moment of my solitude, hoping I would not be drawn into conversation by those who drifted in and out, alone, bored or merely looking for something to do. I heard the chair being drawn out before I glanced up to see a complete stranger about to sit down. 'Waiting for someone?' he asked. My first impression of George was a flashing smile, fair and handsome and very suave but I did not want to be bothered so I replied shortly 'No.' 'Put that book down and talk to me,' he said. 'I've been watching you most of the day. Where are your friends?' I was annoyed at his tone.

'They're either swimming, sleeping or lying about with face packs on their faces and curlers in their hair. They're where they can be alone, where they can't be picked up or molested by strange men,' I said and I picked up my book. 'Touché,' he said but he settled down in his chair and then asked: 'You're not a local girl, and I know you don't live in Bulawayo, where are you from?' 'Salisbury,' I told him, 'and you?' Within the space of a few minutes I learned that he was here with a football team, as their manager. He worked in Bulawayo at one of the banks, lived in a hotel, was thirty-four years old and unmarried. I picked

314

up my book again. Gently he removed it and put it on his lap before glancing at the title. 'But you're not English, are you?' he continued. Why is it, I asked myself, that that question is always being asked of me? Am I destined to be picked up on trains and hotels? Is there something about me that makes me so different from the usual run-of-the-mill Rhodesian girl? Shall I perhaps invent a whole family of Italian or Spanish grandmothers, aunts and cousins to stand behind me in their battalions, guarding me from the attentions of strange men?

I surrendered as graciously as I could. I gave him the barest details of my life until then, resisting the temptation to embroider my background, and I took care not to say how old I was. 'Have dinner with me tonight,' he begged, 'and then we can go across the border, there's a casino the other side.' I looked at him with dismay. 'I don't know how to gamble,' I told him. 'I was brought up very strictly and haven't the slightest idea.' 'That's what it is,' he said when he'd stopped laughing, 'you're one of those Convent girls, aren't you? Confession every Saturday, communion on Sundays, holy days and feast days, mortal sins and guardian angels?' 'Yes,' I said, 'but not a spoil-sport I hope.'

For me the next two days passed too quickly. We spent all our time together. I forsook my party of friends and sat at George's table for dinner, ignoring the angry looks from Malcolm who glowered at me from across the room. We danced and left early to take a taxi across the border into Livingstone, to the casino where I was excused from playing the tables. At three o'clock in the morning I climbed up the steps in the train and I found Rhoda waiting for me. 'Malcolm's furious with you,' she said. 'He says he was humiliated by your going off with someone who picked you up, he wanted to come over and punch your friend on the nose.' She laughed. 'I don't know why you put up with him all this time,' she added, 'he's so conceited and such a big baby.' 'He was also very persistent,' I told her, 'but he caught me at a bad time. I told him then he was too young for me.' Rhoda burst out laughing. 'But he's nearly thirty,' she said.

Malcolm was at the swimming pool when I found him the next day. 'I'm sorry you're angry,' I said, and I handed him an envelope from my purse, 'I don't think it was fair for you to pay for me to come up here, so I'd like to square the debt.' He took the envelope and riffled through the notes, then stowed them in a jacket pocket. 'That fellow is old enough to be your father,' he spat out. 'He's smooth enough to have dozens of girls in Bulawayo. Or did he say he couldn't live without you?' 'Don't be silly,' I told him, 'we'll probably have forgotten all about each other this

315

time next week.' 'Are you trying to say you're sorry?' he asked. I considered him for a few seconds and then replied 'No, I'm not sorry.' There seemed to be no more to say and I left him sitting there with his friends.

With George I again explored the Rain Forest and we slipped and slithered down the little path which wound down the canyon to the Silent Pools where crocodiles lurked waiting for the suicides or the unwary tribesmen who had fallen into the river upstream. Upturned canoes, logs and other detritus of a large river floated to the top and were carried away by the whirlpools, and with the roar of the mighty torrent in our ears we climbed back to the summit of the cataract to look again at the foaming crest of the river.

We swam in the hotel pool and then took the launch up river to Elephant Island, where a solitary bull and a small herd of elephant cows and their young lived, isolated from the herds on the shore, and we watched as the angry bull raised his trunk and screamed his rage at us. 'We're going over to Livingstone again tomorrow, the team's playing there,' said George on our way back to the landing stage. 'Our train leaves early so I shan't see you after tonight, it's been a lovely weekend.' I said. 'What about your friends?' he asked. 'They've been ignoring you since we met, do you mind?' 'Not at all,' I replied, 'none of them are special.'

He drew me closer and asked 'Why don't you come to Bulawayo?' 'Why?' I asked. 'Well, we could get to know one another better,' he replied. 'Come to Bulawayo, please. I've been looking for someone like you for years; we could get engaged, get married, I'd take great care of you.' I looked at him in astonishment. 'You're joking,' I retorted, 'or is this a proposal?' 'Don't try and be clever,' he said, 'you know very well what I mean.' 'But I thought it was just a holiday flirtation, you know, like ships that pass in the night,' I told him. I could see he was getting angry. 'It hasn't been a flirtation for me,' he said. 'I'm quite serious.'

We would return to our respective homes, he said, and I would ask for a transfer; George would book me into a private hotel near where he lived and after a few month's of getting to know each other, if we felt ready for it, we would become engaged. I suddenly felt five years older but I was not sure I wanted to be married. Shall I mention my father and his obsession about custody I asked myself? But no, I decided that could all be discussed later if the proposal was really serious. The thought of a transfer to a new town, new friends and fresh fields was very enticing, more so than a proposal from a sophisticated stranger. 'Can I think about it?' I asked as we stood together on the platform the next morning waiting for the engine to be coupled to our carriage. 'I'll phone you next week at your office,' he told me, 'and I'll expect to hear that you've spoken to your boss about a move.' Fondly he kissed me and then he stood waving until the train rounded a bend and steamed south to Bulawayo.

I sat alone on the return journey to Salisbury. The whole crowd was aware of my treatment of Malcolm; even Rhoda had deserted me and I was ignored. There was no sign of Carrie at Bulawayo station and I began to wonder if I had not truly deserved the opprobium now being meted out to me for what I considered a light-hearted flirtation but which I now began to view in a different light.

From the station I went straight to the office and when I rode home in the late afternoon, I found Malcolm had been to Kenthurst during the day. He had persuaded Jeremiah to unlock my door and he had removed everything he had ever given me, my precious tweed coat, bottles of perfume, small presents of jewellery, the cushions from my bed and the radio set. Wires dangled in mid-air where he had torn them from the set, drawers were left open in disarray and coat hangers were strewn about the room. 'Did he say anything?' I asked Jeremiah who stood there wringing his hands. 'No Missy,' he replied. 'If I had known he came to steal your things I would not have let him in,' he said. Nothing for nothing, I told myself, but to Jeremiah I replied, 'It is my fault alone, not yours.'

It was a time for change. I drew my money from the bank, gave all my clothes to Jeremiah and spent a week buying a completely new wardrobe, determined that my departure to the south would herald a new era in my life, and I applied for a transfer to the head office in Bulawayo. I decided to make one last visit to my father, not to tell him of my plans but to ask for news of Stella and Tom.

'Nothing from Tom,' he told me as we sat on the verandah. The house seemed unnaturally quiet and I had had no answer to my knock on the door, but I had found my father busy in his garden down near the river. Of Doris there was no sign as yet. 'Any news of Stella?' I asked. 'Not a word,' was the reply. 'Have you got her address?' I asked. He got up to search through a magpie collection of papers, bills and old letters on the side table, and drew out a small photograph. 'She sent me this 'ere,' he said. 'It's a photo of her on her wedding day.' He held it away to get a better view and passed it to me. Stella stood by a decorated table about to cut into a large wedding cake, her dress and veil as I remembered them, the pearl bandeau setting off her fragile beauty. On the table lay her bouquet of white roses and carnations, but there were no signs of a wedding party or a bridegroom. The picture had been scissored off close to Stella and on the back was written only the date.

'Was there a letter with this?' I asked. He rummaged through the papers again and drew out a tea-stained envelope. 'Nothing, only that photo, but there's an address written 'ere on the back, in pencil.' 'Did you ever write to her?' I asked. 'Nah,' he replied. 'I musta forgot it, things ain't been too good around 'ere lately,' he said rubbing his hand over his unshaven chin. 'Doris not well?' I asked. 'Something like that,' he said and he rose to resume his work in the garden.

'I see you've done a lot of building,' I told him as I followed him out to the back of the house. He had built a crenellated façade around the top of the little house, giving it the appearance of a mediaeval keep and the two rows of rooms which he had added were separated by a dark, gloomy courtyard roofed over with the rest of the house. Rows of washing hung on the wire stretched across the courtyard and an untidy heap of dogs lay on the pile of unwholesome sacks in a corner. Doris stood calmly ironing on a rickety table but she glanced up when she saw me and smiled. I was shocked at her appearance. Gone was that smart, finely drawn picture of a shy, reticent girl; she had let herself go and looked a slattern in a dirty scarecrow black garment which hung unevenly to her ankles. No stockings, trodden down slippers and a badly washed cardigan completed the ensemble. She wore no make-up and her hair was tied back with a rag of some sorts. She looked sulky and dirty and when she came forward to speak to me, her cardigan flapped aside and I saw she had grown fatter. Perhaps she's expecting a baby, I thought, but I decided not to ask unless she told me first. 'How's your mother?' I asked, at a loss for something to say.

'Gone,' said Doris. Tears flooded her eyes. 'Bill kicked her out, she's just a little old lady, but he kicked her out, she's got no one now,' and she started to cry. My father had disappeared down the garden path and I felt embarrassed, but sorry for Doris, and wished I had gone with him. 'I'm sorry,' I said. It was the signal for the floodgates to open, for all her resentment and bitterness to be exposed, and she huddled down in a chair and wept into her hands. 'He promised me when I said I'd marry him that she could live with us, he said she'd have a home for the rest of her life,' she wept, 'but now he's gone and chucked her out. My poor old mum, at her age too.' She blew her nose and stood up. 'I'm going to lie down,' she said and without another word she left me.

My father was down by his old shack when I caught up with him. 'I'm going,' I said. 'Just came to say cheerio.' He looked over my head, sniffed and then said, 'Let us know if you hear from your sister,' and made ready to leave me. 'I'm sorry Mrs Kemp's left,' I said. 'Old Cow!' he burst out. 'She caused nothing but trouble from the day she first came. Wouldn't leave us alone, made trouble with the houseboy, interfered with the garden boys, wanted Doris to sleep with her in her room and tried to boss me around,' he cried, 'and then there was Pogo.' He blinked rapidly and I could see the tears in his eyes.

'Where is he,' I asked, realising that I had not seen the angry, barking animal. 'Gorn,' said my father in a sepulchral tone, 'gorn.' He wiped his eyes. 'I took him back into the bush, I had to, Doris said she would leave me if I didn't. Couldn't go through that all over again, not now.' He sniffed loudly and spat. 'Why?' I asked. 'Had to, didn't I?' he replied. 'I told them bleedin' boys to let him loose during the day to run with the dogs; he used to curl up with 'em on their beds but the minute he heard me car coming up the road and stop, he was out like a rocket. Into the bleedin' car, on to my lap, chattering nineteen to the dozen for the sweets I kept in me pocket. He was that tame.'

'A coupla weeks ago, I come 'ome and there's the old lady with her bags packed, Doris crying fit to bust. It was them bleedin' niggers. They'd taken the dogs across the river to look for rabbits, they knew Pogo hated water and wouldn't cross so he was left running up and down the bank; 'e musta got tired of waiting and he come back 'ere and got into the house through the fanlight.' He glanced up at the offending window. 'I told 'er to see all them winders are shut when they go out. They was over at Ma English's for morning tea and the poor bloody baboon climbs in through the winder and has a look around. 'E made a fair old mess of the place. Tore into the old lady's room, threw everything off the dressing table, ripped up all her clothes and tore open the pillows. Gawd blimey, the place was knee deep in feathers when they come home, and Pogo gorn.' He smiled grimly. 'There was a fair old how-dye-do when I come back. The old girl's got me gun and looking for Pogo but I got it away from her. Doris was boo-hooing in the bedroom, the boy was trying to sweep up the feathers,' and he paused for a moment to add 'd'ye ever see a nigger covered in chicken feathers? Laugh, I nearly laughed meself to death,' and he slapped his knees in delight as he recalled the ludicrous scene.

'We got the place straight,' he continued, 'and I went out to find me mate. There he was, cool as could be sitting up a naartje tree eating them sour things, but when 'e sees me, he comes down quiet as a lamb. I chained him up but the old girl went mad. "Get rid of that bobbijan" she screams at me, "I'm not staying a minnit longer, I'll take me daughter with me 'an all" she yells. There was all her things and Doris with her 'at on. So what could I do?'

'What did you do?' I asked. 'Bought twelve loaves of bread, tins of that there jam 'e likes and a big bag of sweets,' he said, 'and I put Pogo into the car and took him out into the bush. Broke up some of the bread, opened up the tins of jam and spread the sweets around. Some of the bread I stuck up in the branches while he was tucking into the jam and when he sloped orf to find the rest, I got into me car and beat it. Poor old bleeder, he got up on his hind legs and stood there just looking at me as I drove orf. Cried like a baby I did, leaving me mate there in the bush,' and once more his eyes filled with tears. 'I'm sure he'll be all right,' I said, knowing that the baboon was doomed. He had been a captive all his life and would have difficulty in fending for himself. He had the smell of humans about him, too, and the troops in the bush would consider him an enemy and would either run away or try to kill him.

But I did not say what I was thinking. I would only add to his misery. 'When did Mrs Kemp leave?' I asked. 'Next day,' he replied laconically. 'Thought it best to put a few things right there and then. Told her to let Doris run the house but one bleedin' thing led to another and she started to accuse me of all sorts of things. There was one hell of a row. Then d'ye know what she does? She turns to me wife, and says "Pack up your things my girl, we ain't staying here another minnit." "Hold on," I says, "she's my bleedin' wife, she ain't yer daughter now you know. If you go with your ma," I says to Doris, "it's the finish. Don't come crawling back, I managed on me own for bleedin' years, I can do it again. And don't go crying to the judge for money, yer won't get any from me, ask your ma to support you." '

'Doris sits there crying, the old girl's shouting and I decided I'd had enough. I calls the houseboy and tells him to put the cases in the car and they both get up and run after me. "Don't go ma" yells Doris, so I gives 'er a clout around the ear'ole and tells her to shut up and get back into the house. I drove the old gel to Iris's and left her there.' 'Who's Iris,' I asked, breathless for the story to continue. ' 'Er other bleedin' daughter, 'er what lives in Hatfield,' he said. 'When I gets back 'ere, Doris 'as locked herself in her room and moved all her things out of our room.

320

She's been there ever since, she don't speak to me, she's let 'erself go and every night after dinner she locks herself in her ma's old room and won't open the door.' He spat in disgust. 'Bleedin' women.' he muttered.

'Why don't you say you're sorry?' I asked. 'Poor Doris. She must be missing her mother, she must be very unhappy. Why don't you make it up with her?' 'Me, say I'm bleedin' sorry!' he cried. 'Not on yer bleedin' life, what next?' Shall I say something about the baby she might be expecting I thought, she looks as though she is; or shall I wait until he mentions it? But he stood there silent and angry and no doubt hurt, feeling that once again the whole world was against him. I knew my own affairs would be of no interest to him and I was surprised that he had unburdened himself to me; I had caught him in an unguarded moment and it was the longest conversation I had ever had with him.

I cycled back to town taking the route past Aunty Betty's house and rode through the brickfields. The same hordes of natives thronged the roadway up to the railway line, but where Sorrow the bread-seller once sat there now stood a brand new Pentecostal church and the pastor clad in a long robe stood at the doorway. Gone were the tribal skins and feathers which had adorned this son of Africa, now he wore the black cassock and the white surplice with obscure hieroglyphics proclaiming his function emblazoned across his chest. He smiled at me as I rode past and I wondered what thoughts were in his mind.

I dismounted to push my cycle across the railway lines and walked up the street, past the station, and then I saw ahead of me a shop where Mario Gomez had once sold fruit and vegetables. When I drew near I saw the windows had been painted white and a sign had been pasted across, reading 'Lease for Sale'. So he's gone too, I thought, my last link with Rui. But I wondered when? Had Rui ever written as he had said he would, although I had had that message and gift via Rhodes. Was there a letter addressed to me lying in the dust of the abandoned shop? I found a side door which swung open to my touch and went in. Dust and cobwebs lay thickly everywhere, old fruit boxes were piled up in the corner, the scale rusty and dilapidated and a pile of old bills, newspapers and letters lay by the door which was shut firmly. I picked them up but saw they were months old; one or two letters from local customers, yellowing documents, a bank statement but nothing else. I wondered what had happened to Gomez.

A native constable was standing by my cycle when I came out of the building. 'This is yours?' he asked. 'Yes,' I told him. 'I was looking for Gomez who had this shop. But it is closed and has been empty for a long time. Do you know anything about him?' 'They were Portuguese people?' he asked and then he smiled. 'They left more than a year ago, they went back to Beira. I know nothing more.' 'Thank you', I said, and I rode home.

That night I sat down to write two letters, one to Stella asking for news and giving George's address for a reply, and the other to George himself saying I had been transferred to the Bulawayo office from the end of the month; I hoped he could meet me on my arrival. At the end of the month an obliging friend took my cases to the station and I rode down to the store and asked for Sorrow. 'Yes missy?' he asked. 'I am leaving Salisbury,' I told him, 'and I'm giving you my bicycle and a few other things I no longer need. I have written a note saying the bicycle is yours, that it is a gift, so that the police will not think you have stolen it.' He looked at me in amazement, his mouth open, and he circled the machine, rubbing his hands with glee. 'Thank you, thank you,' he said over and over again, and then he asked. 'Why Bulawayo? You do not speak Sindebele. You are a Mashona like me.' 'My office is sending me,' I told him and we shook hands and I left him admiring his prize. I walked around the corner to see Anne and I found them both in the café.

Stathes sat on his usual stool behind the counter but his face creased into smiles when he saw me and excitedly he called to Anne. 'I've just come to say goodbye,' I told them. 'I'm leaving for Bulawayo, I've been transferred.' I regretted that I had not seen a lot of them, but I had often called in when passing to the office. They had very few friends but had always waved at me and given me advice and cups of tea when I had stopped to talk. 'Have you told your father?' Anne asked. 'No,' I said. 'Please don't tell him if you ever see him, I'll write.' She looked at me. 'None of that crowd have ever said a word since I left years ago,' she said. 'That part of my life is a closed book. No, I shan't say a word, it's just between us.' I bent down to kiss her and then Stathes took my hand. 'Kyria, I am sad to see you go. You have a good psikhi, you will do well. But come and see us if you return,' and we kissed.

They came to the door with me and suddenly we heard the sounds of a great commotion coming nearer, the sounds of running feet and children's laughter. We stood in the doorway and beheld an amazing procession bearing down upon us, picannins in their dozens came running and dodging, escorting a grotesque figure in their midst, natives on foot or on cycles stopped and joined the hulla-baloo and in the midst

322

of the crowd we saw the majestic figure of an old white lady, her dyed black hair surmounted by a large ostrich-feather-laden picture hat, her rouged cheeks, heavily pencilled eyebrows and dark red mouth giving her an almost clownlike appearance. Her very low-cut pink lace dress clung to every line of her tall, voluptuous figure hugging her formidable breasts and girdling her ample hips, to fit tightly about her knees and then spreading out into an enormous floor length bouffant skirt from where her pink satin shoes peeped. White court gloves covered her hands and arms, the folds of fat about her shoulders blending unobtrusively into the whole colour scheme. But underneath that splendid dress, she wore nothing. She was completely naked and we saw the nipples of her massive bust, the creases of her stomach and the darkness of her navel and her pubic hair. She was totally unaware of her surroundings, of the crowds which followed her and of the embarrassed smiles and sidelong looks of the passing traffic. She smiled and bowed to invisible friends and strode down the pavement as though to the beat of an unseen orchestra always smiling and simpering, completely oblivious of the attention she was attracting.

Motorists slowed down to have a better view, pedestrians stood on tiptoe to see, but turned away when they saw she only wore a lace dress, wondering where she had come from or who had allowed her to perambulate the streets in that state. Those who knew who she was ran for the nearest telephone to call her sons to come and fetch her. Others, more foolhardy, attempted to cover her with their coats once they had fought their way through the crowd of picannins, but her smiling glance turned to fury and she attacked them with her parasol, cheered on by her followers.

'She is crazy,' observed Stathes as we watched the procession pass the café. 'Every Saturday afternoon the same thing. That poor woman,' he shook his head in sympathy, 'always in that dress, walks through the town like a queen. But wait, her sons will come and take her home.' We saw in the distance a car had drawn up and two men were standing, waiting for the procession to draw nearer. As it did so, they gave each other a sign and advanced, bowing low; one advancing to offer his arm, the other to throw a handful of pennies down the street. During the scramble for the largesse, the old lady was escorted to the car, the door closed gently and off they drove without any sign of the embarrassment they must have felt. She is lucky, I thought, to have such loving sons to treat her so courteously with never a harsh word or glance, as though she was indeed the queen she imagined she was.

Goodbyes were said at last and I went back to the station and saw the train was in. I was full of apprehension at the step I was taking and still I wondered if I had not been foolhardy to put my trust in a man I had known only for a short time. But it was too late to turn back, I had burnt all my bridges and must face the challenges which lay ahead; new friends would be made, a strange town to call home, an office where I would be one of many instead of the manager's secretary and a proposal of marriage from a virtual stranger. There was not the same excitement I had felt at seventeen and I was full of doubts as I lay in my bunk, listening to the eerie whistle of the engine and the drumming of the wheels over the track. Was it the desire for marriage and security, or the prospect of escape from my background and an unfettered and free mode of life which had enticed me away? What would I do if George regretted his hasty proposal or if I could not come to terms with all that marriage would demand of me? Would he respect my religious beliefs and the constraints it put upon me, I wondered, and I knew that whatever happened the decisions were mine alone.

Although there were no loving parents to care for me, no happy home to leave, I possessed two enviable qualities, my faith in myself and my freedom. Low in the order of priorities came the job I was going to, but this held no fears for me, I had not been intimidated by any employer and I knew that often my abilities and knowledge were superior to theirs, and I was not afraid of hard work. As Carrie had told me, it was a new beginning and I began to look forward to all that lay ahead.

The next few months were like a protracted party. I was welcomed and fussed over by George and his friends; not many Salisbury girls came happily and willingly to Bulawayo, which was considered a backwater, lacking the sophistication and élan of the capital city, but I loved the wide streets, the beautiful silver oaks and jacarandas which lined them as far as the outer suburbs, and the kind and friendly people. There were night-clubs in the town where we danced and dined, cinemas and a lively theatre where overseas companies came with their productions, places of historical interest where the first missionaries had built their schools and churches, the Matopos Hills where the founder of this country lay buried in the granite kopjes. Best of all, there was the enjoyment of meeting new friends, and the relaxed atmosphere of a large city devoid of the heavy hand of bureaucracy.

With one of the older staff members, I was sent to a new office at the railway station where we would assist new immigrants through the Customs; during the last year there had been a flood of European refugees coming into the colony from Germany and Austria, and we began to hear that foreign word 'pogrom' as we struggled to understand their explanations as to why they had left their native countries to settle in this new frontier town. Our way of life, our language and customs were different from theirs, but they opened little shops in the avenues selling groceries, mending shoes, making jewellery and opening elite dress shops; most strangely of all, they did not employ domestic servants. They were fearful of the black men and could not speak English or the local patois used between master and servant. Although not everyone welcomed the refugees, we became used to the sight of the white women cleaning their own windows, hanging out laundry and working in their gardens.

'No,' said Mrs Baum, one of the newcomers, when I offered to find her a good domestic servant. 'I am too poor, we were only allowed to take very few things when we were driven from our country. Money, no, only some clothes and a few of our treasures, everything else they took. We are refugees, nowhere welcome,' and she began to cry, dabbing at her face with her fine monogrammed handkerchief. 'Why did you leave Germany,' I asked, 'and why did you come here?' 'Questions, questions all the time,' she replied, 'always questions. We were driven out because we were Jews. For no other reason. And we came here because the Agency arranged it so. Enough. No more questions,' and she picked up her elegant crocodile handbag, gathered up her passport and swept out of the office to join her compatriots on the pavement. Sophisticated women, well-dressed men in their good tweed suits, and those well-cared-for hands were evidence enough that they had never been used to the every-day tasks in a home. Many were of the professional classes and the people Germany and Austria had lost were our gain.

There was talk of the approaching war and every newspaper carried stories which dispelled our ignorance of their sufferings and hardships, of their escapes and torture by the dreaded S.S. Gradually they assumed their place in the hotch-potch of a colonial society, appearing to be part of it but in reality remaining aloof and foreign. Daily the newspapers carried reports of Germany's expansionist plans, of the occupation of the Saar and of the re-armament proposals. It would not affect us here, we told ourselves; but soon the young men began to speak openly of their penchant for the armed services, preferring the glamour of the Air Force, that new and exciting arm of Britain's military capability. Not one would admit that he was afraid or did not want to take up arms. Such a despicable admission would earn him the ridicule and pity of his friends and several years in prison as a Conscientious Objector.

'Will you be called up?' I asked George, dreading his reply. 'All the men under thirty will be,' he said. 'But I can't be called up for the Rhodesian Forces, I'll go back to England and get myself a commission in the Air Force.' 'What will become of me?' I asked. He looked at me warily and then replied, 'I hope you'll wait, but we can be married before I go; nothing will happen for a few months I'm sure.' He spoke with such conviction that I felt foolish for having asked the question, but I was afraid for the future.

On every possible occasion, he reminded me that we were engaged to be married; he would take me in hand, he said, to groom me for the position he was offering. My reading would have to change, no more of that ridiculous Chinese philosophy I read and an end to Colette's books. 'Rubbish,' he described them. 'I'm surprised a young girl like you reads such dirty books,' he said, and I felt besmirched and decided that my newest craze, an adventure into Russian literature, would be kept a secret. My hair was to be cut by a top professional recently arrived from Johannesburg and my clothes, quite frankly, embarrassed George. Nor did he like the way I returned an interested glance, or responded to other men: 'They think you're trying to flirt with them, especially when you look at them with those bedroom eyes,' he remarked. I cringed with shame as his words flayed me, and summoning up my courage I asked 'What attracted you when we first met?' He eyed me for a few moments and smoothed back his hair. 'You were so different from any other girl I had ever seen,' he said. 'And now you are trying to make me look like everyone else?' I asked. He did not reply but reached out to help me from my chair. 'I've got to go to my tailor for a fitting, come with me and I'll take you around to that new dress shop and we'll see if they've got anything for you. I'll pay.'

I sat on a stool listening to the conversation in the fitting room of Mr Stanley's august establishment. Was not the position of the buttons on the new jacket perhaps a little too high? And the cut of the lapel? Too narrow? Or too wide? Perhaps one button after all, and what of the lie of the pocket? Too slanted or not enough? And he was not too sure about the material, perhaps a creamier shade or a lighter linen would have been preferable? Poor Mr Stanley, his mouth full of pins, his fingers smeared with chalk as he marked or eased out a seam, chalked in the slant of the pocket or ripped out his tailor's tacks. I longed to get up and run out of the shop, to join the gaggle of hockey players who rode up the main street, their legs encased in long black stockings, their scarlet tunics giving them the appearance of a flock of Red Cardinals, those beautiful birds only seen in this part of the country.

But I was too much in awe of George to do so and meekly accompanied him to the dress shop to try on, under his critical eye, a selection of day and evening dresses just arrived from England; a choice was made under the jaundiced and envious eye of the assistant and George took my arm saying 'You'll be a credit to me yet,' as he led me back to my hotel. But inwardly I rebelled and took my problem to Carrie, who I had at last located in a nearby solicitor's office.

'Why do you put up with him?' she asked me. I was silent as I too, wondered why. 'You're a fool, what's happened to all that spirit and your independence?' she asked angrily. 'I can't tell you how surprised I was when I heard you were involved with him, he's a philanderer, he's far too old for you and he boasts he can have any girl in the town.' I was dismayed at her words but I knew they held some truth. Those knowing looks exchanged with other older women, the excuses when plans had to be changed at the last minute, the frequent absences and the veto on any phone calls to his hotel. To my mind came the words of the police driving instructor as he had rested his hand for those long few seconds on my knee instead of the gear lever when I had gone for a driving test. 'He's a bad 'un all right,' he'd said. 'Can't keep his hands off any girl,' and he'd patted me kindly on my shoulder as I retorted angrily, 'do you think you're any different?'

'Are you in love with him?' Carrie asked. I thought for a long time before I answered. 'I don't know. I don't think I know what love is or how I should feel,' and I began to wonder if I was capable of that elusive emotion; I was too afraid of admitting to myself that I did not really know what it meant to be in love or to be loved. I had not known any love as a child and felt no attachment to my father or to my aunt and her family. To my sister and brother there was a kind of loyalty, and to kind Mrs Samuels there had been deep gratitude for her concern; those Africans I had known so long ago, I still felt a great affection for, as I did for the nuns at the convent. But Love, no. And what of Rui, that first man in my life? A feeling of gratitude for giving me confidence in myself, flattered and enchanted by his attentions, devastated by his departure; at seventeen total commitment would not have been difficult and I would have enjoyed the restraints he would have put upon me. They would have been a continuation of my life as it had been but with the added

327

bonus of his love and care together with his physical presence. But I was crying for the moon, I knew, and I made up my mind to confront George and tell him that I felt I was too young to be married.

But there was no need for me to make the first move. We were dancing at the Round House Club and as he ran his hand up my arm he remarked 'You have a lovely colour, like honey, quite different from anyone else.' 'Sunburn?' I volunteered. He led me off the floor and when we had seated ourselves, he asked, 'Do you know someone called Julia McCready?' I thought for a moment and replied, 'No, I don't even know the name.' 'She knows you, or rather your family,' he said. 'Tell me about your mother, where did she come from? Who was she before she married your father?' I confessed I could not tell him anything, my mother had died many years ago and I could no longer even remember what she looked like. 'But she was dark like me,' I volunteered. For a few moments he avoided my eye, then, still looking away from me, he said, 'Julia told me your mother was a coloured woman, that everyone in Salisbury knew she was. They knew too that she passed herself off as French or Spanish. It's a favourite ploy amongst that kind when they're trying to catch a white husband.' I was horrified, burst into tears and ran from the room.

Was it true, I asked myself as I desperately turned my mind back to those dim and distant days, trying in vain to see my mother again, to see her face, searching for signs of miscegenation, the tell-tale frizzy hair, the purple tinge to her fingernails, the slightly blurred features. I cringed as I thought of the coloured people in the town, their seeming lack of pride, their shamefaced look as though they were constantly apologising for their presence, knowing that they were despised and dishonoured, unable to acknowledge their begetters. I knew too how deeply they were despised by both white and black, the whites refusing to admit their part in the siring of this race as though they had come from another planet or had always been in the country before the Europeans had come to it; the blacks scorning them for their mixed blood, saying they were mongrels with all the faults of both progenitors yet none of their good attributes. To be purely black had its own rewards; the disadvantages were many in this white society, but I had never known any African who silently apologised for, or was ashamed of, his skin colour. To be white was of course, to be unassailable, but to be in between was considered by everyone to be a living death. For me I knew it would be the end. I

328

remembered the pitying looks from other parents when I was introduced to them at school, the constant questioning about my dead mother. I had always supposed it was because of my motherless state, but now I wondered – was it because of my looks? I was in a state of panic when I heard George walking towards me in the dark. He put his arm around me and said quietly, 'Don't cry, I still love you, but you must realise I could never marry you now, I don't want a lot of coffee-coloured children. Blood with always tell.'

'It cannot be true,' I said desperately. 'There are no signs of coloured blood in my family. If you were to meet my father and my sister, you would see how ridiculous this all is. Both my grandparents came from overseas, there is absolutely no truth in what you've been told.' I hiccuped and snivelled in my distress. 'I'm quite prepared to take you out,' said George, 'but forget about marriage, I can't afford to take the chance. Of course if your father will tell me what he knows, I may change my mind.' My hurt turned to anger as I turned from him. 'You are too generous,' I cried as scathingly as I could, 'you told me you loved me. If you truly did, this would make no difference. It is not my fault if what you say is true. But I know it's not. How many other people has your friend told this story to? Who else, tell me?'

'It's only between Julia, you and me,' he replied. 'But she did say people in Salisbury knew.' 'It's not true,' I said once again. 'This is the first time such a thing has been said to me. I had many friends in Salisbury and no one ever hinted at anything like that.' I removed his ring from my finger and flung it to the ground. 'You can believe what you like,' I said, 'I'm not asking my father to confirm or deny such a canard. You are despicable and have said dreadful things to me. I hope you will be punished.' 'You're getting hysterical,' he told me. 'Perhaps you ought to consider leaving Bulawayo before the story gets out. If you do go, leave those things I bought you at Highbury, I'll collect them and sell them to Ben Baron down by the railway yards. He takes second-hand goods and no questions asked.' With that jibe he turned to retrace his steps into the nightclub and I walked though the moonlit night, through the avenue of whispering jacaranda trees, the silvered grasses and on to the main road.

Carefully, I lifted the hem of my dark red velvet dress, remembering as I did so that indeed George had paid for it, and I considered removing it there and then and leaving it in the road for him to see on his homeward ride. But that would be silly, I told myself. A certain amount of satisfaction would be gained but I would also catch a cold and did not

329

wish to be found striding along a deserted country road, miles from the town, in a thin petticoat, brassiere and high-heeled gold shoes, in the early hours of the morning. Suddenly I heard the approach of a car and presently a police car came into view. It slowed down and the voice of the police sergeant called out, 'It's my lucky night, you're a long way from home aren't you?' 'Are you offering me a lift?' I asked.

He opened the door and I climbed in. 'Do you Salisbury girls always walk around the bush in the middle of the night?' he asked. 'We do all sorts of funny things,' I replied. 'We even ride in police cars.' He switched on the overhead light. 'You're a mess,' he told me, 'have you been crying? Had a quarrel with the delightful Mr Ross? Not before time.' He leaned forward. 'If you touch me,' I cried, 'I'll jump out. And yes, to all your questions.' He asked no more but took me home, promising to say nothing about the night's event. He was to become a good friend and we enjoyed a mild flirtation for some years; I knew I could always turn to him for help but I never told him why I had been walking along a dark bush road in the middle of the night.

For a long time doubts surged through my mind. Perhaps it was true, perhaps Grandma was not from France and they lived miles from any town so that no one would see her and deduce that she was a Coloured; but she had spoken a language different from any other I had ever heard. No, it was not possible – but then what about Charlotte? Dimly I pictured her as I had seen her last, kneeling in the sandy road, an arm around Stella and the other around Tom and me. I recalled her black eyes, her olive skin and her fine dark hair free from any give-away kinkiness, straight as my own was, bound in a low knot on her neck. Perhaps she was coloured and I, in my ignorance had not seen the tell-tale signs? And what about my affinity with the tribesmen? I had always felt great sympathy for them and I remembered Vinyu whom I came close to idolizing. Were these feelings all because I was really one of them?

I realised I was torturing myself with these doubts and uncertainties and there was but one solution. I would have to return to Salisbury and confront my father and ask the truth, and sooner rather than later. I crept to my office each day, feeling sure that written across my forehead was the word 'Coloured' and feeling that I would return to Highbury to find my clothes packed and an angry landlord pointing towards the Coloured suburb of the town and urging me to go back to where I

330

belonged. But it was not so. Invitations to every event were left at my door, the office telephone beckoned me with requests from every man I had met and I responded to each and every one, almost with an air of bravado. I frequently saw George in passing and we smiled grimly at each other, but I refused to give anyone any satisfaction by discussing him, or any explanation as to why we had parted and were no longer to be married.

I left Highbury where I had made so many friends and which had been my home for some months, and moved across the town to a single room in a tenement block. I stood on my small balcony looking across the bare stretch of land which separated the edge of the town from the native quarter and beyond, where lay the Coloured township. Smoke from the cooking fires mingled with the dust of the donkey carts as they were driven across the valley, and I thought to myself, perhaps that is where I really belong, amongst those people who are neither black nor white, but mongrels, despised by black and white alike and said to have inherited the worse of both cultures.

To my mind came the picture of an occurrence many years ago when I had been running through the bush with my cousin. We had found ourselves near the brickfields where there stood a long row of one roomed shacks occupied by coloured families. I had stood at the doorway looking in, afraid to enter because of my dirty feet, when the lady who was sitting at a sewing machine, turned to look at me. 'Come in, little girl,' she had said, 'don't stand there with your finger in your mouth. Come in, or are you too proud?' I continued to stand there, curious about her but more inquisitive about the array of photographs standing on the dresser and afraid to answer. I knew she was coloured and that I should not be in her house, that it was forbidden to mix with people like her and that I would be beaten if my cousin told his mother.

'Is that yours?' I asked pointing at the largest photograph. It was of a white man, young and fresh faced, in uniform and written across the bottom were some words. She leaned forward and picked up the yellowing picture and handed it to me and smiled. 'He was my friend,' she said, 'he was a British Tommy. He used to come and visit me here. He was my sweetheart.' She sighed as she gazed fondly at the young man. 'What happened?' I asked. 'He said he'd come back for me, but he didn't', she replied as she replaced the photograph. 'Perhaps he was killed?' I asked. 'Perhaps,' she said. 'Your friend's waiting for you,' she said, but before I could go, I was pushed aside and a young girl came into the room. She was about sixteen I judged, the same age as cousin

331

Jack, and I saw the resemblance to her mother. 'This is my girl Poppy,' said the lady. 'What's your name?' I told her but I was fascinated by the daughter. Her skin was lighter than her mother's, her eyes were that strange colour between green and grey, but her hair was a rusty krinkled ginger like the coir in my mattress at Aunty Betty's. Coloured, I told myself, both of them, and that young man in the picture is Poppy's father. I was more shocked because her mother had not been married, I had not seen any wedding ring and she had referred to him as her sweetheart, than I ever was because her father had been a white man.

Now as I stood looking across the valley I resolved that I would return to Salisbury and find out the truth from my father. The following week, after a convincing tale to my employer, I was once more on the train heading for the capital. Letty and Grace were pleased to see me they said, and yes I was welcome to share their beds and borrow their bicycles. I cycled back to my father's house and found him sitting on the back verandah on his old motor car seat, sipping his tea from a saucer.

'Wotcher,' he cried when I walked in. 'Where you bin?' he asked, 'I wondered where you'd got to? Heard from Stella have you?' Would it matter, I thought, if I said nothing about my move to another city and pretended that I still lived in town? 'I was transferred to Bulawayo about eight months' ago,' I told him, 'and I came up to see the Godley girls. But mainly to see you.' 'Oh yers,' he said nervously, 'in some sort of trouble are you? Come to ask your old dad for help, 'ave yer? What you bin up to then? Cooked the books or spent the petty cash? 'Oo yer workin' for then?' I answered all his questions and then asked if we could walk down to his garden on the river bank. 'It's something very confidential, I don't really want Doris to know,' I told him. 'She's taken the kids for a walk,' he said 'we got young John just over a year old and the baby Ellen just a coupla months.' He grinned with satisfaction. 'So you're a family man again, are you?' I asked, 'What about Mrs Kemp? Is she living with you.' 'Stone the bleedin' crows,' he cried. 'I put a stop to that once and for all more 'n a year ago. She lives with her son Bob but I let her come and spend a day once a week with me wife. Just as long as she's gorn by the time I gets 'ome.' He chuckled with glee.

'Now what's it all about,' he asked at length. 'What you come all the way from Bulawayo to ask me? Yer not thinking of getting married are you? I wouldn't allow it, you know, I still got custiddy of you. You can do what you like when you turn twenty-one.' I wondered what small satisfaction that fact gave him and why he took such a perverse delight in reminding me, but I consoled myself that whatever I did, I could safely keep it from him here in Salisbury.

332

'Do you know anyone called McCready?' I asked. He thought for a moment. 'McCready? A widder woman? Her wot worked at the Steam Laundry?' 'I don't know where she worked', I said, 'but it's Julia McCready I'm asking about.' He thought for a moment. 'Could be the ma I know. Silly woman. Didn't 'arf set 'er cap at me. Years ago it was when you was all small nippers, when you first come to live with your Aunty Betty. Yes I remember her, had to give her the cold shoulder, but she didn't 'arf chase me.' He smiled again, re-living the experience and enjoying it in retrospect.

'Yus', he said at last, 'I remember she did have a kid, a girl with long fair hair, but I don't remember the kid's name. Julia you say?' He sat down on the rusty old wheelbarrow and lit a cigarette. 'What about her?' he asked.

I told him, using the same words George had spoken to me, but I did not mention George's name, merely referring to him as a friend in the same boarding house. 'Strewth,' cried my father, 'I'll sue her, I'll sue her for bleedin' defermation of character, that I will. Gawd Almighty what a thing to put around, me married to a coloured woman! What bleedin' next?' He shook his head in disbelief. 'Is it true?' I asked. 'True,' he shouted, 'of course it ain't true. D'ye think I don't know the difference between a white woman and a coloured?'

'What about Grandma Williams?' I asked 'Was she coloured?' ' 'Ow the bleedin' 'ell can you say that? She was a foreigner, couldn't speak a word of English, came from somewhere in France. Or Belgium. Somewhere where there's a big steel works. She was always tellin' yer ma about her cousins and her brother who worked in a foundry. Leege it was, somewhere in northern France I think. Coloured, what next.' He spat in disgust, aiming the glob at a lizard which scurried past. 'And yer such a bleedin' fool, you come all this way to ask me such a damn fool question,' he said. 'Why don't I have a birth certificate?' I asked. He rubbed his chin thoughtfully for a few moments and then said. 'That's another matter, it ain't got nothing to do with what you just said. I'll tell you some other time. It weren't my fault. But saying my wife was coloured, if that don't beat the band.'

'Why would she have said it then?' I asked. 'Gawd Almighty, how should I bleedin' know,' he asked, and then a crafty smile lit his face. 'Her ma might have started it, she was a spiteful woman as I remember 'er.' He blew several smoke rings into the air, considering them as they wafted upwards and melted away. 'Coloured? I ask you? What the 'ell next.'

'But what about me?' I asked him. 'What am I going to do if it's said again? Denying it's no good. I wish I had my birth certificate.' 'Well there ain't one,' my father said, 'it weren't my fault as I've told you, but anyone with a brain's just got to look at yer to know you take after yer ma and that old cow Williams. That bleedin McCready woman will find herself in trouble if she goes on like that, see if she don't.' I could see he was anxious to change the conversation now that it no longer revolved around himself, but I persisted. 'Can't you ask the Registrar for a copy of my baptismal certificate then?' I asked. 'It would be better than nothing.' 'It ain't got nothing to do with him,' said my father. 'It's where you was christened and I ain't fagging all the way out to bleedin' Hatfield to ask any favours. Bleedin' priests.'

'I cried when I was asked if it was true,' I said. 'You always was a soppy kid,' he answered. 'What about me? D'ye ever think about the 'ard time I had?' 'Yes,' I replied, 'I always felt sorry for you when you lived in that little house down the plot and when you used to come to Aunty Betty's and sit there playing your banjo and singing those sad songs.' He looked surprised. 'Gawd blimey,' he said, 'you ain't 'arf a queer one.' He got up and we walked back to the house.

Satisfied by my father's reassurance that I was not a half-caste, I put the whole matter from my mind, only remembering it when I saw George. More disquieting was the talk of war in Europe, and rumours flew thick and fast; we would be invaded from the north where Mussolini's airmen were already strafing the Abyssinian villagers and where a war had raged for over a year. We had gold, coal and precious metals in our country, coveted by those who would overrun us, but most precious of all was our space, millions of acres of good land which would satisfy any greedy dictator of an over-populated country. Of our neighbours the Portuguese on our eastern borders, who could be sure? I recalled those young Germans we had met on our holiday so long ago in Beira, suspected by the British community of being spies. They lived on their ship and that could only mean one thing, said the pundits; radio equipment, which would allow them to send messages back to Berlin. To our west lay the wide emptiness of Bechuanaland with its swamps and deserts, but this was not a problem; our friends in the south, the South Africans, were British to the core and would deal with any subversive element which filtered through from German South West Africa. We'd be all right, we told ourselves, it'll never happen here. We continued to watch the newsreels and listen to the radio broadcasts, but our main thoughts were on the next party, the next dance or picnic and the newest dresses just arrived from the south.

334

PART SEVEN

At the end of that winter, war in Europe was declared. As if the world was about to end, every man in the colony raced to his nearest Drill Hall to sign on, notice was given in offices, coats and aprons hung up in shops and stores, workers under the threat of the sack were hastily forgiven their misdeeds and throughout the towns and villages it seemed as though the men were all off to a world-wide spree, to a glorious adventure. Not a thought was given to the possibility that there would be death and destruction, to broken families, terrifying experiences and to the change it would bring to all our lives. Amongst the frenetic clamourings to serve King and Country, there were the more sober-faced whose knowledge of events was more complete than ours, who had been brought up knowing what had happened during the First World War, whose families had been devastated but whose words went unheeded.

Uniforms appeared on the streets, clubs for servicemen were opened and the pig styes and cattle pens at the Showgrounds were converted into quarters for the men in uniform; engagements were announced, marriages hastily arranged and gradually the male population was reduced to the under eighteens, foreigners, the medically unfit, those in essential occupations and the old. The drain on commerce and industry threatened to become so crippling that conscription was hastily introduced and a system for orderly call-up was substituted. Employers now had time to assess and re-organise their staffs and there arose that phenomenon, the working wife.

As men were gradually siphoned off and absorbed into the Services, employers and typists did their utmost to run the businesses until replacements could be found. But from where? The native population of many millions of Africans was completely uneducated and would remain so for many years; the coloured community consisted of some hundreds and their men had been called up to form the nucleus of the

Transport Corps. Those of us who could add, speak on the telephone properly and write a legible hand filled the gaps.

I had seen the advertisement for a Customs clearing clerk in the newspaper and telephoned for an interview. 'Are you sure you have had enough experience in this sort of work to take on the job?' asked Sonnie Fox the senior partner of the business. I looked around the small office, at the three desks and the small staff, and asked 'What do they actually do?' They were, he informed me, contractors to the railways and delivered goods and merchandise which arrived in the colony to the firms which had imported them. I would have to clear everything through the Customs, he told me, and then he added 'You will have to meet passengers off the train, refugees mostly, who come in as immigrants. I'm not sure you're the right person to deal with that.' 'You're wrong,' I told him boldly, determined to have this job which I knew would pay well. 'I attended to many of the refugees who came in these last few months, I can give you their names and I know one or two who would definitely speak for me.'

He jingled the loose change in his pocket and looked me over again. 'You'll have to work by yourself, none of us know anything about it and we couldn't help you.' Hastily I reassured him that I was the right person for this job which until that moment had always been the prerequisite of men only; to hire a girl was unthinkable. 'What salary would you want?' he asked. 'The same as Mr Hunt,' I said. 'I believe he has been called up?' He looked at me as though I had made an improper suggestion, laughed falsely and shook his head in disbelief at such an outrageous proposal. 'I can't pay you the same as a man', he said at last. 'Why not?' I asked, 'I would be doing a man's work.' His mouth fell open. 'I'd be the laughing stock of the town if I were to pay you a man's salary,' he said.

I rose and picked up my handbag. 'I don't get any reduction for my room and meals, I have to pay exactly the same as a man does,' I told him. 'Surely if I'm to do the work of a man, I should expect to be paid the same as he does?' 'No,' he shook his head, 'it's out of the question. A man's salary for a girl?' and he began to laugh, while the two girls and the junior looked at me from under their brows. I made as if to leave. 'I'm sorry,' I said, 'but I have one or two others to see, thank you for seeing me,' and I walked to the door. But he was not prepared to let me go. 'If I did take you on, when could you start?' 'At the end of the month,' I told him. I could see he was desperate but was unprepared for the next question. 'Any chance of your getting married?' he asked. 'I don't employ married women and any way, the job would only be for

338

the duration; I will have to take Mr Hunt back if he's discharged or invalided out of the army.' 'I'm not engaged and have no plans to get married,' I said, 'and if Mr Hunt comes back, I realise he would have to have his job back. I'm sure I could find another job quite easily.'

'Can I let you know?' he asked at length, but I was determined to have my way. 'No, don't bother,' I said, 'if you can't offer me the job, just say so. I have two other people to see and I want to get the whole thing settled.' 'What about a trial period?' he asked. 'No, Mr Fox,' I said. 'Either I have the job now at the salary I want, or I don't. I have no parents to look after me and I must also think of my future. I am quite alone and have to make my own way.' He stood for some minutes chewing at a thumb nail, then suddenly said 'The job's yours on the salary you've asked for, but on one condition. That is that you don't discuss it with the staff or any of your friends. I'd be the laughing stock of the town if it got around that I'm paying a girl the salary of a man. You'd spoil the market.'

Silently we shook hands and I went back to my office to give in my notice, alternately fuming at the injustice of the system and laughing because I had won the day. I was to stay with Fox Brothers for more than two years, thanking Providence on every pay-day that I had stood up for myself and had not shown the timid and cowardly side of my nature. The company had been formed from the defunct remains of the original transport company started by the Zeederberg family after the First World War. Flat bed wagons pulled by teams of two or four or six mules rumbled through the town, picking up and delivering the imported merchandise to the shops and offices, and the drivers, all Matabele tribesmen, knew every inch of the town and the outlying suburbs. Recently a daring innovation had taken place, the purchase and delivery from South Africa of two ten-ton lorries for the carting of steel rods from the newly built Steel Works, but like Mr Hunt, the coloured drivers had also been called up for the Transport Corps. The day I started with Fox Brothers saw the introduction of the first African driver, a dour, unfriendly man whose name was Johannes and whose first task had been to drive the flat-bedded lorry down to Plumtree with a load of empty coffins. There had been a train crash during the night and bodies had been brought back to Bulawayo for burial in the cemetery. 'Johannes is still thinking of those dead people', said the office boys, as explanation of Joannes' surly and unfriendly face.

* * *

339

Suddenly the whole face of the town changed with the arrival of the Royal Air Force in their blue uniforms. Barrack huts had been hastily erected on the small airport at Kumalo a few miles from the city, where the weekly arrival of the bi-plane from the south carrying mail from Britain had been the high point of the week. Empty houses were commandeered for the commissioned staff, clubs were established for the servicemen and the women of the town were called upon to lend a hand, to befriend the young strangers, to serve meals, to change the gramophone records at the clubs and to collect books and magazines for the messes.

We discovered that these Englishmen spoke with different accents, some of which we could barely understand; they hated the heat, the flies, the incessant rains of the summer, the searing winds and cold of winter and they openly told us we were only on the verge of civilisation. Sharp distinctions were drawn between those who went out with the non-commissioned men and those who preferred the company of the officers; with other friends, I belonged to neither of these groups, preferring to wait for the return of friends on leave from their service in the North.

News came of our men killed in action, missing or taken prisoner and at last the war became more real and our complacency was cracked. Familiar faces re-appeared in strange and wonderful uniforms; the red trousers and beige jackets of the 'Cherry Pickers', the dark green of the Kings Royal Rifle Corps, the tartan trews of the Scottish regiments, the sober khaki of the Royal West African Frontier Force, of the Somaliland Camel Corps and the King's African Rifles. Short leaves were spent in a whirl of parties and many romances blossomed and culminated in marriage. We were all swept up in a hurricane of frenetic enjoyment, brought to earth only by the announcements in the papers of fatalities and losses.

To the south events took an ominous turn. An underground movement surfaced, the Ossewa Brandwag, sworn to sabotage the Allies' cause, and notices appeared on hoardings and in the papers, that we were to be careful what we said about the war, about our men coming on leave or departing to rejoin their regiments. Railway lines in the border areas were blown up, ships off the coast were mysteriously sunk and General Smuts, the South African Prime Minister, stated that South Africans would serve only in Africa and would not see service abroad. Rifts opened between friends and families with connections in the south and plans were made for our own men to be withdrawn from the South African Division if they so wished, but many took the opportunity to remain with the Imperial army.

There was no one whose life was not affected in some way by the course of the distant war and gradually that well-worn phrase 'There's a war on you know' became the excuse for any shortcoming, any deficiency or inadequacy. It justified the faithless abandoning their partners, the sudden addition of an unwelcome baby, the proliferation of the 'dirty weekend' and the good-time girl. Soldiers returning from the north as well as the servicemen in the colony, suddenly found themselves with more money and allowances than before, and very few gave more than a passing thought to the days when peace would come. We all lived for the moment, thinking no further than the next dance, the next party or the next man.

'There's a flat to let in Fourth Avenue,' said Carrie over the telephone, 'old Stern who owns it says we can go and look at it after work. Are you interested? Stern doesn't want the Air Force to get hold of it, says he wants a tenant who'll take it for a long time, not just a few months.' Slowly we walked through the avenues in the late afternoon, savouring the beauty of the silver oaks bordering the road, and came to the small block. We would take it, we assured the landlord and plans were made to move in at the month's end. We had long spoken of sharing a home, of getting away from our present depressing rooms to somewhere we could entertain our friends, where we could come and go as we pleased without the twitching of every curtain in the building or the disapproving looks when we came in after midnight.

We engaged an umfaan, a young African boy of some sixteen years; he would make beds, sweep and clean, and with a note written by one of us, do our shopping. After office hours one of us sat in the small kitchen and taught him to read and write, but he sulked and pouted when he was corrected. 'You don't want to be a kitchen boy when you grow up,' I told him. 'There will be office jobs for young men like you when you say you can read and write English. One day perhaps you will have your own business and become rich, stop crying and let's start again.' The tears hung on his cheeks, he sniffed from the bottom of his feet and smiled. 'When I am an older man,' he said, 'I will be rich.' 'You won't be if you don't listen to me', I told him, and he snivelled and threw down his pencil. 'You are not my friend,' he cried, 'it is too hard, I cannot write.'

But he persevered and was soon able to read out paragraphs from the newspapers I brought home. 'Are you my friend?' he asked one day as we sat reading, 'my people say the white man is our enemy.' 'Am I?'

341

asked Carrie from the doorway. He smiled his engaging smile, and his eyes twinkled. 'You are both Mashona. The white men are our enemies. We must obey all they say and work for them but when I am an old man, my sons will change all those things.' He laughed and fiddled with the paper. 'Who tells you these things, and why do you say we are Mashona, we too are white people.' He wriggled in his chair, avoiding our eyes. 'You are just people,' he said.

A subject of such depth was never discussed between us again and Tobias applied himself diligently to his domestic and his school work until the day I saw an advertisement which read 'Smart youth, coloured preferred, wanted for department store in city.' I telephoned and asked for the manager. 'Your advertisement for a coloured youth?' I asked. 'Can I bring someone around to see you? He's very young, but can read and write English. He's very honest. I've known him for a few months and am sure he's just what you're looking for.' It was arranged we should present ourselves after hours, at the back door of the establishment.

Mr Harris was waiting when I walked in with Tobias, but his face fell and angrily he asked 'Didn't you see I said "a coloured preferred"? This fellow's a native.' 'Yes I know, Mr Harris,' I replied, 'but he's clever, he can read and write. He's very polite, he knows the town well and he's also coloured. Black.' Mr Harris glared at me. 'There's no need to be cheeky,' he said primly, 'but I can't employ an umfaan, I want a young coloured.' 'Then you shouldn't have said preferred, you should have just said Wanted a Coloured youth.' Behind me I heard Tobias cough. 'Why not give Tobias a test?' I asked. 'At least give him a chance. You might even be commended for being the first company to employ a native in an office.' 'You've got a lot to say for yourself,' said Mr Harris. 'What's your interest in this job?' 'None,' I told him, 'but when I went to work for the Fox Brothers, they didn't want a girl, they wanted a man for the job. I'm not being conceited when I tell you that they are satisfied with me and since then, the other Customs agencies have employed girls. Why don't you also aim for being a first?' He was thoughtful for a few minutes and then rose to show me to the door, motioning to Tobias that he was to wait.

'You've given me something to think about,' he said. 'I'll give him a written test and see how good his English is. If he comes up to scratch, I'll take him on, but if not, he'll have to go.' 'That's fair,' I agreed, 'I don't think you'll be disappointed. I hope you will pay him what the advertisement says, it would be a pity to spoil such a radical step.' We

342

smiled at each other and shook hands. 'If you ever decide to change your job, come and see me,' he said. 'There are going to be big changes in this country when the war is over.' Tobias was engaged for the job and I often saw him when I went into the shop to buy vegetables; he sat behind his desk checking in bags of potatoes, crates of cabbages and boxes of fruit, pausing only to answer the telephone or to answer a query from a customer. We smiled at each other and he always arose from his desk or abandoned his customer to walk with me to the door. Afraid that he would feel patronised or under an obligation, I hesitated to engage in a conversation with him until he made the first move, but he too was shy and only once said 'I will always remember what you and Miss Carrie did for me. I was not grateful then, but I am now. You were both truly my friends.' But we missed Tobias and were only consoled by the fact that he was destined for better things than a life as a kitchen boy. The remark he had made to me however, that 'one day my sons will change all those things' gave me a few moments of unease; surely I thought to myself, the natives are quite happy, why would they want to change things? I was completely unaware of what they thought, not realising that under that smiling face and humble mien, there lay a seething mass of bitterness, resentment and desperation. It would be many years, decades even before their aspirations were realised; at that moment such a development seemed as unlikely as a man going to the moon.

Suddenly we noticed a change in the uniforms on our streets. New Zealanders, Australians, the Free French, Yugoslavs and Greeks arrived to train with the Air Force. We met them at the Service clubs and some we invited to our flat for tea, for meals or simply to listen to our new records. They were homesick and longed for the end of their training so that they could return to their own units and families back home – but not Etienne, who spent all his time with Carrie, taking her dancing or out to dinner and then she told me he had asked her to marry him. 'Are you going to?' I asked. 'Are you in love with him?' 'Yes I think so,' she said after some thought, 'but I can't help thinking of what happened in Salisbury,' she added. 'That was more than two years ago,' I reminded her. 'It's got nothing to do with Etienne.' 'But I shall have to tell him,' she said, 'he's a Catholic, he's got the same ideas as you have. About purity and things like that.' She looked embarrassed. 'How can I marry him when he thinks I'm a virgin, and I'm not?' 'Then you'll have to tell him,' I said. 'Better now than later surely?' I'll loose him, if I do,' she retorted.

I thought very little more of our conversation; a letter from Stella had come to me, addressed care of Mr George Ross. Could she come and spend two weeks with me, she asked, would there be room for her in my hotel room, she had very little money but would explain everything when she arrived? I was excited at the prospect of seeing my sister again; two years had passed since I had stood on the station platform saying goodbye to her, envying her her good fortune and dreading the prospect of life without her. I wondered what changes we would see in each other but I wondered too, about her present circumstances and why she had no money; but I wrote to say I shared a flat with a friend and there was a spare room and that I longed to see her.

As she stepped out of the railway carriage, three men scurried around carrying her heavy suitcase, passing out packages from the window, raising their hats as they bade her goodbye, reminding her they would be staying in Bulawayo for a few days on business and would be only too pleased to be of any help. 'The same old story,' she told me laughing, 'men are such suckers aren't they? Those three pestered me all the way from Johannesburg, but I couldn't be nasty could I?' I was more interested in her pretty clothes than in her admirers, and I lay on the spare bed as she unpacked. 'Don't you have to go to work?' she asked when the last pair of shoes had been safely stowed away. 'Not today,' I told her. 'I've got the day off, but tomorrow I have to be back at work so we'll have to make the best of it until the weekend.'

'How is Stanley?' I asked. 'That sod,' she spat out, 'he was a fraud right from the beginning and I was a fool not to see through him. Do you know that Margie, who introduced us, was his ex-wife? He'd come up to Rhodesia to find her, she had run off with that fellow Surtees and although Stan had been divorced from her, he was hoping to find her to ask her to release him from paying alimony. She'd been living with Surtees, living in sin mind you, all that time.' I looked suitably shocked but my heart sank as she continued. 'When I got to Jo'burg he had made all the arrangements for the wedding and we got married right away. Then I found out that his mother was to live with us. A real old witch she was, caused trouble right from the beginning; seemed to think I was her skivvy. It was Stella do this, fetch that, get me a cushion for my back, run down to the store for me and when Stan came home, he'd go to her straight away and sit there holding her hand and talking to her as though she was the bride, not me.

344

'But worst of all was his job. Do you know he's a nightwatchman at the Power Station? I nearly died when he told me. Every evening at five o'clock I had to pack up a meal for him and he trotted down the road off to work, swinging his bag as though he was somebody important. I didn't want any of you up here to know, so that's why I never wrote. He never gave me any money and that old cow did all the shopping, he gave her his pay packet every week and she'd hand me two or three pounds for myself.' 'But what about his car?' I asked as soon as I could interrupt the flow. 'That was another thing,' she said bitterly. 'He had to sell it, he'd borrowed the money to come up to Rhodesia that time and when I got to Jo'burg, there was only enough left to spend on the wedding. If I'd known about it, I would have come straight back here.' she said. 'You wouldn't, you know,' I replied. 'Why have you left it so long before you did?' She said nothing and went to stand before the mirror, to re-arrange her hair and to smooth down her dress. She smiled at her reflection and turned sideways, smoothing her dress carefully over her hips.

'For this past year I've been working,' she continued. 'At an estate agent's office in the mornings. I've made lots of new friends. My special friend Glenda, she gave me this load of slippers she'd got from somewhere, stolen I think by one of the office nigs, and we sold them. She often gets stuff and we sell it after work, to the people who live nearby.' She sounded very pleased at her enterprise. 'What's your house like?' I asked. 'I've made it nice,' she said, 'but it's in an Afrikaans suburb, I don't like the Boeties who live around us, the men whistle at me in the street. They've got a cheek.' I felt sorry for her. 'So how did you get enough for your train fare?' I asked. 'From selling stuff, but my friend who sometimes gives me a lift to the tram stop, he gave me a present.' She said it innocently enough but already my mind seethed with speculation.

'What did Stanley think of your coming back to Rhodesia?' I asked. 'I don't care what he thinks,' she said nonchalantly. 'He never asked how I was going to manage it, but the old lady had plenty to say when he was at work. Said I was a trollop, whatever that means. I told her to mind her tongue, if it wasn't for me her precious son would have to engage a nigger to look after the house and to fag around for her. That shut her up.' 'I'm sorry everything's gone wrong,' I told her. 'You can stay as long as you like and if you need anything, let me know.' 'So you've got a good job then have you?' she asked. I knew she wanted to know what I was paid, but I was not going to tell her. 'It's not bad,' I said. 'I took over from a man who was called up but it's only for the duration. I'll probably get the sack when the war ends.'

We spent the next two weeks together happily enough. Stella put on her startlingly pretty dresses with hats and shoes to match and strolled the length of the street to my office where she would stay until lunchtime, but in the meantime she would wander into the accountant's office and giggle and talk to him, or flirt with the men who came in on business. In the afternoons she went on her way, but at five o'clock she waited outside for me and we walked to the hotel across the road for tea or drinks, or waited until it was time to go to the Services Club or on to dates with my friends.

'What are your plans when you get back home?' I asked when the time came for her to leave. 'I'm going to take a full time job and one of my friends has asked me to come and live with her. Her name's Isobel, she lives in a posh suburb and they've got a tennis court.' 'What about your husband?' I asked. 'If he changes to day shift and puts his old ma into a home, I'll stay with him, but if not, I'll leave. My friend, the one who gives me a lift, he says I'm wasted on Stanley. I'm far too good for him, he says.' She giggled at the memory of it. 'He's even offered to find me a good job.' 'But you're not thinking of a divorce are you?' I asked. 'Why not?' she said. 'I didn't get married to be a servant, you know. He promised me a good time, said I could have anything I wanted, a nice little house, a motor car and he'd take me to all the night clubs and bioscopes. Instead, he reads comics at the power station, walks about looking at the gauges and twiddles the knobs while I'm left alone with that old cow in that awful house surrounded by Afrikaners, all members of the Ossewa Brandwag I'll bet. I don't know what Aunty Betty would say if she knew.' 'Poor you,' I said, 'but cheer up, let's get changed, we're going to the flicks tonight with two of my friends.' But Stella had little time for servicemen. They were not very well paid, did not own cars because they spent such a short time on leave and they talked about themselves and had got out of the habit of flattering women.

'I wonder when we'll see each other again,' I asked as we stood once more on the station platform, and at last Stella asked: 'All those boy-friends of yours? Are any of them special? Some of them seem quite nice, anything serious?' 'No,' I said, 'just that, boy-friends, nothing more.' 'But you're quite old, almost twenty,' she went on. 'You'll have to start thinking of settling down or you'll be left on the shelf.' I burst out laughing. 'Just look who's talking,' I said. 'After all you've told me! No thank you, when I meet the right person I'll know and when I get married it will be for ever so he'll have to be the right one, someone very

346

special. But if I don't meet anyone, I'm going to China, perhaps I'll be a missionary or something like that.' She looked at me with her mouth wide open, while I wondered where on earth that idea had come from; had I simply snatched it out of the air or was it in my subconscious mind? 'You do say some silly things,' she said, 'that's the daftest I've heard. But you'll have to do something quite soon, you aren't getting any younger you know, you can't go on playing hockey with a lot of girls and staying out all night; catch me living in a dump like this, you should come to Jo'burg.' 'Not after what you've told me,' I said, but the remark was lost. The bells rang and the passengers were urged to join the train. I stood and waved until I could see Stella no longer and then I went home. Years would pass and fortunes change before we were to meet again.

'No,' said Mr Fox. 'You can't have two weeks off; you've had days off here and there, your sister was always hanging around the office and I let you go off with her early almost every day. What do you want a fortnight off for anyway?' 'I've got to have my tonsils out. I've always got a cold or a sore throat and I'll have to be in hospital for as long as that.' 'No,' he repeated 'your leave's due in three month's time, you'll have to wait until then.' No amount of arguing or pleading would change his mind and Carrie and I debated the problem. Apart from the doctor's fees, the hospital would have to be paid, but the main problem was the time the operation and convalescence would take. Suddenly Carrie said she might have a solution.

'Dr Schwabach at the White Father's mission near Balla Balla does the operation and only keeps his patients at the surgery for a morning. My firm acts for him, he's buying a practice in town, why don't you go and see him?' 'Balla Balla's miles away, how on earth can I get out there?' I asked. 'Write to him,' she sensibly urged, and at the end of the week a reply came to my letter. The doctor would be glad to see me, he had the loan of a fellow-surgeon's rooms right here in the town every Saturday and Sunday. He attended to natives only he said, but was quite willing to see me if the matter was urgent.

'Next Saturday then,' said the dapper little doctor. 'Be here at nine sharp and you'll be back at home by noon.' He beamed at me, his eyeglasses twinkled and glinted in the bright light of the clinic but my heart sank with fear. 'Will it hurt?' I asked. 'Chust a little,' he said. 'I do it for many people. I am a good surgeon, qualified at Heidelberg in Chermany but I have to wait for my licence before I can practice here.

347

My brother, he is with the White Fathers, that is why I am here.' I nodded. 'Why can you do it so quickly when I would have to stay in hospital for two weeks?' I asked. He helped me on with my coat and walked to the doorway. 'I give only a few injections, local anaesthetics they are called. No ether or chloroform and Zut! a small cut here, another there, and I pull the tonsils out. You will feel no pain, it will take only a few minutes. Then a prick of the needle, a small dose of morphia and you will be back home to rest for a day or so.'

I was terrified, but the urgency of the matter drove me to present myself at the surgery as requested. Off with my dress, on with a rubber apron and seated in a chair, I was handed an enamel basin and instructed to open my mouth, hold the basin firmly and to sit still. What followed remained a nightmare which haunted me for many months after, and as I had sweated with fear that time, I later sweated with relief that I would never have to undergo such a terrifying, painfilled ordeal again. Four injections into my throat on each side and with a tongue depressor, as promised, a small incision was made each side; a loop of fine wire was guided into my throat and the tonsils gouged out and deposited in the basin which I still held firmly. Gouts of blood sprayed the doctor and my apron, I retched with the depressor in my mouth and eventually I mercifully fainted. But only for a few minutes. When I came to, swabs had been inserted, the basin and its bloody contents removed, my face and hands cleaned and order restored. I hardly felt the prick of the morphia needle as I lay back on the settee. Two hours later I was riding my cycle back to the flat where Carrie and Etienne waited for me.

'You poor thing,' said my friend as she helped me undress, 'what's that tape for?' I reached for a pencil and paper and wrote, 'Can't speak, they're swabs in my throat, they'll come out later', and I lay down in bed and went to sleep. On Monday morning I went to work as though nothing had happened. I could not speak, but I got on with my work. Mr Fox lounged against the doorway. 'I hear you had your tonsils out on Saturday morning?' he asked. I nodded yes. 'Cost a lot did it?' he enquired. I wrote on a piece of paper 'Nothing. The mission doctor removed them. I gave him a donation. Ten pounds.' He looked sharply at me. 'D'ye feel all right?' Yes, I nodded. He jingled the money in his pocket. 'I'd have let you have the two weeks off if I'd known it was so urgent, you know. You should have told me.' I thought of a dozen answers but said nothing. My head ached, my throat burned and I could not swallow but this time next week, I told myself, it will all be over and I'll be yelling and shouting with the best of them.

Then suddenly everything changed. Etienne was posted to Canada as an Instructor at an Air Training School and he and Carrie were to be married in a civil ceremony. They would have only a few days together and then she was to follow on a later ship, but in the meantime they would have a short honeymoon at the Victoria Falls. 'I'm so pleased,' I said to Carrie, 'you and Etienne are suited to each other. I do envy you, going all the way to Canada. I don't suppose we'll ever see each other again.' Her eyes filled with tears and she laughed. 'But not right away, it'll be weeks before my passage is arranged. The French Consul in Johannesburg is seeing to it all, but I'm so glad Etienne is not going on to active Service; I couldn't bear that.'

There was a tearful farewell on Bulawayo Station as the train drew out and the new Madame Vascieux stood by my side waving to her departing husband, knowing however that it would only be a matter of months before she joined him in Canada. We went home to the empty flat: plates and bottles lay around, glasses, some still half-filled, sat on the table and everywhere around us was the evidence of the farewell party we had had. Carrie paused in her clearing up and said 'It all seems a dream, the last few weeks. The weekend at the Falls was heaven, I wish I'd met Etienne years ago.' I knew her remarks were leading to something more serious and so I asked, 'Did you ever tell him about that awful time in Salisbury.' She smiled but she replied as though she was thinking of something else. 'I told him everything when he said we were to get married right away. He said he didn't want to know about it, that it had nothing to do with us, nothing to do with him. He said he loved me and that was all that mattered. He asked if I was telling him for some other reason. To put him off perhaps, but I said I wanted him to know, that you had said I would regret it if I didn't. You were right.'

'Now what?' I asked. She thought for a moment and then said 'It's back to school for me,' but she burst out laughing and said, 'no, not to learn French, but to take instruction. Etienne wants me to change my religion so that we can have a wedding ceremony at his church when I arrive in Montreal. I shall be a good Catholic wife.' Every afternoon after work, she cycled to the cathedral and spent some hours with her tutor, but the question of her religion remained foremost in our thoughts. 'I must have been a pain in the neck,' I told her 'with all my pious maxims to you in Salisbury. What a prig you must have thought me.' 'I thought you were silly at the time,' she admitted, 'but now I realise that you had nothing else.'

But Carrie alas, was destined never to arrive in Canada. She had been gone some weeks when one of the girls in the office asked, 'Have you seen the paper today? One of the ships from Cape Town was sunk by a U-boat and everyone was drowned. Your friend's name's in the paper.' I felt everything dissolve around me and my heart thudded with fear as I frantically scanned the long column of names. I saw the names of girls I had been to school with, girls who had married Air Force men and were being sent back to England and then the last name in the list, Madame C. Vascieux. Oh God, I cried, why poor Carrie? I looked at the date of the incident and saw that the sinking had happened almost two weeks ago. My thoughts turned to Etienne, but my mind was full of the awfulness of Carrie's death. Had she been killed instantly I asked myself, or had she drifted in the sea and drowned from exhaustion? I could not speak or think coherently and was devastated.

Mr Fox's voice brought me back to reality. 'You'd better go home, one of the girls can go with you. Take the car, one of the boys will look after your cycle.' He patted me on my shoulder, embarrassed but concerned. I did not go home but instead went to the Catholic church and asked for Monsignor Brown. Yes, he told me, he had seen the news in the paper, he held my hand tightly and begged me to stop crying, saying, 'It is the will of God. There is a reason for everything, let us concern ourselves at this moment with her young husband. We must pray for him, but let us not forget to thank Our Lord for Carrie's life, it has touched us all. Yours and mine.' I knelt down with him but again into my mind swam the picture of Carrie in that black sea, calling for help perhaps, injured and terrified and then sinking into the blackness of oblivion. I heard the priest's words as though from a distance and I got up and ran from the church. Oh God, I prayed, help me, help me to understand why and most of all, help me to accept that Carrie is dead.

But how soon these thoughts left my mind. Was this the help I had so eagerly prayed for, the surcease I longed for? The horror of Carrie's death slowly faded and I thought of it less and less, remembering the time we had spent together, the confidences exchanged, the admissions we had made to each other and the delight we had found in each other's company. I came to realise for the first time in my life how tenuous is our grasp, how fragile are our dreams and aspirations, how suddenly the custody of the vital principle can be relinquished. A line of Shakespeare's came to mind – 'The stroke of death is as a lover's pinch'.

350

It was Ray who delivered me from my wretchedness. Would I come with him to a farewell party at the Round House? he asked. Two of his friends and he were anxious to repay hospitality they had received and he was without a partner for the night. When I demurred, he added that there was someone anxious to meet me, a friend of his, and this seemed a good opportunity, if not the only one, to make the introduction. 'You can't go on like this,' he added. 'What would Carrie have said?' 'She would have said life's too short,' I replied. 'Pick me up at eight o'clock and I'll be glad to meet your friend.'

The lights had been dimmed and couples were dancing on the floor when we walked into the Round House, and when the music stopped we all sat down at the table. Drinks were poured, couples sorted themselves out and introductions were made. 'This is a friend of mine, John,' said Ray, and I looked up into the smiling face of a very tall, dark man also in uniform. 'I'm so glad you came,' he said. 'I've been pestering Ray to introduce us; he told me about your flat-mate, I am sorry.' I had the impression that something strange was happening to me, that my life was about to change and I could not speak, but I nodded in reply and groped for a handkerchief. He placed his hand over mine and asked, 'Do you want to dance or just talk?' 'Dance', I said and we rose and went on to the floor.

All at once I seemed to emerge from the daze I had felt myself in and I looked up at him, thinking with wonder that here was the man who I had surely been waiting for, someone who would be part of my life; all my unhappiness dissolved and vanished and I was suddenly conscious of him, of my hand in his, of the constriction in my throat as I struggled for something to say. He smiled. 'You're not engaged, are you?' he asked. I felt his presence so strongly, I could hardly reply, wishing that time would stop and, like a fly in amber, I could stay forever fixed in this moment, untouched by events, isolated from everyone around me, alone with this man. 'No,' I replied, suddenly determined to enjoy every moment of his time, the few short hours left to us, in a crowded ball-room surrounded by his friends.

'I've been trying to meet you ever since I saw you years ago, when you first came to Bulawayo,' he told me, 'but I never had a chance, you were engaged then, I was told.' 'Yes,' I told him, 'but I think it was just an excuse to escape.' 'From where?' he asked. 'Salisbury, my home town,

351

my father,' I said, 'but also from a miserable childhood.' He looked surprised. 'What else?' he asked. 'That was all,' I told him. 'Don't you think it was enough?' 'What are your plans now,' he asked but I told him I had none, I lived from day to day, I had a responsible job which I enjoyed, many friends, and I read a lot. 'Write to me while I'm away,' he asked, 'and when I come back, perhaps we can see a lot more of each other.' I don't know what I expected him to say but my heart sank at the casualness of his tone and I experienced a momentary feeling of recklessness. 'And then?' I asked.

'Do you believe in love at first sight?' he asked. Instantly I was drawn back in time and I heard Rhodes say, as we had sat over lunch, discussing the ill-fated romance with Rui, 'for him it was a *coup de foudre*, love at first sight,' but I was at a loss for words and replied, almost as though I was once again sitting next to the Portuguese soldier, 'You will go away and may never come back. What will I do then?' 'Oh, I'll come back, you can be sure of that.' It was not Rui's voice, but this stranger beside me who replied with such certainty as though he too, had glimpsed not into the past as I had done, but into the future to be able to say with such conviction 'I'll come back.'

The following six months passed slowly. Letters were received and replied to, friends arrived back on leave with messages, and rumours began to circulate that all Rhodesians serving with the South African Forces or the Imperial Army were to return to the colony to form an independent unit. I was called to the telephone. 'I'll be back in Bulawayo in a week's time,' said John, while I struggled to collect my wits and to give the impression that this was a normal occurrence. 'I'm in the south visiting my parents whom I haven't seen for some years. I'll explain when I arrive. Can you meet me? I'll be on the mail train.' How, I wondered will I feel when I see him again? More important, will he still be of the same mind? Perhaps he had changed his mind about me, perhaps I had been wrong to read too much into his letters, wrong in assuming that he still wished to know me better.

I stood on the windswept platform when the train drew in and saw him alight and walk towards me, towering above the other passengers but smiling broadly. 'I'm so glad you came,' he said again. It was after midnight when he summoned a taxi to take me home; for hours we had sat in the lounge of his hotel exchanging news of the past six months and discussing the future. 'Will you marry me?' he had asked, and although I had said I would, I added that I did not want to do so until the end of the war. 'I don't want to be a war-wife.' I told him, 'married, but alone.

Target for every man who thinks because you're lonely, you're easy. I'd lose my job too, and I need it. Let's wait until the war is over. We will both have more time to think about it, to make sure it's right for both of us.' He sat silently for a few minutes. 'Are you sure you want to wait until then?' he asked at length. And I wasn't sure, I didn't want him to leave me again, our only contact letters and messages, but reason urged me to say, 'We don't know much about each other, we're almost strangers, you may have regrets.' He said no more and I felt his kiss on my cheek and climbed into the taxi and went home. But I regretted my action, knowing that I might lose him as I had lost Rui. But the situation was entirely different, I told myself, I had only been seventeen then, uncertain of my own feelings, incapable of any depth of emotion, vulnerable and unsure of what I wanted.

Two weeks later we were married. It was a sudden decision, activated, he told me, by the fact that he had come to the conclusion that 'you will get tired of waiting until the end of the war, and marry someone else.' No, I had said quite adamantly. 'I've waited all my life, a few more years would have made no difference,' but secretly I was overjoyed. I had once more taken the train to say goodbye to him the weekend before the newly formed regiment was to entrain for Durban and North Africa. I had gone only for the party and as I sat swinging my legs from the goods van on the Saturday afternoon's 'Kaffir Mail' to Gwelo, I had pondered over the events of the last few months. What will I tell my father, I wondered, will he utter another of those idle threats about custody? My twentieth birthday had passed a month since, unheralded and unnoticed as all my birthdays had been, but I reminded myself it would be years before I was married and beyond my father's control.

'Have you brought any other clothes?' asked John, when I stepped off the train in shorts, shirt and tennis shoes minus laces, carrying only a brown paper bag. 'No,' I said, 'only my evening dress, it's in the packet with my night things.' He seemed surprised and it seemed to matter, but he said no more and we joined his friends. Curious looks followed me and I felt everyone's eyes on me and at last asked: 'Is something happening that I don't know about?' 'Yes,' said John, 'I've asked my Commanding Officer for permission to get married, I have a Special Licence and have arranged for the Padre to marry us tomorrow morning at the Anglican Church.' No wonder I was the subject of such scrutiny, I thought, everyone imagines there's an odour of the shot-gun about this, but I pulled myself together sufficiently to say 'But why?' and: 'What am I going to wear?', and: 'What about my job?'

A frantic rush around the small town to find a dress, a hat, shoes and stockings; a ring from Morry Cohen's Jewellery Store but no bouquet. An intense drought had reduced the province to a windswept plain, dried up river beds, scorched and withered trees, desolate abandoned homesteads and the bleached bones of animals dead from starvation and thirst, and no flowers. 'Take these,' said the hotel receptionist, handing me the abandoned bouquet of a newly married pair who had arrived on honeymoon. I waited until the appointed hour and walked alone to the church in the next avenue, carrying my bouquet and trying in vain to get used to new shoes and a ridiculous hat, and as I walked up the aisle alone and unescorted an officer stepped out from the gathering and took my arm to lead me to the groom. A sea of unfamiliar faces turned to look at me, several wives and girl friends smiled conspiratorially and the service proceeded. What am I doing, I thought, why am I here when I only came for a farewell party? And who is this man I'm entrusting my future to? I don't know him, he's a stranger, I've only spent about six or seven days in his company and then I've been too tongue-tied and bewildered to speak to him. Will I feel different now I'm married?

Two hours later I stood on the station platform once again, this time to say goodbye to my new husband, still a complete stranger, still in his dress uniform. There had been no time or opportunity to have more than a few minutes alone in the vestry while the register was signed; since then what was laughingly referred to as a reception had been in full swing. Heads peered out of compartment windows, soldiers waved and called out congratulations to me, some winked knowingly but I was surrounded by other officers' wives while I longed for only a few minutes alone with John. As though he had read my mind, he drew me aside and we walked away from the crowd. 'As soon as I know what our movements are, I'll let you know. We think we'll be in South Africa for some time, and then I want you to come down, we'll have our honeymoon, if it's at all possible.'

I managed to answer that I would do whatever he asked, but I was apprehensive, everything had happened too quickly and I felt my life was out of control. 'I will go back to Bulaayo and wait until I hear from you,' I said, but already I was dreading the departure and our parting and thinking of the ludicrousness of the day's happenings. The ringing bell interrupted my thoughts, a quick kiss, a frantic grasping of hands and he was on board the train. We stood for a long time watching those waving hands and heard the soldiers shouting their farewells, and then people retraced their steps to their taxis and cars, but I remained on the station platform until a train left for Bulawayo.

'D'ye hear about the wedding in Gwelo today,' asked the guard in the van. 'One of the officer's got married in a rush I heard, to some girl he'd only known a few days. Wonder why?' 'You're talking about me,' I told him, 'and there's no need to wonder why, it was just a sudden decision.' 'Oh yers?' he said and he winked slyly at me. 'D'ye play draughts, we could have a game, it'll be five hours before we arrive in Bulawayo, after midnight.'

'What on earth made you do it?' shouted angry Mr Fox when I returned to the office. 'Was it . . . er . . . you know . . . er?' he asked as he looked me up and down for signs of a significant change. 'I didn't have to get married, which is what I think you mean,' I replied. 'He had got the Special Licence and told me there was no reason why we should not get married, and so we did.' Should I tell him more? I wondered: that we had spent barely more than a few minutes alone together in all the time we had known each other, there had always been friends around, or our conversations had taken place over telephones or amongst crowds. What would he think if I told him that my husband and I had only had time to sign a register, exchange a chaste kiss and then said goodbye surrounded by a complete regiment of men? I knew Sonnie Fox, like the rest of the population, would not believe me or would treat the whole matter as a farce.

But I was more concerned that instant dismissal might follow, and tentatively asked 'Will I have to leave?' We both knew that it would be almost impossible to find another girl to take my place; most of the female population over sixteen was married, engaged or housebound. No more was said and life resumed its previous slow pace.

Letters came from North Africa suggesting I try to get to Britain. Many of the Rhodesian servicemen were asking for secondment to British regiments and would be stationed there and already there were many of our men serving in the Royal Air Force. I made up my mind to go, and applied for an exit permit from the colony, on the pretext that I wished to visit my parents-in-law in South Africa. Nothing was said of any intention to get to Britain. I could not think where to begin, who to approach, how to set about such an unconventional request, but I gave notice at my office, calling at the Convent before I did so to ask if there were any aspiring school-leavers looking for work.

Before Mr Fox could shout at me or threaten to veto my exit permit, I produced Harriet like a rabbit out of a hat. He was completely taken aback and offered to lend me money, take me to the station and answer all enquiries as to why I should so suddenly have bolted, and he was delighted with my replacement. 'If you don't like South Africa, come back,' he said. 'Can't see you fitting in there and don't ever admit you're married to a soldier in the British Army, some one'll take a shot at you,' but I knew he was only trying to frighten me.

Johannesburg was an exciting city to live in. There were theatres, the University, cinemas almost on every street corner, shops such as I had never seen before, Arts centres and Museums, night clubs, civic groups, medical centres and suburbs full of extremely wealthy people. I could not sit at home with my sisters-in-law and their mother and the only way to find out how I was to get to Britain seemed to be to find work and start from there.

'Can you use a dictaphone?' asked the Senior Partner in a radiology consultancy, 'and do you understand Latin terminology? We need a competent typist to do our reports daily here at the clinic. You will have to wear nurse's uniform, it puts the patient at ease; they might imagine you're a doctor if you wear an ordinary dress.' Yes, I replied to every question, wondering as I did so what a dictaphone was and how much of my Latin I still remembered. A hurried call to an office supplier was made, saying 'My employer wants to buy a decent machine, what can you recommend and could you show me how to use it?' A demonstration was given and I returned to my parents-in-law armed with a glossary of Medical Terms (Latin version).

I telephoned Stella and arranged to spend a weekend with her. She still lived in the same sad little house with Stanley, and although she now had a two-year old son, they barely spoke to each other, each going their own way. 'Why can't I get a decent job like yours?' she asked. 'I've been here for years and am still stuck in the estate agent's office, getting a pittance for all I have to do.' 'If you wanted to go overseas, what would you do?' I asked. She looked at me blankly, 'Don't be daft,' she said. 'Ships are being torpedoed right outside Cape Town, you'd never do it. I'd stay where you are if I were you, earning all that money each month. By the way what did you tell the old man? Did you tell him you'd got married?' 'No,' I replied, 'I'll wait until I'm twenty-one in a few months time, then I'll write to him.' I had never ceased to be amazed that he'd not found out, although there had never been an announcement in the daily papers and unless I had told him, there was no means of doing so.

A letter arrived from an acquaintance I had met in Gwelo. She was, she wrote, joining her husband in England, he was in the same regiment as mine, and she enclosed the address of a bureau who would assist in the repatriation of dependents of British soldiers. 'Please come over,' she said. 'Perhaps we can stay together, I have relations in Britain who would help us find a flat or rooms.' Encouraged by my father-in-law I wrote to the bureau asking to be considered for a passage to the United Kingdom where my husband was stationed with his regiment. I waited, and the months slipped past. I began to enjoy my work and forget about going to England. I was transferred to a Military Hospital outside the city, I played tennis at weekends or spent them with my sister and eventually she told me she was leaving Stanley and moving in with an office friend. 'Will there be a divorce?' I asked. 'You don't think I'm spending my life with him,' she said. 'I want something better out of life, he's a complete fraud.' I felt sad for Stanley, that much wronged and misjudged man who had known for years that he was no match for his young wife.

The weeks ran into months, and there was still no word of my much-hoped-for journey, and there was an underlying tinge of fear in my mind. I began to lose my enthusiasm for the project. My mind drifted to memories of Carrie. Will I join her, I wondered, at the bottom of the ocean? How long does it take to drown if the ship is torpedoed? Should I try to save myself, look for something to take hold of which could keep me afloat, or should I just give up and say it is the will of God and let the fishes and sharks eat me as I sank into the blackness of the ocean? I grew frightened at my recklessness in asking for a passage and I could no longer remember what John's face looked like. I began to think of returning to Rhodesia, my year's residence in South Africa was almost up and my permit would expire very soon.

'You'd better come home immediately,' said my mother-in-law over the telephone, 'I can't speak over the phone but someone is here to see you.' He was an officer of the Royal Marines and my first thought was that he had brought bad news. 'I've got a rail warrant here for you and instructions as to your movements this next week to Cape Town. Please do not speak to anyone about this, there are subversive elements in this country, so be careful.' A week only I thought, to get packed, to leave my job. What would the partners have to say? Would they release me?

'Leave?' thundered the senior partner, as he shook my letter of resignation in my face. 'Going where?' 'I'm leaving the country,' I said. 'I'm not going home, I'm just leaving the country.' 'You won't leave,' he shouted, his face reddening with fury. 'I'll have your passport cancelled.

Who do you think is going to do these reports? Have you no thought for all the soldiers sent down from Nairobi, brave boys sacrificing their lives for people like you who can only think of their own selves?' 'You can't do anything about my passport, I'm Rhodesian,' I shouted back, 'and I am sorry for all the wounded soldiers who have to come here, for the people who are so ill, the cancer patients and the children, but I'm leaving.' He stamped up and down the room in fury. 'It took months to find a competent typist,' he said, 'you can't leave, that's all there is to it. I will oppose your exit permit.' 'You can't, it's all arranged,' I told him, 'and my sister's downstairs, she can take over from me, she's looking for work.' His mouth fell open, and he sat down. 'Bring her in, fetch her quickly,' he cried as though Stella would vanish before he had set eyes on her.

The ship lay rocking gently at the quayside when the train drew in. I read the name on the bows, *RMS Andes* but my mind was full of foreboding. Will my tombstone or memorial read 'drowned at sea, passenger on *RMS Andes*? Morbid thoughts possessed me, but failed to deter me. I was caught up in the mechanics of this repatriation scheme. The very word caused me some amusement, I was colonial and had never been out of Africa and I listened with fascination to my fellow travellers, wives evacuated from Palestine and living along the Natal coast these past two years. They spoke longingly of Home, of high tea, of bloaters, of their mums and dads, of threepenny tram rides, of three 'apence and of the air-raids , the black out and the horrors of rationing. 'What part of the Old Country were you born dear?' they asked kindly. 'Salisbury,' I replied truthfully. 'Lovely town,' they murmured, 'with that lovely Cathedral, nice part, the West Country.'

Boat drill occupied most of our day, and when I had overcome my seasickness, I began to enjoy the voyage. Such an expanse of water I had never seen before and it seemed unlikely that at any moment the black hulk of a U-Boat could surface and sink us, or that we might strike a floating mine and be blown apart. I was thankful to share a cabin with only seven strangers, having been shocked when I walked through a dormitory where hundreds of soldiers' wives and their babies slept. Tiers of bunks arose in spirals from steel poles screwed into the decking, babies cried, mothers quarrelled amongst themselves, there was no privacy and the smell of wet napkins hung in the air.

On the other side were quartered the men; officers in cabins of eight, other ranks crowded together, sleeping in hammocks on the bottom decks below the water line. Day and night soldiers patrolled the decks. There were random inspections to see that all doors were hooked back, that no one was having a forbidden bath or several quiet moments behind the lavatory door. We slept fully clothed with shoes and life jackets on, with our one and only suitcase at hand in case of emergency.

By day we sat on deck, gossiping with new friends, speculating about conditions in England, waiting for the shrill ringing of the bells to summon us to Boat Drill and watching with pity the desperate married couples searching for a secluded spot where they could retire under cover of their steamer rugs to enjoy a few minutes of privacy. We appeared to have disengaged from normal life, there was no other world, only this disembodied existence governed and controlled by the voice of the Tannoy and the Daily Orders pinned to notice boards, which you ignored at your peril.

Fraternisation between ship's crew and passengers was strictly forbidden, but it was the saloon stewards who organised the drinking parties in their cabins and to one of these I was invited. 'I am Kosla', said the girl who sat next to me at meals. 'I am Egyptian, married to a British soldier and I'm being sent to England to his family. There is a party tonight, come with me, I do not want to go alone, I know none of the others.' She was a statuesque brunette, her hair gathered smoothly into a pigtail which hung down her back, but her beautiful face was marred by a wall-eye. As though she had read my summary of her appearance, she pointed to her face and said, 'This I got in Jerusalem during the troubles there, it was a bullet. I was in the market square, my little daughter was killed and I was shot through the head.' She lifted her hair and I saw the deep scar there, white and smooth like a fish belly. 'We may be killed at any moment, let us enjoy ourselves tonight, come with me I have a bottle of sherry, we can get drunk.' When she saw I hesitated she asked 'You are shocked?' I said nothing. 'Do not be, my friend,' she continued, 'why ever not? I have nothing to live for, I have always been a good girl, strictly brought up. But God saw fit to punish me and for what? Now I do as I please, I drink, I think only of myself and I have lovers. That way I earn my punishment.' There were tears in her eyes but she looked away from me. 'I will come with you,' I said and then I asked, 'Is your husband on board?' 'No,' she replied. 'I have not seen him for almost a year. Many letters came. He is with his regiment in England but I have not been lonely, there were many to comfort me as I travelled south to board this ship.'

She smiled softly to herself and then asked, 'Your husband, where is he?' 'Also in England,' I told her, 'he is with a cavalry regiment, I haven't seen him for nearly two years.' 'But you spent some time together before he left?' she asked. 'No,' I replied, 'I had only known him for a short time, a matter of a few weeks. We got married very suddenly and he left the same day with his regiment.' She looked at me in amazement. 'So the marriage was not fait accompli, is that what you are saying?'

'That is so,' I told her. 'You are the only person to whom I have admitted it. I did not think anyone would have believed me, had they asked.' She burst into loud peals of laughter, but when she saw how embarrassed I felt, she asked, 'So you are still a virgin after two years of marriage?' I did not answer. 'That man you married was extremely sagacious, if not cunning,' she said. 'He would know immediately if another man had fished in his waters.' I tried not to look shocked. 'It was force of circumstances,' I replied, 'he asked me to marry him within the first hour I had met him but I told him I did not wish to be a war-wife, that I would marry him after the war. But he persuaded me and there were no reasons why I should refuse.'

'Was that your first proposal?' she asked. 'No,' I said, 'when I was very young, seventeen, I nearly married a Portuguese soldier serving in the colonial army. He was a lovely man, a castiço, an aristocrat, very religious and very, very honourable. I was swept off my feet and very flattered to have his attention and he wanted to marry me. But there were many difficulties, religion, my age, his career and while he did everything to resolve them, it was decided he was to re-join his regiment and then suddenly they were sent to the Far East. I never saw him again but I thought about him for a long time. There were many others who asked me but I could not submit to another emotional entanglement – perhaps I instinctively knew they were not right.'

'But this man to whom you are now married? He is different?' she asked. 'Of course,' I replied. 'I knew when I first saw him that he was the man for me. I was quite determined to have him and would have pursued him relentlessly, but it was not necessary, he had the same idea so I let him do all the work.' 'And you are happy?' she asked. 'Yes I think so,' I told her. 'Marriage is a very serious business, do you not agree?' She shrugged her shoulders and then said jokingly, 'I shall call you Virginie, it will be just between you and I.' 'If you dare to,' I said, 'I will not come with you tonight.'

It was the only party we went to. For a dare, Kosla had eaten ten hard-boiled eggs in as many minutes and afterwards lay costive and sulking on the deck during the day or in her bunk at night asking 'Why did I do it? I could have spent the night elsewhere, the second engineer wanted to show me his cabin and his treasure. What a fool I was. But what barbarians those people at the party are.' There were other fields for her to explore and possibly she was the only one who was able to turn a frightening and dangerous sea voyage into a pleasure cruise.

'I am collecting books for that poor man down there,' she told me when I saw her up on deck some days later. The ship was standing off the coast under a grey sky and lashing rain and I saw the dark and sombre line of the jungle, green palm trees, corrugated iron-roofed houses, natives standing on the shore looking at the ship, pirogues coming towards us through the surf and when I looked overboard, I saw the waterboat drawn up against the towering sides of the steamer. Men were fastening ropes and connecting pipe lines.

'That's Freetown,' Kosla told me, 'and the books are for the poor man on the waterboat.' 'How do you propose to get them to him?' I asked, 'throw them down?' 'I have already spoken to the Commanding Officer', she said. 'He has given me permission to take them down, come with me, we will go through that little door at the waterline, where you see the gangway.' We hurried through the decks and scrambled over the rickety gangway. I heard the surge of water being pumped through the pipes, hands reached out to help me across and then we were on the waterboat.

He was quite young I guessed, dressed in immaculate white shorts and shirt, but he was reluctant to let us return to the ship. 'Have a drink,' he asked. 'I've got some fresh lime, stay for a few minutes. It's ages since I've seen any white people and it will be ages before the *Andes* is ready to sail.' He clapped his hands and a youth of about twelve darted in with a jug of fruit juice, some assorted glasses and a large bottle of gin. 'You can go,' said his master dismissing the boy.

For a few minutes we sat and chatted and then he turned to Kosla and asked, 'Care to look over the old tub?' He turned as though to include me but I saw her shaking her head and replied, 'No, I think we must go when we've finished these.' But no, he said, he would give me just another small drop of gin and I was to wait there, there was something he wished to show Kosla. I took the drink, already regretting the first one, and sipped at it.

It was the beating of the rain on the cabin roof and the loud drumming of powerful engines which woke me. It was almost dark and I was alone in the day-cabin; there was no sign of either the master or my friend and I jumped to my feet realising that it was the ship vibrating and then I heard the sound of voices and the thud of ropes as they were being cast off onto the water-boat. 'Kosla,' I screamed banging on the closed door, 'are you there? The ship is getting up steam, it's going, we're going to be left behind.'

The next few minutes were a nightmare. They emerged from his cabin, he pulling on his jacket, Kosla fastening her clothes, while he shouted at the men who were about to raise the bridge. Above me curious passengers leaned over the ship's rail. Swiftly we were bundled out of the cabin, across the deck and on to the bridge once again being lowered to our level. A door was flung open, hands leaned out to pull us through and we came face to face with the Master at Arms and a curious gang of the crew, relishing our near misfortune. 'Up to the C.O's office,' said the guardian of the law, 'he's waiting for you.'

'Just what do you think you were doing?' he roared, coming around his desk to confront Kosla. 'I gave you permission to deliver books, not to spend the day over there.' Ingenuously she smiled at him but his heart like his eyes was stony. 'You did give me permission sir,' she said. 'Only to deliver the books,' he repeated. 'But sir,' she said meekly, 'he told me he was so lonely. He doesn't see a European for months at a time. He was showing me his snapshots and we sat talking. For ages. I dozed off, it was very hot and sticky in the cabin and the next thing I knew was Virginie banging on the door and shouting. I think she must have fallen asleep too.' He glared at me. 'I didn't know your name was Virginie,' he said. I felt myself blushing but I said nothing, looking down at the floor and wondering what he was going to do with us.

As with the melting of winter snows, his mood changed. 'I quite understand my dear, you were very kind to keep him company.' He came to sit between us. She took his hand in hers and said in a small voice, 'I didn't do anything wrong did I? I was so sorry for him, stuck out here in Freetown, it must be awful.' He fiddled with his moustache with his free hand, the other resting on Kosla's knee, and he turned to me. 'The gong will go for dinner, I'm due on the bridge, run along.' I went towards the door. 'Thank you,' I said, and I left, but Kosla did not accompany me. Later that night I met her in the ironing room. A heavy silence had fallen over the occupants as they waited their turn, when she came in; she winked at me, but we did not speak. I wondered if she closed her eyes when he had kissed her, as surely he had. She looked at me and said, 'If only every day was like today.'

Slowly the colour of the sea changed from the dark grey of the tropics under a leaden sky to the blue white flecked ocean of the northern hemisphere and I knew that after five weeks we were now in the sea lanes approaching Britain. There was no sound or sign of any other living thing, even the flying fish and porpoises had been left behind, the voyage was almost over and life and all its problems lay just over the horizon.

Driving rain and cooler temperatures kept us indoors but when the bells rang with more frequency than before, we seized our life-jackets and ran for our boat stations, hoping for another rehearsal and not the real thing. 'Day after tomorrow we'll come in sight of land,' said the worthy ladies who knew, and they went on to tell us that the Isle of Mull would be visible tomorrow. We were about to enter the North Channel and then the Irish Sea and would dock in Liverpool. I began to wonder what lay ahead. What would become of me and where would I live?

'Will we ever meet again?' asked Kosla, her arm around my shoulders, her blind eye towards me. 'Perhaps.' I said, 'if you come to London or I come up to Scotland. I am to report at Rhodesia House in London, that is the only address I have.' 'What kind of address is that?' she asked jokingly. 'Will you camp on the pavement, or perhaps the foyer?' 'I don't know anyone in England,' I told her, 'but I am sure I will manage. Give me your address, I will write to you.' I looked at her scribbled note. 'Take no notice of that title, to you I am your friend Kosla, but that is the address that will find me. Let us remain friends. We have shared many good and bad times together, it would have been awful without you.' 'For me it has been a wonderful experience although I was very frightened very often,' I replied, surprised that she bore a title although she had behaved so recklessly.

Suddenly I heard once again my grandmother's voice saying in that long forgotten patois of hers 'He would have done better to marry a prostitute who wished to be a lady, rather than a lady who wished to be a prostitute.' I had not understood a word of her expression then, nor to whom she had referred. For many years it had lain dormant in my subconscious mind only to leap out and apply itself to my friend. But I told myself, a prostitute took money for her favours whereas Kosla had given herself for her own pleasure, and for her partners'. We put our arms around each other and kissed. 'Don't forget me,' she murmured, 'we may meet again, who knows?'

'Indian Army? British Army? Palestine Police? Royal Navy?' asked the sombre-suited officials who had come out to the ship, holding on to their bowler hats and grasping firmly their brief cases as their boats tossed and swung through the rough sea. 'Form queues,' barked the Master at Arms, herding us into line. 'This is something new to me,' hissed Kosla behind me. 'We are like sheep but I was told it is the order in England.' She raised her eyebrows to heaven.

I barely recognised my erstwhile travelling companions who appeared in smart two-piece suits, tailored dresses, high-heeled shoes and pinned-on hats, smelling faintly of Eau de Cologne. Their children no longer ran around in dirty old clothes but were clean and combed in pretty dresses or long trousers and jackets. Gone were the bare legs, the sloppy old clothes and the dirty tennis shoes or slippers they had worn at sea, those had been thrown overboard and now drifted away with the ship's trash on the out-going tide.

Warrants were issued, ration books filled in, money changed and directions given to the relevant railway stations. I stepped off the *Andes* full of excitement and anticipation, and very grateful that I had accomplished the journey of such a distance and duration alone. Kosla stood at the foot of the gangway, nearby purred a grey car and beside it holding open the back door, a smart uniformed chauffeur. 'Goodbye my dear,' she said as we hugged each other, 'I pray you have good news of that husband soon, he is a very lucky man.' I laughed, remembering our conversation when we had first met. 'And you Kosla? I hope all goes well.' 'If it does not,' she replied, 'and I have to wear a black patch I will look like a brigand, no man will be safe from me.' She laughed and climbed into the car and then she pointed to the back of the chauffeur and then to herself and winked. I stood and watched until she was out of sight, grateful for her friendship but uppermost in my mind was pity for her.

So this is England, I told myself. So small, so compact and so orderly. This is where centuries of history have been made, where I shall remain until the war is over. How fortunate I am to be here where everything is happening. I stood looking at the buildings, I touched everything, remembering the many who had passed by this place, those who had made earth-shattering decisions and who had helped to form our vast empire. I thought of the slave traders who had sailed from this port and who, by their trade, had dissipated Africa's men througout the world, debauching and degrading them and reducing them to decades of slavery and servitude. But I remembered too, those who had sailed away from this port in their wooden ships to colonise North America, Australia and Africa, and I was grateful.

An elderly man was waiting for me when I reached Rhodesia House. I had been directed to his office by the girl in the foyer; she had openly admired my tan but she looked curiously at me. 'He's expecting you,' she said. He leaned over his desk to shake my hand and motioned me to be seated. 'How long have you been at sea?' he asked. I told him. 'So you haven't heard any news for almost five weeks? A pity.' He looked uncomfortable but in my euphoric state I did not reply but I wondered why he looked so troubled. As though from a distance I heard him say, 'There is no definite news, he's still missing I am afraid.' 'Who?' I heard myself ask. 'Your husband,' he replied. 'He's been posted as missing. Believed drowned in the Channel, two weeks ago. There were others with him.' I felt as though I was falling through space. 'But he can't be,' I said foolishly. 'He couldn't be drowned, it must be a mistake, it's not true.' 'I'm afraid it is,' he said. 'Missing only means no one is sure, he did not join up with his regiment when they landed so that's the reason he's posted as missing.'

But drowned? I asked myself, it could not be true and I refused to believe it. I heard his voice from far away. 'It's not official yet, so there's still hope.' 'What am I to do now?' I asked. 'I know absolutely no one in this country. Can I get a return passage.' He looked at me and then sat down in his chair. 'Not for years,' he said, 'not until the war is over. All the shipping is tied up with troop movements, it will be ages before anything sails for Africa again.' What is to become of me, I wondered. What shall I do, where can I live until then; it might even be years and I shall be stuck in this strange country alone, a widow, not knowing another soul and with only a small amount of money.

'I've arranged for you to stay in the West End at a small hotel until the end of the week. After that perhaps you would consider moving out into the country. I live in Haywards Heath and a neighbour of mine has offered to take you as a paying guest. It's a lovely small town.' He did not tell me that it was in the direct line of the buzz-bombs which had devastated so much of London and the suburbs and it would have made little difference if he had. The few days I spent in London saw me dejected and dispirited. I dreaded the distant sounds of exploding bombs, the eerie wail of the air-raid siren, the lack of a friendly face, the knowledge that I might be killed in the street and I began to wonder what had possessed me to leave the peace and tranquillity of Rhodesia.

'After three months,' said Mrs Hutchings 'you'll have to get a job, otherwise you'll be directed into something you may not like. But in the meantime I hope you'll be comfortable with us. We play tennis with friends in the town and you'll be very welcome to join us.' I helped around the house, and dug in her garden and twice a day I milked the family goat. I had been too cowardly to admit that I had never approached the udder of any animal before, but the Hutchings family firmly believed Africa to be densely populated by wild and domestic animals of all kinds and that we lived a pioneer style of life; I wondered if I dare to confess that my knowledge of cooking and housekeeping was nil, as well as the care of domestic animals. But I had watched my grandmother's farm boys and those at Aunty Betty's and Mrs Smith's, and was able to extract the milk without any obvious damage to the goat although she had glared at me, her vacant yellow eyes never leaving my inexpert hands.

I made friends with an Amercian girl in the village and together we cycled through the leafy lanes on bicycles borrowed from our landladies, but we were ready to leap into the nearest ditch at the ominous sound of approaching aircraft or flying bombs. We waved to the Canadian servicemen as they lolled around the entrance to their camps, refusing their earnest invitations, and we ignored and rode faster past the prisoners-of-war working in the fields, but when I emerged from my morass of self-pity I began to take an interest in everything around me. I played tennis, and with Billee I went to London to the ballet, to the museums and sat for hours in trains, stationary as becalmed yachts, waiting for the all-clear to signal our onward journey. I felt safe under the flocks of barrage balloons glinting silvery as they turned and swayed in the air currents, looking like a field of metallic sheep; on a lovely sunny September morning we sat on the edge of a ditch watching the armada of aeroplanes towing gliders across the Channel to Arnhem.

'Any news?' asked Billee on every occasion we met. 'No,' I told her, 'but I'm still hoping. I don't really believe he's dead.' 'Oh sure,' drawled Billee in response 'mistakes have often been made. But you're young and there'll be other men.' But she was not impressed when I confessed a longing to join the Land Army. 'I like the uniform they wear,' I said. 'Not those damn-awful breeches?' she cried, 'and those woollen stockings? And I ask you, those clod-hopping shoes.' I would have to arise at four thirty every morning throughout the year, she told me, to cut swedes for the dairy cows, 'and look at that mud and manure,' she wailed, 'you'd be better off in a civilian job.' I applied for and took the post as secretary to a member of the Brains Trust, but I spent most of my time typing the editorials for the Church of England Newspaper of which my employer was also chairman.

'You've had a phone call,' said Mrs Hutchings when I returned home one autumn evening. 'It was a lady, she wants you to ring her back.' Could it be Kosla I wondered? I knew no one else in England. I dialled and presently a completely unfamiliar voice answered. 'I've tracked you down at last,' she said. 'I wondered if you'd arrived in this country, John gave me your last letter just before he went across to France. Can we meet?' Arrangements were made for us to meet at Tonbridge the next day. I stood at the entrance to the station and saw a tall, elegant Englishwoman coming towards me. She was not the person I had visualised. My mind had turned to a grey-haired woman, in tweeds, twin set and pearls with a spaniel at foot but she was quite different; she was tall and slender and quite young. 'I'm Diana,' she said. 'We met John when his regiment was stationed near our place near Ashford. Have you heard any news of him?'

'No,' I told her. 'But I don't believe he was drowned. I think there has been a mistake somewhere.' 'Do you have any plans?' she asked. 'Yes,' I told her. 'I will wait three more months and if he is officially posted as dead, I'll ask for a return passage right away. That is all I can do.' We sat and talked and then she asked. 'Why not come and stay with us? There's no reason for you to stay in Haywards Heath with people you hardly know. Old Whats-it can find another secretary quite easily. Give him a week's notice but if you like, I'll give him a ring and tell him what the position is.' She searched in her diary and wrote my name in on a day the following week and then she walked with me to my platform.

'Do you keep in touch with that Egyptian girl you met on the ship?' she asked. I closed my eyes and saw Kosla's face again, her hair drawn down over her scarred neck, her blind eye disfiguring her beautiful face and I remembered her recklessness, her impetuosity and her scandalous behaviour. 'She was to have an operation on her eye, the nerves were damaged when she was shot. She may still be in hospital or may have returned to Egypt' I said. 'I wrote to her just after I arrived in England but there was no reply. I can't even remember what I said, I was still stunned by the news, I couldn't think properly.'

Severing my uncertain connection with Haywards Heath was not difficult, and a week later I arrived in Ashford. My friend's small son was clearly disappointed in me. 'I thought you'd be black and have a bone through your nose,' he cried when we were introduced. 'Say something in African.' In Shona I said I was glad to meet him which appeared to satisfy him and to make up for my white skin. 'When it snows, will you come on my toboggan with me?' he asked, 'there's a big hill behind the house.'

He took me for long walks through the woods and I was enthralled with the beauty around us. I sniffed the bosky scent of the woods, we waded through the small streams looking for fresh-water shrimps or watercress and we picked the wild berries in the hedgerows. Everything would be perfect I thought, if only I didn't have this awful burden on my shoulders, but I could not bring myself to pray for the repose of my dead husband's soul. That act would be tantamount to admitting that he was irrevocably lost to me and I steadfastly refused to accept that it was so.

'When we first met,' said Diana, 'I don't think I appreciated how you felt, but then I thought about it and realised that you hardly knew each other; it would have been worse for you if you'd spent a long time together but you say it was only a matter of a few days and hours.' 'Not even that,' I told her. 'We'd only known each other for a few weeks and we got married at four o'clock and at six o'clock I was saying goodbye to him.' She gave me a startled look. 'Yes,' I admitted 'I'm still wondering what it's all about.' 'So,' she added, 'as they say in the Bible, you never knew him?' I did not reply. 'Well, it's rotten luck all the same,' she said at last. 'I wish I'd been more sympathetic when we first met and I'm sorry it's turned out this way.' 'I didn't expect you to throw your arms around me,' I told her. 'We were complete strangers and it was kind of you to ask me to come and stay. You are right when you say it would have been worse if we'd been married for ages but for me it seemed like the end of the world. He was everything I ever wanted or hoped for but I still do not believe he won't come back. I do not believe he was drowned.' 'I wish I had your faith, dear,' she said. 'Now you must think of this as your home for as long as you are in England and we must pray for John's safe return.' Her husband said very little but he soon treated me as an old friend and was not averse to a quick squeeze as I rushed past him to draw the black-out curtains.

I was introduced to all their friends, many of whom already knew John, and on Saturday nights we went in a large crowd to the cinemas or to the hospital dances. This was the first time I had seen women dancing together, and I was flattered to be asked to take a turn with the Matron.

I did the housework and learned to make tea, boil an egg and cook and I was entrusted to take the next-door farmer's bicycle and cycle to Ashford to confront the butcher. 'Look foreign,' Diana would urge me, 'pretend you're stupid, act as though you can't understand English and ask him for a leg of lamb enough for six people for two meals. We've used our meat ration for the month and I'm not killing off my hens just yet.' I mounted the cycle and pedalled furiously the six miles to the butcher shop. 'Offal A to L' read the notice in his window but I did not pause to decipher that and went into the little shop. As though half-witted I pointed to a small leg of pork, shook my head vigorously and made what I imagined were sheep-like noises. I held up my hands showing six fingers twice but he looked at me in astonishment. I extracted the ration books from the bag and handed them to him. 'She's that foreigner staying with the Ramsays,' said his assistant, 'I think she's saying she wants a leg of lamb, quite a big one.' 'But there ain't any coupons 'ere, they've used the lot,' said his master. I stood there dumbly and then began to cry, wondering if I should not perhaps tear at my clothes, but before I could put my plan into operation, the butcher sighed heavily and reached for his steel. He cut and sawed while I sobbed, and he led me to the door bundling up the illegal joint and ushering me out. I seized his red, meaty hand and bestowed a kiss on it, wondering if perhaps I was overdoing it. 'There, there,' he said, patting me on my bottom, 'don't cry, come and see me any time, I'll see you right,' and he squeezed me, but I could see he was anxious to be rid of me, whether because of my red tear-streaked face or because of the size of the joint I was fastening to Mr Chown's bicycle carrier. I refused to enter his shop again, feeling that I could not rise to such a performance a second time.

Parties were held throughout the beginning of winter, and friends came from as far away as London, each with something in a bottle or a plate of food, the unattainable sausage roll which turned out to be Spam, black market Gin and Expectant Mother's orange juice, mysterious joints of meat – either the illegally reared pig or a nice piece of horse. We played the gramophone and danced in the sitting room, I heard giggles from upstairs and frequently stumbled into bodies when I went out for a few more logs of wood for the fire. The ladies all spoke in loud penetrating voices, calling each other darling, the men stood about in groups, hands in pockets, rocking on their heels as they boasted of their day's shooting, reaching out to fondle any piece of female flesh within reach.

Next morning after church, there would be a post-mortem while we cleared up the mess. 'Old whats-it isn't looking too good don't you think?' or 'Did you see what that fool Marjorie was wearing? I threw that out to my char's daughter years ago, she must have a market stall.' 'Poor old so-and-so says she's left him at last, d'ye remember that time we all went to the Riviera and he found her in bed with Freddy?' I was fascinated. 'Why do you invite them if they're all such idiots?' I asked. They looked at me in surprise. 'But they're the only gentry left in the district,' Diana would tell me. 'But what about the people you speak to in Ashford? You seem to have a lot of friends there.' There was a deathly silence. I heard the coals shifting in the grate. 'My dear,' she said, 'they're in trade. We don't mix with that sort socially, they're all right for a bit of chat in the street or in the shops but not to have at one's home.' I was mystified at the distinctions drawn and could not understand how one qualified to be gentry, tradespeople or the common herd, but the lines were strictly marked and there would be no crossing. Even clothes could betray one's humble origin and my navy blue overcoat was banished in favour of a more middle-class checked tweed. No wonder we can't even agree with other nations I thought.

The day before Christmas I answered the telephone and stood there transfixed, rooted to the spot. 'I'm in London, I'm catching the train to Ashford station,' said the voice. 'I've had a devil of a job to locate you. Phoned Rhodesia House and they told me you were with Diana.' 'It's John,' I screamed as she came running down the stairs, and in true Jane Eyre fashion, I fainted. 'Wake up, pull yourself together,' she said slapping me urgently. 'He was calling from a phone box, but the pips went. He's arriving at ten o'clock tonight, we'll go and meet him.' Suddenly I was afraid. 'Perhaps it was a hoax, someone playing a trick,' I suggested. 'You're being silly,' Diana said, 'we both need a drink. Any of that ghastly orange juice left? There's plenty of gin.'

He came towards me in the darkness of the winter's night, hurrying past passengers who groped their way through the blackness of the station. He seemed taller and then he bent down to kiss me, lifting me off the ground. 'I never thought I'd see you again,' I mumbled, 'I thought you were dead, I cried for months.' 'I'm here now,' he said, 'I've got two weeks leave. It's wonderful to know you're here and not six thousand miles away.'

Later he explained that the vessel carrying his squadron had landed far up the coast of Belgium, behind the German lines. For days after they had disembarked, they lay low and then by stealth and by night, the whole group had made their way south. Four weeks after they had left

England, they joined up with their regiment, then heavily engaged in the fighting. No one had thought to inform him of my arrival, Rhodesia House still assuming he was drowned and the War Office was unaware that I was still in the country. By chance he had met a fellow Rhodesian serving with the Air Force who had mentioned he'd seen my name in the visitor's book at Rhodesia House with the address in Haywards Heath. As soon as it could be arranged he was on an aircraft and sent back to England where he'd traced me through Mrs Hutchings. 'And Helen?' I asked. It was she who had told me in South Africa how to get here but she had gone to Ireland to live with a relative and had left no address.

In the middle of January I waited again on the station platform. 'I'm always doing this, always saying goodbye to someone on a railway station. There have been so many friends and people whom I've had to say goodbye to; some of them never to be seen again, others fortunately have returned.' He held me close. 'The war will soon be over I'm sure. We'll go home together, there won't be any goodbyes for us after this I promise you.' I watched the train until it was out of sight and then, happier than I had been for a long time, I returned to Ashford.

The course of the war had indeed changed. Good news came more frequently, everything looked brighter, the people had shaken off their winter lethargy and I stood in the queue for Expectant Mother's orange juice and an extra egg on my ration book. Diana and I sewed baby clothes and I was engaged as secretary to the Agent for the local Conservative candidate. An election was imminent and with the only other member of staff, an elderly lady who confessed she was pleased my English was so good considering I came from Africa, I roneoed election addresses, attended meetings to hand out leaflets, harried the laggards to vote and strung up bunting and checked voting cards. Suddenly the winter's gloom had gone, the war was over, peace negotiated and lights throughout the country were switched on. We stood on the rise by the orchard looking at Ashford as it sparkled and glittered in the distance and I understood how Cortes had felt when he had first beheld the Pacific Ocean.

Men began to return, more of them to be seen in civilian suits, expatriates spoke of their sailing dates, the exotic uniforms of Allied soldiers disappeared, notices appeared in the press asking for news of missing sons and husbands, households speedily re-arranged with the departure of the incumbent boy-friend and every man in the kingdom began to wonder and assess the future.

John returned and was given a sailing date which did not include me;

it was better we decided, for me to stay in my job and to wait until the baby was born, and then to follow as soon as was possible. My son was a week old when his father sailed for Africa. 'Don't go,' pleaded Diana. 'Wait until the baby is much older and the rush over. The seas are still full of mines, you might be struck.' I was tempted, but I felt I had wasted enough time and was restless to go. The election was over and the A-bomb had been dropped on Hiroshima. Peace negotiations and War trials were being held and suddenly I found I did not want to leave England. But it was a foolish wish, a desire of little duration and I packed and waited for my sailing orders.

Early in December I took the train to Liverpool, crying all the way, sad to say goodbye to such good friends but also afraid to find myself alone with this small child and wondering what lay ahead of me. There would be month's voyage through the Mediterranean and the Suez Canal before we entered the Indian Ocean and arrived in Durban. Cables came saying I would be met and with confidence and optimism for the future I boarded the *Franconia*.

Slowly the ship steamed down the channel, harried and fussed over by the tugs on either side. Slowly the shore line disappeared in the gloom of the wintry night, the bright lights flickering through the rain and I wondered if I would ever return to this enchanting country again.

I thought of the thousands of people who had left these shores for a life in the colonies; those like my father's family who had been brought up in the slums of the big cities, who had struggled for a meagre education or had learned all life had to offer on the streets where they lived. Of the struggles they had endured to better themselves, but defeated had packed up and travelled steerage to far away continents to make a better life for themselves and their children. I felt a grudging respect for their efforts, for their tenacity and their endurance.

I began to understand their constant reminders of how things had been back 'home' and their adherence to the forms of speech they had learned as children, to the habits and way of life they had taken with them. In spite of their improved circumstances, they clung to their old ways, reluctant to let them go, feeling perhaps that they would have nothing to cling to, nothing with which to identify, no traditions to pass on to their heirs.

But like them I knew now that I too would suffer pangs of longing for this mother country and would come to understand the meaning of that word 'suadades', that untranslatable Portuguese word, so eloquently explained to me by the Portuguese soldier; a state of longing for a person or place, a bitter-sweet feeling akin to the Greek 'pothos'. The words of the poet Camoës came to mind. 'What do you want of me? Perpetual suadades? With what hope are you still deceiving me? For time past will never return and if it did, I should no longer be the age to enjoy it.'